THE NUTRITIONAL NICHE

LAND AND WATER
ENVIRONMENT=
PHYSICAL GEOGRAPHY

FOOD PRODUCTION
AND RESOURCES=
ECONOMIC GEOGRAPHY

TRADITION AND
CULTURE=
HUMAN GEOGRAPHY

DIETS AND NUTRITIONAL
DISEASES=
MEDICAL GEOGRAPHY

AMERICAN GEOGRAPHICAL SOCIETY

THE ECOLOGY
OF MALNUTRITION
IN MIDDLE AFRICA

(Ghana, Nigeria, Republic of the Congo, Rwanda
Burundi, and the former French Equatorial Africa)

Studies in Medical Geography, Volume 5

Jacques M. May, M.D.

HAFNER PUBLISHING COMPANY
New York   London
1965

First Edition 1965

Printed and Published by

HAFNER PUBLISHING COMPANY, INC.
31 East 10th Street
New York, N. Y. 10003

———————————

Library of Congress Card Catalogue Number 65-16440

*This study was sponsored by the U. S. Army Natick Laboratories
under Contract No. DA19-129-QM-1946(N(*

TABLE OF CONTENTS

ACKNOWLEDGEMENT

The author wishes to extend his thanks for their generous cooperation to Mr. Howard L. Ohman, Project Officer, Earth Sciences Division, U. S. Army, Natick Laboratories, who has on several occasions given good and pertinent advice, far beyond the call of duty; to Miss Frances Lanzisera who has acted as researcher with her usual skill and efficiency; to Mr. Douglas Waugh who has done the cartography with much talent and patience; to Mrs. Rhoda Durkan who has taken inordinate pains in the reviewing and typing of the manuscript; to Miss Helen Mears who has patiently edited the last version of the manuscript and to Mrs. Marie-Anne May who in spite of her many other duties has always smilingly provided assistance when a deadline had to be met.

Jacques M. May

March 1965

PREFACE

The current volume in Dr. Jacques May's Studies in Medical Geography is concerned with the food geography of Middle Africa, involving primitive tropical agriculture and limited livestock economy.

Each of the regional volumes of this series has examined a completely different food complex in basically different cultures and environments. Volume 3 treated the food geography of the monsoon and desert lands of the Oriental tropics, and Volume 4 dealt with the mixed crop and livestock systems of east central Europe.

The food geography of these three major regions differs in almost every respect. In southern Asia the food is chiefly rice, millet, and fish or dates, grain, and meat; the central agricultural technique is irrigation. East central Europe relies on bread and animal products and the use of the plow. Middle Africa depends on manioc, sweet potatoes, beans, sorghum, and plantain raised in a dry-farming economy in which the chief implement is the hoe.

Studies such as these are of the utmost importance in the world today. Any attempt to solve the problems of malnutrition must begin with a knowledge of the distinctive food geography of the region, as must the plans of any group that may have to support a staff of its own in the region.

The U.S. Army Natick Laboratories are fortunate to have secured the services of as qualified a medical and scientific authority as Dr. May in preparing this study. The publication of this volume has been approved by the Department of the Army, though endorsement of all statements made is not implied.

PEVERIL MEIGS, Ph. D.
Chief, Earth Sciences Division
U. S. Army Natick Laboratories
Natick, Massachusetts

This volume is the 3rd in the Food Geography Series sponsored by the Natick Laboratories, U.S. Army, 5th Volume in the Series Studies in Medical Geography published by Hafner Publishing Company, Inc.

LIST OF MAPS

Ghana

1. Ghana
2. Annual Rainfall
3. Agriculture

Nigeria

1. Nigeria
2. Topographical Units
3. Agriculture
4. Vegetation

Republic of the Congo

1. Republic of the Congo
2. Agricultural Organization
3. Staple Food Crops
4. Cultivation of Export Crops

Rwanda and Burundi

1. Rwanda and Burundi
2. Rainfall
3. Agriculture
4. Communications

The Former French Equatorial Africa

1. States of
2. Relief
3. Gabon
4. Republic of the Congo
5. Central African Republic
6. Chad

LIST OF TABLES

Ghana

1. Population
2. Production
3. Calories and Proteins

Nigeria

1. Imports
2. Exports
3. Mean Daily Food Intake
4. Nutrient Composition of Diets
5. Mean Composition of Diets
6. Seasonal Variations in Calorie and Protein Intake
7. Protein and Calorie Intake
8. Estimates of Daily Calories and Certain Nutrients

Republic of the Congo

1. Provinces of the Congo, 1963
2. Main Tribal Groups by Provinces, 1960
3. Population Data, January 1, 1959
4. Detribalized Population, 1959
5. Production of Agriculture, 1949-1962
6. Acreage and Production of Food Crops, 1958
7. Acreage and Production of Cash Crops, 1958
8. Composition and Distribution of Livestock, 1958
9. Agricultural Exports 1959-1962
10. Estimated Per Capita Caloric Intake and Food Consumption, 1953
11. Adequacy of Food Resources, 1959-1974

The Former French Equatorial Africa

1. Food Resources, 1948-1961
2. Nutrient Values in Some Equatorial African Foods
3. Summary of Food Resources, Central African Republic, 1960
4. Foods Consumed Per Capita Per Day, Central African Republic, 1960
5. Daily Per Capita Caloric Equivalents of Diets, Central African Republic, 1960
6. Nutritional Deficiencies in Selected Areas, Central African Republic, 1960

INTRODUCTION

The emergence of Africa into the Industrial Revolution and the money economy is one of the greatest problems of our times. The new nations of Africa, suddenly deprived of the support and tutelage of the colonial powers, regard with some bewilderment the two competitive political and economic systems fighting for preeminence in the world today. The choice they make, the compromises they strike, will influence their diets in a significant fashion.

"Fiat panis" says the seal of the Food and Agricultural Organization of the United Nations. One wishes it were that easy, for if bread or, in this case, porridge could be produced by wishing it, the choice Africa has to make would lose much of its drama. But Africa is poor; food has been painfully extracted from its soil in past centuries. How will the land fare under the heavy technology of the twentieth century? Which of the two systems is best suited to introduce that technology? Mistakes are paid for dearly, and in this case the price of error could be famine and death for millions of human beings.

This book is not intended to help the reader decide what is best for Africa. That is a problem that no individual can solve. The solution, if any, will, as always, emerge unforeseen from the actions of many people. This book, which deals with nine countries of equatorial Africa, intends only to outline the conditions under which food is at present produced and consumed and to give a glimpse of the problems created by the current transition from a mainly subsistence tribal way of life to a money economy dominated by mechanical technology. As is usual with the ecologic approach, these problems express the maladjustment between environment and host.

THE ENVIRONMENT OF MIDDLE AFRICA

The soils of the area under study are generally poor, shallow, and leached. Water is either too abundant, causing erosion, or too scarce, causing aridity. In addition, wherever animal husbandry occurs, there is a man-made aridity due to overgrazing that results in the early destruction of the best grasses and their replacement by annual grass of poor nutritive value (see chapter on Burundi). The best grasses are not very good either, having in most places a low nutrient and a high cellulose content. Pests and vectors of disease affect both crops and animals; the most damaging of these are the Glossinae, vectors of trypanosomiases, which exclude animal husbandry from most parts of the area under study except under special and costly programs involving breeding resistant animals and controlling tsetse expansion. No animal

manure can be counted on to improve or to replenish the soils, and
even where cattle are numerous, the herdsmen are migrants and
nomads, divorced from agricultural endeavors. This cultural separa-
tion between the farmer and the cattleman is one of the universal
problems of the area. The soils must be replenished by fallow periods
of various durations. This becomes more and more difficult to ac-
complish when population pressures gradually absorb more and more
land (see chapter on Nigeria).

Water resources vary from the Sahelian Subsahara Zone, where
surface water is very scarce and often literally nonexistent, to the
Guinean equatorial areas, where large rivers, such as the Congo, the
Niger, and the Volta, offer enormous water supplies. To put this water
to good use, however, is another matter. Much of the problem centers
on protecting the fields from floods during the rainy season and irri-
gating them during the dry season. Here technology could help, but the
selection between big schemes and small schemes is difficult to make.
The cost of big schemes demands returns that the local economy may
not be able to provide, manpower that disrupts the social structure,
and maintenance technicians that are not available; small cooperative
schemes seem better adjusted to the present possibilities but require
widespread guidance and technical supervision that has been lacking
since independence.

LAND TENURE IN MIDDLE AFRICA

Systems of land tenure varied widely in the past, from the feudal
system of Rwanda and Burundi, now mostly destroyed, to the tribal
systems of West Africa. The population pressure, combining its action
with the pressure of imported Western technology, is continually clash-
ing with tradition. These clashes have undoubtedly created a crisis in
production, as the figures collected in most of our tables will show. In
the African social context, land belongs to the tribe, to the clan, or to
the family. In many cases a council of elders or a landman representing
the council assigns the plots, taking into account the size of the family
and its production potential in tools and manpower. The only fertilizer
known is the ashes of the bushes burned before the crops are sown.
When the land is exhausted, the farmer, clan, or tribe moves elsewhere,
allowing the depleted earth to remain fallow for as long as is needed to
restore fertility.

This system was perfectly adequate as long as land was available.
It became less satisfactory as more and more land became exhausted.
Moreover, in the eyes of the ultracompetitive Western culture, the
system has many disadvantages. It excludes the idea of personal property, discourages any desire to work harder to improve one's lot, and,
because of the transitory nature of occupancy, keeps the standards of
housing and living low.

FERTILIZER

The problem of restoring the soil to fertility is basic in African development. Deficiencies in phosphorous and nitrogen primarily but also in calcium, magnesium, potassium, and sulphur are widespread. Zinc deficiencies have been noted in the Congo (Brazzaville) and in Ghana. Considerable research and experimentation remains to be done to determine quantities and proportions of fertilizers required to maintain fertility under different soil and climatic conditions; but even when the necessary data are known, problems with reference to purchase or manufacture, financing, and distribution will arise, which are at present insoluble for the average subsistence farmer. The value of animal manure is well known, but the tsetse fly prevents livestock development in most parts of the area, and wherever such development is possible, the farming and cattle cultures are totally separate.

MECHANIZATION

The history of the mechanization of agriculture in Africa is one of many failures and few successes. To be successful, mechanized farming needs a rich soil, access to fertilizers and fuel, and machine parts essential for the use, upkeep, repair, and replacement of the machines. In the future such a development can be expected; but as a rapid method of bringing Western technology to African agriculture, mechanization is premature. The cost, the rapid rate of depreciation, the scarcity of skilled labor, the lack of technicians, and the shallowness, lightness, and erosion of the soil discourage its use. Examples are many in which the powerful blades of mechanical plows have quickly buried the few inches of surface humus under the deep-seated stones that they were turning up. In addition, the introduction of machines where a large surplus of manual labor is available may immediately result in a disruption of the social equilibrium.

PRODUCTION AND DIETS

For many reasons manioc has become the most popular food item in tropical Africa. It grows in poor soil, it easily beats its rivals in calories per man-hour of work, and it keeps in the ground without spoiling, sometimes for more than a year. Manioc has therefore become the logical protection against the hungry season of the pre-rain months. Manioc, yams, and plantain are essentially foods of the tropical rain forest, but they are gaining popularity in the north and are found up to the seventh parallel for the reasons just stated. In the dry northern belts south of the Sahara sorghum and millet are the staple foods as long as the seasonal supply lasts. Rice and corn are subsidiary foods; they are also raised in many areas of the forest zone. Rice in particular is popular everywhere that it is available.

Fats come from peanuts in the north and from palm oil in the south; in some areas the shea tree (Butyrospermum parkii) provides the well liked shea butter, more often used for cosmetic than for nutritional purposes.

Meat is eaten only on rare occasions. Most of it comes from small animals killed in the forest or infrequently game, such as elephants and monkeys, but they are becoming scarcer and scarcer. Fish is important near lakes and rivers but is not important inland, although Africans know how to preserve it by smoking and drying. Milk and blood are drunk by some cattlemen. Total caloric intake varies with the season and with the country. Averages lie between 2100 and 2600 calories per capita per day, but during the seasonal shortages in northern Ghana, for instance, the total intake sometimes drops as low as 650 calories per capita per day. The percentage of animal protein in the total caloric intake is less than 6 percent. Meat consumption varies from 7 kilos per person per year in Chad to 1 kilo per person per year in the Congo, Brazzaville. The main problems common to all countries studied are: seasonal food shortages; protein and vitamin deficiencies; undernutrition and malnutrition of children; lack of nutritional education; adverse influence of food taboos; and the absence of storage space for food and of a marketing organization.

THE PEOPLE

The predictable alternation of periods of plenty with periods of starvation does not frighten or upset the average African. The cycle has occurred for centuries, and most Africans prefer that way of life to a mediocre fare all year round. In spite of the hardships, many Africans prefer their traditional system to the frustrations and anxieties that go with a competitive system such as the money economy. One of the most successful schemes of improving living standards without upsetting tradition too much is the paysannat system. This was established in most of the countries studied, with local variations. The system allocates land to a farmer and his family, often preparing the ground for him, making sure that there is an accessible market nearby, building schools and health centers in the vicinity, and letting him enjoy the proceeds of the venture while exerting some guidance on the selection of crops, seeds, and farming methods. We shall see that the system was giving good results wherever it was applied, but the withdrawal of adequate supervision after independence has resulted in its deterioration.

Basically, the African wishes to produce no more than he needs. Surplus production for money is not part of his outlook on life. Given better seed, he will rejoice not because it will give him a better yield but because he will get the same result from a smaller plot. Surpluses are not particularly appreciated. First, they spoil in the harsh African climate. (In the course of this book, the longevity of the various foods will be discussed.) Second, when food is abundant, there is no demand for the surpluses in the local areas; transportation to distant markets is difficult and the price uncertain. Therefore when food is abundant, it is better to gorge oneself than to carry it away for little or no profit. Even if money can be made by selling food, what can be done with the money? There are few articles for sale in the local area, and even in the distant towns there are only a few small items, not worth the risk and fatigue of a trip to buy them.

THE PROBLEM OF POPULATION GROWTH
AND URBAN SETTLEMENT

As a result of the control the colonial powers had established over endemic diseases, the growth rate of the population has been steadily increasing in past decades. Ghana, Nigeria, and Chad were probably growing at a rate of 2.5 percent a year, while the two Congos, Gabon, and the Central African Republic were growing at the lower rate of 1.8 or 2 percent. Rwanda and Burundi, however, are among the fastest growing countries of Africa, with a possible rate of 3 percent annually. The population under 15 probably represents about 40 percent of the total. This implies that if the death rate can be kept at its present level or lower, an increase of about 60 percent is to be expected within 20 to 25 years. Unless considerable economic improvement takes place, unemployment, malnutrition, and social unrest are to be expected. An indication of things to come is found in the cities of Leopoldville, Brazzaville, and even Bangui. They give an inkling of what can become of a destitute group of detribalized people seeking to play a role in the money economy (see chapter on the former Belgian Congo). As it is, there is an overgrowth of petty traders and government officials, a distressing pool of totally unemployed men separated from their tribe, and women whose meager resources do not meet the cost of living in cities. Urban diets have lost their tribal character, and the workers try to round up enough money to feed themselves white bread, canned foods, and imported spirits. It has been said that Nigeria will be confronted with 800,000 unemployed school graduates by 1966. It can only be hoped that other factors will develop soon that will allow the absorption of this literate group into some productive enterprise. In summary, the problems encountered in these regions illustrate the difficulty of "leapfrogging" a medieval type of culture into the twentieth century. The fact that some amount of "telescoping" in time is possible is not doubted, but it may have to be a smaller amount than had been hoped. While it is true that the machines of modern technology exist so the time it took to develop them can be saved, it is no less true that the physical, social, psychological, and cultural factors of "developing" countries also exist. Those factors are not compatible with the machine age. It will take some fresh thinking and careful experimentation before we know how long it will take for modern machines to create a new and livable culture.

GHANA

TABLE OF CONTENTS

1

TABLE OF CONTENTS (Continued)

GHANA

Weights and Measures

1 kilometer	=	0.621 mile
1 square kilometer	=	0.386 square miles
1 hectare	=	2.47 acres
1 ton	=	10 quintals
1 quintal	=	100 kilograms
1 kilogram	=	2.205 lb.
1 hectolitre	=	22 gallons

The unit of currency is the Ghana £ equivalent with the £ sterling

1 £ Ghana = $U.S. 2.80

GHANA

I

BACKGROUND

A. GEOGRAPHY [1] [25]

Ghana is a fragment of West African territory located between 4° 30' and 11° north and between 1°30' east and 3°30' west of Greenwich. The zero meridian passes through the eastern half of Ghana, intersecting the coast at Tema, where a rock protruding out of the sea is known as Meridian Rock. Ghana formerly belonged to Britain and is now a republic within the British Commonwealth. It is bounded on the east, north, and west by the French-speaking states of Ivory Coast, Upper Volta, and Togo. Its southern limit is the Atlantic Ocean, whose inhospitable, strong surf line forbids any safe natural anchorage along its 567-kilometer coast. Ghana covers 237,873 square kilometers, just about the area of the United Kingdom. Its political unity is entirely artificial and has no ethnic, cultural, or geographical basis. Its only cementing factors arise from its recent status as a British colony and the culture and other consequences that have derived from this historical circumstance. For the purpose of this study, this is of great importance. It explains the fragmentation of its land resources, production, and even diets. It explains the artificiality of its regional structure, since all its geographical regions continue into neighboring countries. There is no coincidence between politics and geography. Politically, the country is divided into eight regions as follows:

Eastern Region	22,662.50 square kilometers
Western Region	24,689.46 square kilometers
Central Region	9,567.58 square kilometers
Ashanti Region	25,123 square kilometers
Brong Ahafo	38,591 square kilometers
Northern Region	70,245.98 square kilometers
Volta Region	20,700 square kilometers
Upper Region	27,138 square kilometers

Geographically, there are three main agricultural regions: 1) the coastal savannah, 2) the forest, and 3) the northern savannah.

Considering climate, land form, and consequent economic developments, Boateng further subdivided these regions as follows: (see Map No. 1).

1) Coastal savannah:

> Accra Plains
> Cape Coast Winneba Plains
> Volta Delta

2) Forest region:

> Akwapim-Togo Ranges
> Kwahu Plateau
> Southern Ashanti Uplands
> Akan Lowlands

3) Northern savannah:

> Afram Plains
> Krachi and Northern Ashanti
> Gonja and Dagomba Savannahs
> High plains of Wa and Mamprusi
> Gambaga Scarp

Notice that these areas or geographic divisions do not coincide with the administrative regions given in Table No. 1.

The Accra Coastal Plain has little rainfall, usually less than 850 to 900 mm. per year. The soil is better further north, where rainfall is more abundant (see Map No. 2). The area practices shifting agriculture except around Accra, where settled farming occurs. The markets of the local towns and of Accra absorb the production of the small farms, which are usually less than one hectare (2.47 acres) in size. Farmers burn the grass for fertilizer, as elsewhere in Africa. Around Accra, however, the absence of tsetse flies allows some animal husbandry; animal manure is available and is used in gardens. In spite of local water shortages, there are pastures near Teshie, allowing some cattle breeding as well as raising of pigs, sheep, goats, and poultry. The Volta Project is intended, among other goals, to develop agriculture through irrigation in this area. Fishing is an important source of food all along the coast and inland in the marshes and lagoons. Accra, Labadi, Tema, Prampram, and Teshie are fishing ports.

The Cape Coast Winneba Plains consist of a narrow band of land extending west of Accra to the east of Sekondi Takoradi. It is a farming and fishing area where tsetse infestation makes livestock husbandry impossible and where water scarcity further hampers agricultural development. The beginnings of a citrus industry is evidenced by a few lime tree groves. The area is inhabited by the Effutu and the Fanti, who have gained fame as fishermen and whose skill in handling the surf-riding boats needed to load the big cargo vessels offshore is well known.

The Volta Delta is an alluvial land that also suffers from a relatively small rainfall. The main agricultural activity is centered on the cash crops of the coconut, copra, and palm trees.

The Akwapim-Togo Ranges represent the Ghanaian part of a highland zone that extends through neighboring countries to the Niger River. Along the deep valleys of that region farming is the prominent activity and produces the forest crops. In the Togo area around Ho two cash crops of great importance are found—cocoa and coffee.

Between the Akwapim Ranges and the eastern end of the Kwahu plateau is the Pawm-pawm basin. The Krobo people located there practice a form of shifting agriculture called "Husa farming." This is a type of cooperative system in which a group of farmers buy land along a river and divide it into long, narrow strips, each with a river frontage. This results in improved water supply and increased yields.

The Kwahu Plateau has an average elevation of 500 meters. It divides the waters that flow south into the sea from the rivers flowing northeast into the Volta. In the Kwahu cash crops like cocoa and food crops like onions are grown in equal proportion. Unfortunately, communications are difficult, which hampers the development of the region.

The Southern Ashanti Uplands are located southwest of the Kwahu Plateau, sloping gently from 400 meters in the north to 250 meters in the south. The Uplands contain Kumasi, the second most important town in Ghana. This area represents the most important economic area of the country for both agricultural and mineral resources; the rainfall is adequate (1250 to 1500 mm. per year) for cocoa farming, the most important single cash crop of Ghana and the mainstay of her economy. Food crops are also grown, making Kumasi an important market that trades in yams, imported meat from the north, shea butter, livestock, and other such commodities. The large mining centers of the area, to which gold gave a former name, import their meat from the north.

The Akan Lowlands are located between the previous region and the northern limit of the Cape Coast Winneba Plains. The average elevation is less than 150 meters. The rainfall reaches 1500 to 2100 mm. per year in the southwest corner, which results in dense forest growth. Under the Akim people, the Densu and Pra Basins have become a cocoa-planting pioneering area. Some rice farming is practiced in the extreme southwest around Axim and Esiama. Copra and palm oil are produced in the same area. An important food market supplying Tarkwa and Sekondi Takoradi is found at the village of Opon Valley. The area of Sefwi and Ateiku produces food for the adjacent mining areas, but communications are limited and the distribution of food is unsatisfactory. An attempt to promote the development of bananas for export has recently been made in the area. There is some fishing along the coast. On the whole, this is a relatively depressed area.

The Afram Plains are located within the area defined by the Volta, the Obosum, and the Afram rivers. The district is a depressed area and is also typical tsetse country. Rainfall does not exceed 1300 mm.

per year. The population is sparse and lives primarily by hunting and localized attempts at cocoa planting. Communications are bad because roads are nonexistent. There is some fishing in the rivers, and the catch is sold at the Asesewa Market.

The Krachi and Northern Ashanti Region includes the Northern Ashanti country, the Mampung-Ejura Scarp, and the western part of the Krachi district; its average elevation is between 200 and 300 meters. The rainfall diminishes from south to north and does not exceed 1100 to 1200 mm. The whole area suffers from the fury of the Harmattan wind, especially between November and March. Tsetse flies and dryness combine to depress the region; communications are poor. The area, however, could be improved, irrigated, and developed.

The Gonja and Dagomba Savannahs farther north average less than 200 meters in elevation. The vegetation is sparse and is frequently referred to as "orchard bush." The area is poor, and the soil is dry and sandy. Some cattle are raised in spite of spotty tsetse fly breeding areas. Simulium damnosum, vector of onchocerciasis, is also present. Cattle, which are mostly found north of Tamale (40,000 inhabitants), are exported, together with some chickens and guinea fowls. The shea tree, which grows wild, produces a kind of vegetable fat called "shea butter," which is also exported to other areas of Ghana and is an important part of the local diet. In spite of these assets the area was for a long time a land of famine, and the dry season still creates food shortages that can lead to grave situations.

The high plains of Wa and Mamprusi are located north of the Gonja Savannahs. The average elevation is between 200 and 350 meters; rainfall amounts to 1000 to 1250 mm. per year. There is a long dry season that becomes longer as one moves north. Cattle raising is widespread, and its products are sold in other regions. These activities, however, are limited in space and intensity. Certain areas are still infested with onchocerciasis. Where soil is fertile, people are crowded together in such high densities that the carrying capacity of the land is overtaken and people survive at bare subsistence level. Bolgatanga and Bawku are the most important food markets.

The Gambaga Scarp, a small area of highland 400 to 500 meters in elevation, is an enclave in the easternmost part of the preceding area. The climate is cool and more humid than elsewhere in the northern region. The main activity is farming millet, guinea corn, and sweet potatoes. There is also some animal husbandry.

B. POPULATION[26][25]

In 1963 Ghana had a population of approximately 7,693,000—if the 1960 census (see Table No. 1) and the yearly rates of increase are correct. This population grew from an estimated 4,478,000 in 1953 with crude live-birth rates increasing from 30 per 1000 in 1952 to 55.8 in 1960. These figures, however, are extrapolated from limited areas

where compulsory registration is in force. These areas include 36
towns and townships but represent only 12 percent of the total population. Ghana has one of the highest rates of late fetal death in the whole
of A f r i c a (66 per 1000 live births), apparently surpassed only by
Mauritius and the Spanish Sahara. Infant mortality is high by both
Western and African standards (113.1 per 1000 live births in 1962) and
has changed little in the past decade (113 in 1953). Crude death rates
are also both high (22.7 per 1000 in 1962) and stable (20.3 per 1000 in
1952). Population data are summarized in the short table below:

Total (1960)	Rate of increase in percent	Density per sq. km.	Infant Mortality	Life Expectancy
6,690,757	6.2	28	113.1	38

Ethnically, the people are fairly homogenous. Most of them derive
from the Sudanese Negro stock; in the north and center there are
streaks of the hamitic wanderers who came from the Sahara or beyond
and intermarried with the local stock. The peopling of the country is
somewhat recent and is believed to have taken place during the last 1000
years. Politically, however, the people organized themselves into tribes
and nations that do not seem to have, at least originally, any ethnic
characterization to distinguish them. These tribes were nomadic, following the impulses of war and the pressure for food. The most important of these tribes are the Akans, who have settled in the Ashanti,
Western, and Eastern Regions. The Guans surround the Akans to the
north and to the east, while the Fantis are established in the lowlands
between Cape Coast and Axim. The Twis occupy the large, tsetse-
infested area south of the Volta and north of the Kwahu Plateau. The
Ga-Adangmes occupy the coast east of Accra and the Ewes the hinterland of that region. The most important tribes of the Northern region
are the Dagombas in the east, the Moshis in the north, and the Gonjas
in the southwest.

All these people are grouped in approximately 108 native states;
some are very small (2000 people), some large (230,000 people). These
native states have no very well defined boundaries, which causes continuous bitter and often bloody rivalries and disputes. Since independence in 1957 the chiefs of the traditional tribal states form a House of
Chiefs in each region, mainly concerned with tribal and customary
problems. The eight regions are in turn divided into 26 districts. Obviously, more people live in the fertile agricultural areas; the coastal
lands west and north of Accra have densities of up to 75 per square
kilometer. Similar densities are also found around Kumasi. In contrast,
the whole center of the country, the Gonja district, has a population
density of less than two per square kilometer. This area has insufficient
rainfall for agriculture (less than 1250 mm. per annum), and in the
Afram Plains the tsetse fly is a handicap to the livestock industry. In

the white Volta area, low population densities are caused by the presence of <u>Simulium damnosum</u>, which causes onchocerciasis or "river blindness." These contrasting population situations produce a great variety of types of land tenure and food resources, which will be discussed later.

As in many African territories, the population patterns of Ghana have been influenced by the administrative requirements of the colonial powers; with the exception of Ashanti, a well defined geographical and political entity, the district lines were often established as a result of political and economic considerations that cut across ancient tribal and traditional arrangements.

The population of Ghana is mostly rural (84 percent) and includes approximately 90 towns of more than 3000 inhabitants. The people's participation in agriculture in general varies with the region. The highest proportion of agriculturists is found in the north, where 90 percent of the population are tilling the fields. Next come the Volta Region, the Ashanti, the Brong Ahafo, and then the South and Western Regions. Accra, the capital and largest connurbation, has 200,000 inhabitants. It was founded in 1876, when the advantage of being in a nontsetse area that allowed animal transportation became understood. The people of Ghana have special food habits that derive from tradition as well as from geographic factors; they will be studied in the section on regional diets.

C. AGRICULTURAL POLICIES [19][1][5][2]

"The African land tenure system is now both fluid and misunderstood."* This sentence applies to Ghana as much as to other countries of Africa. Agriculture in Ghana faces four major problems that government policies have so far failed to solve to any significant extent. These four problems are: scarcity of water in certain areas; lack of transportation from producer to market; low productivity of the soil; and inadequate coordination of food production, storage, and distribution.

In the north and in some parts of the coastal savannahs water is probably the most important problem since it also involves the problem of soil erosion caused by the torrential character of the intermittent rainfall. Thus, the traditional policy of migrant agriculture makes sense because it allows the bush to cover depleted soil and to prevent erosion to some degree. Unfortunately, this procedure allows only a small fraction of the land to be under cultivation at any given time. Boateng** remarks that the untidy aspect of some Ghanaian farms is due to an overgrowth of bushes that, however untidy, keeps the topsoil in place.

---

*Source No. 19
**Source No. 1

It follows that this policy should not be condemned or disturbed without good reason.

Low rates of rainfall in certain areas cause another water problem since the scarcity of water hampers the development of pasture land. It is hoped that adequate irrigation policies and plans will grow out of the present land-and-water survey for which the government of Ghana has contracted with the United Nations Special Fund; it is to be administered by FAO at a cost of $1,181,700.

Another problem related to agriculture is the lack of adequate transportation. Farmers are reluctant to carry their heavy loads to market centers since their produce will bring low prices.

A road-building program would undoubtedly improve the food-marketing situation. Storage facilities and feed roads to the few main transportation lines are planned, and some are even under construction.

The low productivity of the soil, indicated by low yields in relation to the number of people employed, could be improved if fertilizers were available and mechanization possible. In a tsetse country the solution to the fertilizer problem is the use of chemical fertilizers; this, however, is expensive and would in most cases be beyond the means of the individual farmers. Mechanization as a solution of the food problem has disadvantages as well as advantages. It must be used with caution wherever the topsoil is shallow. It can be used to create new farmlands from forests, but the cost is high and the results uncertain. Moreover, with the destruction of the forest erosion would be increased; the very nature of agriculture would change since humidity and shade would disappear; irrigation would have to follow, involving further capital expenditure. This unhappy chain of causes and effects is one of the basic problems of rural development in Africa.

The inadequate coordination of food production, storage and distribution is of concern to the government. A start at coordination was made in 1961 with the marketing of grain, groundnuts, and eggs. It is planned to extend this domestic marketing organization to other foodstuffs, following a system developed for the cash-crop cocoa by the Ghana Farmer Marketing Council. A marketing organization is being developed by the Agricultural Development Corporation, operating for the Producer's Cooperatives. Much of the success of this venture depends on improved transportation and roads, which will help avoid glut in some areas while famine conditions exist in others.

Improvements are planned also for fisheries, port facilities, shore plants, fishing vessels, refrigeration, and wholesale and retail distribution of seafood. Here too the problem of transportation of fish from curing centers to consuming centers is inadequately handled. A costly chain of middlemen is reported to deprive the producer of a fair return for his work and the consumer of a product priced within his means. The planned organization may improve this situation.

While the development of the cocoa and coconut industries has been spectacular in the past years, only 25 percent of the farmers of Ghana grow these crops. Most of the food crops are still grown as they were hundreds of years ago. Therefore, the major objectives of agriculture during the next five years will be to develop new crops and to teach new agricultural methods to the 75 percent of the people who do not grow the cash crops. The following priorities have been established:

(1) diversification of agricultural products
(2) establishment of large acreages of rubber and bananas in the rainy southwest of the country
(3) establishment of a cattle industry
(4) improvement of cereal yields in the Northern Region
(5) development of irrigation in the Volta plain and elsewhere
(6) development of fertilizers

These priorities will presumably be included in the new seven-year development plan. This is a successor to the suspended five-year development program (1959-1964) and should be part of the comprehensive planning functions entrusted to the recently established National Planning Commission. In addition, a policy of establishing large-scale cooperative farms is being pursued.

II

FOOD RESOURCES

A. GENERAL [20] [4]

The soils of Ghana are mainly formed of laterite, rich in ferrous oxide and aluminum hydroxide. To make these soils productive, a high degree of fertilization is needed, which is at present not readily available.

Agriculture in Ghana provides 75 percent of all export revenues as well as all of the food crops consumed by the rural population and most of that consumed by the urban population.

Climate, soils, and traditions bring about a great diversity of crops; cash crops include cocoa, palm kernels, coffee, copra, lime juice, bananas, kola nuts, and groundnuts; food crops include guinea corn, millet, sorghum, rice, Indian corn, yams, cocoyams, sugar cane, plantain, cassava, and dried peas. Sources of animal proteins from the sea, lagoons, and rivers are available although not utilized to the fullest extent. In the cash-crop areas most people get their food from markets, although some practice mixed farming (cash and food). In the food-crop areas most people get their food from their own land or from the nearest village. Some people subsist on both, getting their basic foods from their own production and some extras from the markets.

The soils are light and poor in plant nutrients because the rains carry the elements deep into the subsoil. Faced with these conditions, the people have developed techniques that are well suited to the environment and that should not, in hope of rapid modernization, be upset without careful study. Farming is done with hoes and sticks, appropriate tools where topsoil is shallow and where stones and pebbles would be turned up by deep plowing. There is little irrigation and little fertilizer; slash-and-burn methods are used. These methods leave stumps and weeds in the fields that consume a share of rare nutrients; but they also prevent more erosion. As in most other countries of West Africa, the farmers depend on clearing new land where needed while allowing depleted land to lie fallow to recuperate. This is cheaper than fertilizer, which at present the Ghanaian economy cannot afford. As shown by numerous examples in many countries of tropical Africa, imported European or American methods of agriculture are not always suitable and can lead to economic failures and food losses.

The system of land tenure is also strange to Western minds. As we have seen, Ghana has more than 100 states or nations subdivided into many tribes and clans; each tribe has its own traditional system of land ownership. Some common traits can be found, such as the fact that ownership of land is everywhere more genealogical than geographical, leading to non-Western concepts of real-estate ownership and transfer. The migratory character of the farming population must always be kept in mind when trying to understand African and Ghanaian agriculture. While these migrations are less marked among farmers than among pastoralists and less marked today than formerly, they are still a significant trait of African agriculture. Only the binding nature of the great cash crops—cocoa, bananas, coffee, palm—has more and more made its influence felt and tied down the African farmer to the land. It is obvious that the migratory nature of farming and the tribal systems of land ownerships result in great complexity and vastly increase the difficulty of reorganizing land ownership.

B. MEANS OF PRODUCTION [25][2]

1. Agricultural Labor Force
Approximately 70 percent of the whole population engages in some form of agricultural labor. This percentage increases in the north to 90 percent and decreases progressively in the Volta, Ashanti, Brong Ahafo, Eastern, and Western Regions. The concept of a labor force needs to be redefined; in Ghana it should include the self-employed farmer as well as the farm hand who hires himself to a large plantation owner. The scarcity of unskilled labor creates a demand that causes the wage earning group to increase at the expense of of the subsistence farmer, resulting in an aggravation of the food shortages because the former produces mainly cash crops.

Despite government pleas of "Back to the Land," the lure of the towns and cities erodes the agricultural labor force year after year. The demand for food increases in urban areas while the farm population decreases; food imports doubled between 1955 and 1962.

2. Farms [5][1][2]

A policy of consolidating small farms into large-scale co-operatives is now being pursued; in some areas farms are merged to constitute estates of 200 hectares or more in the hope that the inherent inefficiency of the small single holding will be overcome. This has been tried elsewhere with mixed results. At the present time, however, farms in Ghana are mostly private or tribal, with the exception of a few experimental state farms. Private farms belong for a time to individual families or tribes (see above), sometimes to private companies. Differences in size and purpose occur in different regions such as coastal savannah, forest, and northern savannah.

In the coastal savannah farms are usually small, covering less than 1 hectare. Three types of agricultural activity occur in this area—coconut and copra, vegetable gardens, and livestock raising (in the east).

Coconuts are part of the regional diet, but they are also a cash crop in some areas, such as around Keta, whence copra is exported. This activity contrasts with the following insofar as it has pinned the farmer to the land.

Garden farming in Ghana is typical of the plant-harvest-leave type of agriculture found throughout Africa. Typical crops in Ghana are cassava and such vegetables as tomatoes, peppers, shallots, and corn. Such gardens as these abound around Accra, where they find a ready market. It is not unusual to find chickens, goats, and pigs in these gardens.

In cattle raising the distribution of pastures and waters governs the type of farm and its location. Pastures are found mainly between Accra and the Shai Hills; they are occasionally kept moist and green by irrigation, especially east of Achimota. Animal husbandry is in the hands of northern pastoralists who have migrated south, attracted by the pastures. They seldom do any cultivation and do not mix with the local people.

In the forest zone farms are again of a different type. This zone extends over the greatest part of the Eastern, Western, and Ashanti Regions and is principally devoted to the famous cocoa farms that are the backbone of Ghanaian economy. Like coconut in the coastal savannah, cocoa is the anchor that keeps the farmer rooted to the soil. It takes five to seven years to bring a cocoa tree to full production, after which profitable yields can be expected for several years. This is long enough to deter the farmers from their shifting and wandering habits and involves a notable change in way of life.

Cocoa was first grown in 1879 and became the most important crop after 1905. Most cocoa farms are small, seldom exceeding two acres; but some industrious farmers have developed larger estates on which they use hired labor, giving rise to the absentee landlord phenomenon. Food crops are grown in between cocoa trees during their first maturing years. Then, when the trees become productive, food crops are confined to the periphery of the cocoa lands. Food crops, in this zone as elsewhere, are produced by shifting agriculture: slash and burn, sow and harvest for a couple of years, then move on to new lands. Mixed farming is the custom; food crops maturing at different times of the year are planted in succession. Between April and December corn, plantain, vegetables, and cocoyams, are sown and harvested; cassava is also popular because of its ability to grow even in poor soil. Rice of the swamp variety is sown in April and harvested in August. Farmers grow these foods for local consumption but sell some in neighboring markets. Throughout the area tsetse infestation prevents animal husbandry.

In the northern savannah farms are again small and entirely devoted to subsistence crops. North of the settlement of Tamale there is some plow cultivation, using draft animals. The crops consist of grain, millet, corn, rice; cassava and yams are very popular; garden vegetables include tomatoes, peppers, eggplants, and various kinds of pulses.* Farming in this area is much affected by the vagaries of the weather. There are only two seasons: the dry and the rainy, the latter sometimes too short to provide sufficient moisture for the soil. As a result, a dangerous gap may occur during the dry season, the "hungry season," and famine conditions may arise. Since the area is free of tsetse flies, the farmers also raise livestock; this provides manure for the fields. In some farms a shifting cultivation is the rule. There is some export of cattle. Some farmers, driven by food scarcity, move on foot to the south with their animals in the hope of finding a market. Soil fertility is generally low and deteriorates still further after cultivation; it must lie fallow three times as long as it has been under cultivation. This fallow period may vary from place to place, but everywhere the problem of restoring fertility after culture is of major importance.

3. Fertilizers [20] [2]

In most of the tropics the lack of nitrogen in the soil is second only to lack of water in causing poor yields. In Ghana samples have shown that soil nitrate is adequate for up to eight years after cultivation under the natural forest conditions; but after cropping yields in corn increase by 26 percent if 120 kilograms of ammonium sulphate per hectare is added to the soil. Forest soils have been found richer in phosphorous than savannah soils, but the potassium content has been found generally inadequate, especially in higher rainfall areas. In a country where cattle manure is not generally available and where the

---

*The government has long-range plans to displace millet and sorghum with new types of hybrid corn, yielding hopefully two and one-half tons per hectare; it has appropriated funds for this study.

economic level of the farmer does not allow the purchase of chemical fertilizers, the problem of soil enrichment or even of soil replenishment is possibly the most important of all. We have seen that slash-and-burn methods and shifting cultivation are the century-old answers. This is being improved by shortening the fallow period and finding plants whose nature, constitution, and rates of growth allow them to be grown on abandoned lands.* As expected in a country in which water is not distributed adequately for the needs of agriculture, plans are made for the development of irrigation schemes. These include the Volta Project, aimed at protecting crops in the Accra Plain against dry spells. Other studies are being made at Kpong and at the University College of Ghana's Agricultural Station at Nungwa. At present irrigated farming is practiced in the areas of Keta and Anloga. Irrigation schemes, if not carefully planned and supervised, carry the great danger of spreading schistosomiasis by creating new sites favorable to the development of snail intermediate hosts.

4. Mechanical Equipment [5]

Mechanical agriculture may appear to be the ideal solution for increasing productivity in a country in which animals are severely limited by the tsetse fly. Yet, as already stated, mechanization in Africa is of doubtful value; it has been only carefully and tentatively undertaken in Ghana as well as in most parts of tropical Africa. Experiments with mechanized agriculture, however, have been made at Damongo in the northern savannah, as well as in the south coastal area of Pokoasi and Nungwa. It is too soon to draw conclusions on the value of these methods in a country like Ghana. In 1958 there were 161 tractors on government experimental stations, of which 146 had wheels and 15 were crawlers. There were also 15 garden tractors, also government-owned.

C. PRODUCTION [4][2][20][6]

Production figures are only approximate since methods for statistical control are elementary. Figures are for only a few reporting areas, are not always recent, and sometimes date back to 1953.

1. Cereals (see Map No. 3)

Cereals include Indian corn (in the south), guinea corn (in the north), millet, sorghum, and rice. Table No. 2 summarizes production figures for all four cereals, indicating slow development. While corn plantings were reported expanding from 142,000 hectares in the base period 1948-1953 to 252,000 hectares in 1961-1962, production has not risen proportionally but only from 168,000 tons to 183,000 tons, a loss in yield per hectare from 11.8 to 7.3 quintals. These yields are not

---

*The fertilizer industry is not yet established in Ghana but is on the list of high priorities in industrial development.

only low by world standards, but are also well below many African yields, such as Gambia (10.1 quintals per hectare), Rhodesia (23.2 in the north and 24.6 in Southern Rhodesia), Rwanda and Burundi (13.9 quintals per hectare). Similar low yields obtain in neighboring countries such as Upper Volta (6.4), Togo (5.2), and the Ivory Coast (6.2).

Rice is grown on more than 27,000 hectares, but yields are poor, and a production of 34,000 tons in 1962 is mediocre. Rice is a cash crop in northern Ghana, where efforts are made to improve yields. In other areas of Africa rice yields are better, reaching 34.7 quintals per hectare in Rwanda and Burundi.

2. Other Crops

Other crops are mainly yams and cassava. Areas under yams have declined slightly from 64,000 hectares in 1948 to 60,000 hectares in 1958, with yields and production practically unchanged at 481,000 tons. Yams require considerable care and demand twice as much work as Indian corn per area cultivated. Cassava, the mainstay of African diets, has expanded from 66,000 to 87,000 hectares, and yields have increased significantly. Production has risen 100 percent from 512,000 tons to 1,092,000 tons, due, no doubt, to the increased popularity of this "poor man's crop," which accommodates itself to most terrains and can be grown almost anywhere except in swamps.

Other food crops include dried peas and groundnuts, the latter covering some 55,000 hectares and yielding 49,000 tons of product, a rate in keeping with or slightly better than the yields of neighboring countries (Ivory Coast 6.3 quintals per hectare, Southern Rhodesia 5.3, Sierra Leone 5.4). Great hopes for an increase in food crops are aroused by the United Nations Special Fund of $1,181,700 for a land-and-water survey covering 800,000 hectares, which indicates that production of millet, rice, yams, and peanuts could be increased several times. Cash crops such as pineapple could also be expanded.

3. Cash Crops

Cash crops are the most important part of Ghana's economy. Most important of them all is cocoa, followed by palm kernels, copra, coffee, kola nuts, bananas, and limes. Cocoa now covers over two million hectares, mostly in the Ashanti and in the Eastern, Western, and Volta Regions. Cocoa is the object of constant careful studies and encouragement by the government. Yields have recently been considerably improved by using better varieties of seeds and by spraying to control capsid* and swollen shoot disease. The Division of Cocoa Industry has 19 stations spread throughout the countryside, and there is a West African Cocoa Research Institute at New Tafo. In recent years the world output of cocoa has increased by 14 percent. More than 90 percent of the increase has come from Ghana and Nigeria. The future of the cocoa industry in these countries would be improved if Ghana could join the Common Market, because expansion of markets is the only way

---

*Phytophtora palmivora

to prevent a slump in prices such as occurred in 1930. Cocoa exports have risen from 253,300 tons of beans per year between 1948 and 1953 to 321,900 tons per year in 1959 and 1960.

Palm-kernel production amounted to between 9000 and 11,000 tons in the 50's. It dropped to 2900 tons in 1960. In the late nineteenth century it was a leading export from Ghana. Copra production is on the increase and has more than doubled since 1948-1953, from 1600 tons a year to 3800 tons in 1960.

Coffee cultivation dates from the beginning of this century. A total of a thousand hectares are planted with coffee in Ghana, of which more than 800 hectares are in the Akwapim-Togo Ranges.

Production is growing and reached 1982 tons in 1960 as compared with 500 tons per year from 1948 to 1953. Kola nuts, an indigenous product that has an agricultural requirement similar to that of cocoa, were once an important economic asset but are now a purely domestic commodity; 8576 tons were traded in 1960. Bananas, which grow well between maturing rubber trees, are found in many places where a rich humus exists and where rubber is being developed. It is basically a food crop, but 1420 tons were produced for export on a cash basis in 1960. Lime is one of the citrus fruits that shows signs of developing into a profitable cash crop. It is found in the forest zone near Abakrampa; there a local factory that produces crude juice for export produced 32,000 hectolitres in 1960. Pineapple has proven a source of revenue to farmers; they can be sold both on the fresh-fruit markets and to the canning industry. The A.D.C. canning factory at Nsawam, primarily designed for tomato products, is utilizing pineapple as a secondary industry. Tobacco, a currency earner, is being encouraged; the previous production was 350 tons, and the current goal is 2000 tons.

4. Sources Of Animal Proteins [4][25][5][20][11]

Livestock. As already indicated, most of Ghana's agricultural land is not suited for livestock raising because much of the forest zone is infested with tsetse.* Livestock are found in the coastal savannah to a moderate extent and in the northern savannah to a large extent. The best pastures in the south for livestock raising consist of guinea grass between Teshie and Ada; the best in the north are found in the low savannah of the Mamprusi region. Ghana had 480,000 cattle in 1961, a fairly good increase from the 373,000 of the base period 1948-1952. It is estimated that 40 percent of the cattle are cows, as this was the proportion existing in 1952. There is little milk sold except in the area between Tema and Dodowa; most of the animals are kept for breeding.

Pigs are also raised in the coastal savannah. Their number was estimated at 49,000 in 1961 and at 28,000 in 1952. Sheep are raised in the Southern Region, in the Southern Ashanti Uplands, and in the high plains of Mamprusi. Pigs were estimated at over 500,000 in 1961, a slight increase over the 1952 figure of 443,000. Sheep and goats are also raised in these areas, and each number 500,000.

*Glossina palpalis, morsitans and other species.

The number of poultry around the farms is estimated at 2,600,000 in 1961 and at 2,343,000 in 1952.

Given a reported slaughter of 98,000 cattle, 28,000 pigs, 84,000 sheep, and 136,000 goats, the amount of meat available at registered slaughterhouses in 1959 can be computed. Phillips states that the carcass weight of the African cattle is very low; approximate weights are: cattle 118 kilograms, sheep and goats 10 kilograms, pigs 20 kilograms. On this basis approximately 16,320 tons of inspected meat would have been available in 1959-1960, or a little over two kilograms per capita; this is an obvious improvement, if correct, over the figure of 4000 tons reported in 1952, of which 3000 were beef and veal and 1000 were pork. At the same time offal of all kinds was estimated at 22,000 tons. No valid estimate can be made of the amount of milk available or drunk in any form whatsoever, but it can be determined that the average cow does not yield much more than 200 litres a year and many yield much less.

In addition to these indigenous resources in livestock and products, over 60,000 cattle and 250,000 goats and sheep are imported annually on foot from Upper Volta into the Northern Region of Ghana. Originally, some of these migrating herds may have come from Mali.

Fisheries. Fishing constitutes an important part of Ghanaian food resources. It involves over 67,000 people who fish the sea, lagoons, and rivers. The Fanti and the Ewe are the tribes most dedicated to seine fishing; the Ga-Andangmes prefer line fishing. The fishing fleet comprises 8900 dugout canoes propelled by paddles and sails and some 185 motor vessels. The fishing season extends from June to September, and fish is then abundant and reasonably priced. Herring (Sardinella) and bream are the most popular species landed. In the lagoons fishermen use casting nets and occasionally hooks and lines. They also catch carp, for which baskets are used. River fishing is important and provides animal protein to many an inland population group. The most important fishing grounds are the Afram and Volta Rivers. In spite of regulations the practice of catching fish by traps after having poisoned the waters still prevails; this practice destroys inedible and immature fish. The amount of sea fish landed reaches over 20,000 tons a year, to which approximately 15,000 tons of fresh-water fish is added for a total of 35,000 tons in 1961, a considerable improvement over 25,300 tons in 1955. The government has shown interest in developing the fishing industry and has set up a Fisheries Division with a Regional Office at Takoradi. Only a few years ago the fish procurement pattern consisted of fishermen landing their catch and distributing it to women who sold it either as fresh fish or as smoked or dried.* There were no wholesale markets or cold-storage facilities. In recent years notable efforts have been made by two successive chiefs of the Fisheries Divi-

*The fishermen were—and still are—completely dependent on the "fish mammies," who pay them either in cash or kind for their catches. Some are married to the "mammies," some are not; during idle months or days (Tuesdays) the men are supplied with food and repay with fish later.

sion to improve the situation. A fishing harbor is being developed at
Tema, where an ice plant has been built; experimental work at Osu has
covered smoking, drying, and canning; a foreign firm has contracted
for tuna fishing and the production of fish meal and canning for export.
The development and promotion of fish meal has been fairly successful
in the Northern Region, where it is consumed in soups and stew. Further exploration of the scheme is in process.

     Eggs. Little is contributed to the animal protein diet by eggs
because few are consumed. Eggs are taboo for women in many African
groups, although certain populations limit the taboo to chicken eggs.
However, 280 certified poultry farms were in operation at Accra in
1959, 12 in the Eastern Region; 54 in the Volta and Togoland areas, and
79 in the Ashanti and Northern Regions. The market for eggs, however,
still centers around the foreign communities and does not include the
most food-vulnerable groups of the population.

     Wild Life. Wild life is an important source of animal proteins.
Snails have been pointed out by several scientists (including Jollans) as
an interesting and acceptable source of proteins in certain seasons.

D. FOOD SUPPLY [5][20][2][1][14]

    The food supply of Ghana fluctuates from abundance to great scarci-
ty. In 1962, for instance, a low grain harvest occurred. Drought reduced
the cocoa crop, and food shortages developed in the Ashanti. The pattern of plenty and poverty is not new to Ghana. Neither is it specific
for that country. Speaking for the whole of Africa, Phillips remarks
that a good season encourages "eating, drinking, and making merry with
little or no thoughts for the morrow and that, conversely, a season of
drought, pests and disease spells depressed harvests, death of livestock, human famine, sickness and abnormal death." In addition, tradition and local taboos interfere with the food supply and nutrition in
many ways, which Phillips lists as follows: "1. Avoidance of a staple
crop easily obtainable from neighbors but not within the dietary acceptable. 2. Little or no use of milk, eggs, poultry, blood, meat and fish,
obtainable locally. 3. Antipathy to indigenous and exotic vegetables
and fruits when these are available in times of stress. 4. Reserving
of protective foods, not for mothers, children, and the aged, but for the
men. 5. Deficiency in the local diet of animal and vegetable protein,
Vitamin A, the Vitamin B Complex, and sometimes in minerals, causing
physiological and mental maladjustment." Thus, in Ghana in particular
and in Central Africa in general, malnutrition occurs because of both
"have not" and "use not." This attitude results in very little, if any,
stockpiling of food either at the family level or at the government level.
In addition, stocking food in Africa is a dangerous venture because

pests, rain, heat, and other factors will soon destroy what has been stored.*

Regional food supplies cannot be measured quantitatively. An indication of the kinds and qualities of food used in the various regions can be found in the sections on agricultural regions.

The Accra Coastal Plain produces cassava, corn, and garden vegetables such as peppers, eggplants, and tomatoes. Some livestock is raised and as a result some milk may be sold occasionally, as well as pigs, sheep, goats, and poultry. Fish is the most important animal protein available. The Cape Coast Winneba Plains is mainly a supplier of fish.

In the Volta Delta cassava and corn are the basic carbohydrate resources, together with garden crops, beans, peppers, eggplants, and okra. The region is known for its shallots, which are grown on 1100 hectares of land with the help of bat manure and fish waste. Nearby ruins offer nesting places for bats, and fishing is an important asset of the region.

The Akwapim-Togo Range offers plantain (cooking bananas), yams (traded with other parts of Ghana), sweet potatoes, cassava, corn, pepper, eggplants, pulses, and in the north of the region near Krachi, rice, palm oil, and palm wine.

The Southern Ashanti Uplands in addition to the important cash crops of cocoa and coffee produces food crops that include cassava, yams, plantain, corn, and sweet potatoes. Some meat is raised as farmers keep animals for local consumption.

In the Akan Lowlands, in the Ankobra and the Tano Basins, rice has become an important crop.

In the Krachi and Northern Ashanti region the most important food resources in some areas are sweet potatoes and rice; in other places the corn-cassava complex dominates.

In the Gonja and Dagomba savannahs millet predominates; sweet potatoes are also cultivated in mounds. Some animal husbandry is undertaken in spite of the tsetse hazard. The shea tree produces shea butter, an important asset of the local diet.

In the high plateau region millet and corn are again the main staples; cattle raising is widespread, providing some milk and meat, both for trade to the south and for local consumption.

The Gambaga Scarp is, in fact, an extension of the previous region and offers the same food resources.

Transportation between regions is limited, with the result that areas of plenty can exist side by side with areas of food scarcity. At the end of 1961 there were only 960 kilometers of railroads and 23,056 kilometers of roads, of which only 3071 kilometers were hard-top. Thus,

---

*In spite of earlier (1935) glowing reports that effective storage methods had been worked out by certain tribes, most modern visitors agree that grain on sale in many markets shows evidence of considerable contamination. Ice plants (Takoradi, Accra and Tema) are still few and the domestic refrigerator still the ornament of a minority of urban households.

exchange of foods between regions is channeled through inadequate communications, and for centuries food markets and market circuits have been established that play a great role in regional food supply.

Food markets in Ghana, as in other mid-African countries, are not only foci of food exchanges and commercial activities, but are also centers for social gatherings and information. As they are held frequently and on successive days in adjoining towns, they form a circuit upon which food supplies depend. They represent a regional clearing house for the local production and export outlets to other regions. Little is known about these exchanges between regions and the routes that the peddlers follow. Their importance as sources of food supplies vary considerably. In certains areas, their social and educational importance is greater than their supply importance. As communications improve, more and more people will depend on markets for supply and more and more will make livelihoods from the markets. The following towns are important food centers: Accra, Dodowa, Accussi, Seuchi, Kpong, Winneba, Saltpond, Cape Coast, Sekondi Takoradi, Keta. One of the most important of all food markets is found at Asesewa, where the Krobo people, using the "Husa farming," get better yields and make more efficient use of their land. Kumasi is the largest fresh fish and processed fish market, drawing its supplies from all of the major landings along the coast.

E. FOOD INDUSTRIES[2][5][4][1]

The food industries are limited to the small-scale enterprises that can be expected in a basically agricultural country. There are larger mills, such as the Crystal Oil Mills and the Nzima Oil Mills,* which squeeze the oil from the palm kernel and groundnuts, as well as village oil presses. Primitive presses extract the juice from the sugar cane, and mills are increasingly replacing the grinding stone in making flour and in pressing vegetables and tomatoes. There is a tomato-canning factory near Nsawam. Between July 1958 and April 1959, 36,707 cans of pineapple juice were produced at Osu, near Accra; between September 1958 and April 1959, 3445 cans of sliced pineapple were also prepared. Other fruit canneries are found in Accra, and a modern lime-juice extraction industry is found at Abakrampa. The production of these preserves alternates with fish-canning work, as the two seasons follow each other.

The distillation of palm wine has been a cottage industry for a long time. A modern distillery plant, producing whiskey, gin, and brandy, has been established recently at Accra. Breweries for European-type beers have been established at Accra and Kumasi.

---

*160 such mills were said to be available in the Accra Volta regions in 1957. No doubt their number has increased since, as 135 salt mills were sold to Ghana in 1958.

Bakeries catering to European and American tastes are found in the major towns. A biscuit factory was established at Kumasi in 1958. In addition to the mixed pineapple-fish canning center, other fish-processing centers are in Labadi, Teshie, Tema, Prampram, Winneba, Saltpond, Cape Coast, and Sekondi. On a smaller scale fish is dried and salted for preservation in various workshops in the Volta Delta. Although cocoa is the major cash crop in Ghana, only the preliminary stages of processing are carried out in the country. The material is shipped abroad for conversion into the final chocolate products.

F. IMPORT-EXPORT [4][5][25]

The import-export trade, while of supreme importance to the general economy of the country, is almost entirely outside the food economy of the people. It is officially stated that large quantities of rice, corn, beans, peas, and flour are imported annually, but quantities are not given and how much is available in the fields is not known.

While it is reported that 42.2 percent of all imports concerned food, drink and tobacco, this figure should not be interpreted as an improvement of local popular diets. Food imports consist primarily of luxuries—such as canned fish and meat, wheat flour, sugar and liquor—that only the well-to-do and Europeans can afford. In the same way, food exports do not deprive the population of any valuable dietary items because they consist mainly of cocoa, coffee, and palm kernels. Markets for exports are: the United Kingdom, absorbing 30.8 percent of all trade; the United States, 19 percent; the Netherlands, 14 percent; and West Germany, 13.7 percent; while the balance goes to a number of different countries. Cocoa exports dropped in recent years from 267,401 tons in 1950 to 257,469 tons in 1960. Copra exports rose from 800 tons in 1950 to 3713 tons in 1960; peak years were 1952 and 1956 when 4889 and 4722 tons, respectively, were available for export. Palm kernels, after a successful year in 1956 when 11,530 tons were exported, declined to 2855 tons in 1960. Kola nuts rose from 5400 tons in 1950 to 8576 tons in 1960 after experiencing significant variations in intermediate years.

Domestic Trade. Boateng, basing his estimate on a 1953 figure, quotes a sum of £ 71 million or U.S. $198.8 million as representing the value of foodstuffs grown locally. Most of the crops are sold locally, but some foodstuffs move, usually from north to south, in domestic trading. They are, essentially, the yams, millet, guinea corn, and groundnuts of the Northern Region and the Krachi area and the cattle from the northern uplands and pastures. Indian corn, plantain, and cassava move in the opposite direction, from south to north, and fish move from the sea inland.

III

DIET TYPES

A. GENERAL [5][15][21][23]

The general level of nutrition is low. Expenditures for food and beverages as a percentage of total expenditures is rising instead of falling, indicating a stagnant level of nutrition and a slight deterioration of living standards. These percentages were given as 60 percent in 1955 and 62.9 percent in 1959.

The country is poor and the individual average income is small. If the average income appears to be as high as $95* on most computations, it is because sales of cocoa increase the annual income of a limited number of people.

The country is divided into a root belt and a cereal belt; the first centers around the tropical forest region and the second around the the wooded savannah of the north. Cassava (Manihot utilissima) is the typical root of the former while millet and sorghum (Sorghum vulgare) are the typical grains of the latter. In many areas corn is added and, to a lesser extent, rice.

In addition to these basic foods, yams and sweet potatoes are found in both zones, as are bananas, tomatoes, peanuts, and peppers. Proteins are largely of vegetable origin, mostly from roots and grains and occasionally also from pulses such as dry beans and peas. Fish, however, is an important item of diet in areas where it is available; smoked fish is preferred; total consumption of fresh fish and its equivalent in the form of smoked fish per capita per month varies between 4.1 lbs. and 11.7 lbs. Milk and meat are not important; egg consumption is negligible. Fats come mostly from palm oil in the south and from shea butter (Butyrospermum parkii) in the north. Most calories are derived from starchy foods; with the exception of certain areas at certain times, however, the Ghanaian does not get visibly hungry.

Mayer reports that daily caloric intakes amount to 2900 along the coast and 2800 in the forest zones. In the north, however, these figures may fall to the starvation point of 1600 calories in July, 1400 in December and 1100 in February. In these same areas high monthly averages reach only 2065 calories per day while low averages may sink down to 675.

The greatest problem appears to be the lack of protective foods in these diets. In the north a typical meal will consist of porridge; in the south tubers are eaten with a spicy sauce that supplies the fats, minerals, and vitamins.

---

*Estimated at $199 by other sources (Africa Report Nov. 1963).

B. REGIONAL DIETS [1][10][4][15][17][19][21]

Diets in Ghana, as elsewhere, are the results of tradition and bio-climatic conditions. It is possible to distinguish five major diet zones in Ghana, keeping in mind the arbitrary character of such a generalization.

In the coastal areas covering the Accra region and the Volta Delta, there is a zone inhabited by Fantis and Ga fishermen and by groups of Ewe. These peoples eat fish when possible, that is, from June to September, Indian corn, cassava, and to some extent garden vegetables, the Fantis eating more green leaves and pulses. Further west small groups of Ashanti eat rice rather than corn. Further north, in the large area where the bulk of the Ashanti people live, there is a mixture of food croppers with large islands of cash croppers whose diets originate partly in patches of garden crops and partly in market purchases. Most of the tribes in this area eat bananas, cocoyams, Indian corn, and cassava. Animal proteins are scarce and occasional. In both these areas fat comes mostly from palm oil. In the past the Andangme ate millet, as shown by the importance of millet in their religious festivals. Unfortunately, this cereal is an uncertain crop, difficult to protect from predators, and it requires much work for small returns. As a result the Andangme have gradually shifted to a diet of cassava, yams, Indian corn, and plantain, all of which grow well on their land.

North of this area, where Brongs, Guans, and Krachis are found, the basic diet consists of yams, corn, and cassava, while fat comes from the shea tree. These people have many taboos influencing their diets. Women at marriage adopt the husband's taboos; abstinence from Indian corn, palm wine, and certain berries on certain days are among them. Another taboo relates to certain totemized animals; these vary with the tribal group and include leopards, monkeys, white fowls, crocodiles, antelopes, and even snails. Still further north, in the areas of the Dagomba and the Gonja, yams are the basic tuber and corn is popular, although the Dagombas prefer rice. Fats in these areas come occasionally from dairy products but mostly from groundnuts. Milk, however, is not rich and has a low fat content. Further north, in the high plains of the Wa and Mamprusi pastoralists, begins the millet and guinea-corn zone. Pulses supply some good vegetable proteins. Other crops include onions, eggplants, rice, taro, and yams. The Wa use rice as their main cereal grain. The Mamprusi are said to use animal and human manure for their crops. This is possible because cattle can be raised in this area where the tsetse fly is absent. Milk, however, is seldom used because the animals represent prestige value and currency more than food. Goats, sheep, chickens, a few donkeys, and dogs are raised. The last are frequently eaten.

Urban diets pose a serious problem. As rural populations move in greater numbers to the cities, the range of local foods narrows and the number of imported luxuries increases. The purchasing power of the recently urbanized labor does not meet the cost differences between rural areas and city areas. Protective foods such as fruits and vegetables, often available for the picking in the countryside, must be paid for in the cities. Two types of hunger can therefore be recognized in Ghana as well as in other countries of tropical Africa: a rural form of hunger between the times when food stocks are exhausted and the next harvest comes in; and an urban type of hunger caused by the gap between the cost of food and financial resources.

C. SPECIAL DIETS [8][24]

The diet of toddlers in Ghana, as well as in other African countries, presents a serious problem. The father in an African family is the one whose food needs have to be satisfied first; then the other male members of the family in the order of their production potential are served; women and small children come last. Previous campaigns to bring skim milk into African diets often met with failure because the supply so provided was sold for money or was given to the adult male members of the family. Sai points to the following dilemma: if the food offered is desirable, it goes to those rating prestige; if it is not, nobody cares. A happy medium should be found. Food should not attract too much interest from the adult males, yet it must be sufficiently attractive for the mothers to give it to their young. How to achieve this end will depend on appearance, nature, and local taboos.

In Ghana taboos are as diversified as regions—eggs are taboo to women and first sons in the north, while in other parts the list of taboos includes poultry and groundnuts, especially where pregnant women are concerned. Such taboos deprive the most vulnerable elements of population of one of the most readily available sources of proteins.

D. GHANAIAN MENUS AND DISHES [4][11]

The Ghanaian corn bread of the south (keuke) is the result of a fermentation process of wet corn flour. Fermented dough is cooked and wrapped in corn husks. There are several variants of this basic recipe; the keuke of the Eastern Region is sour, that of the Western Coastal Region is sweet and whiter in appearance.

Another corn food is porridge made of corn flour mixed with hot water (akassa).

It has been stated that the custom of milling the corn when wet increases the nicotinic acid content of the product.

In the north, where Indian corn is replaced by millet and guinea corn, a similar porridge is made. The housewife keeps a "sourpot" from which the base for the daily porridge (tuwonsafe) is scooped. Soup, with tuwonsafe, forms the main meal of the day.

Cassava is dried in the sun and ground into a flour (konkonte or garri). Grinding is essential to liberate the toxic cyanide that may be left after the root has been peeled. When the root is boiled, it produces a puree called ampesi or fufu. The dish is often prepared from a mixture of cassava, yams and plantain.

Groundnuts serve both for the preparation of oil and as a delicacy called kuli-kuli, made from the fried residual paste (after oil has been squeezed out by pounding).

Soups are made, especially in the north, with a small variety of green leaves, collected by the housewife or bought at the markets.

Vegetables are not in great demand except among foreigners living in the large cities; but a trend is noticeable, and the market is expanding among the native population.

Jollans reported in 1959 that beef, mutton, and goat meat were preferred by a majority of the consumers interviewed; local preferences for pork were noted among the Ashanti and certain southern tribes. The Northerner's Islamic background may explain this difference. Goat meat is also preferred to beef in certain parts of the Ashanti area. All parts of the animal are eaten when there is a chance, but the consumer, adequately supplied with fats from palm oil and groundnut oil, prefers his meat lean and tough.

The Fulani pastoralists drink milk in competition with their own calves; this has a detrimental influence on the herds as it stunts the young animals indiscriminately.

IV

ADEQUACY OF FOOD RESOURCES[15][10][20]

Food resources in Ghana are inadequate and vulnerable. They are inadequate because conditions of climate and soil, as well as the low level of technology, do not at present allow a crash program of food development. They are vulnerable because any such program, if not carefully thought out, may, like other such programs in Africa, make the situation worse instead of better.

There is a danger that under pressure for land and food crops more forests may be thrown open to exploitation. This will result in decreasing the area's forests with its unfavorable consequences on climate, fertility of the soil, and erosion. In these areas people are often without any food reserves and survive on wild leaves or "bush food" that may be the only food resource available.

In normal times, and until the various programs listed in this report have borne fruit, it is to be feared that considerable malnutrition will continue to exist both in rural areas during the dry season, where

soil and climate govern the food supply, and in the cities, where economic and social conditions create serious problems.

In times of stress, climatic or man-made, the situation could only
be worse. An extension into Ghana of the kind of tribal warfare and
guerrilla fighting that is smouldering in certain areas of the Congo and
Angola would rapidly destroy the economy and drive the people to a
state of lawlessness and to the kind of violence that can be expected
of famished, primitive populations.

V

NUTRITIONAL DISEASE PATTERNS[15][21]

It is very difficult to assess the nutritional intake of the Ghanaian.
Because no detailed study has ever been published covering the country
on a regional and sample basis, only general impressions can be
gathered. According to Platt and Mayer, malnutrition is widespread
throughout the country. Infantile mortality is high (113 per 1000), iron
deficiencies are common, and anemia is widespread with hemoglobin
levels often below 50 percent of normal. Widespread tropical ulcers
attest the deficiency in proteins. In the coastal savannah and in the
southern forest region where cassava is a basic food, calories are
usually adequate; but the prevalent protein shortage is expressed in
terms of kwashiorkor. In the north marasmus and vitamin A and ribo-
flavin deficiencies are more frequently observed. Mayer has found a
goiter area in the north where it is suspected that the iodine content of
the water and the soil are low.

Certain groups of the population are particularly vulnerable; pregnant and lactating women, conditions which often occur simultaneously;
children, especially toddlers after an addition to the family has displaced them at the breast; and people whose physical or mental condition prevents them from procuring their own subsistence. One can
endorse the conclusions of the Food and Agriculture Organization
Report No. 1449 on Ghana:

"Alleviation of this situation can be expected after physicians and
public health personnel have become more numerous, when the food
supply has become more abundant, when education has reached the
masses, and when the purchasing power of the masses and especially
of the more vulnerable groups has increased."

VI

CONCLUSIONS

The food problems of Ghana can be summarized as follows: The soil
is poor and needs a great deal of fertilizer to become productive. This

fertilizer cannot be supplied by animal manure because of the suscep-
tibility of the livestock to the tsetse fly; neither can it be supplied by
purchase because the economic level of the farmer is too low. In addition to these geographical and social factors of malnutrition, traditional factors are also important. Food taboos, male priority in food
distribution, and discrimination against undernourished pregnant and
lactating women and children also play their part in the inadequate
distribution of nutritional foods. The future may bring improvements
because of government awareness of the problems and its willingness
to organize food planning and education. Ghana may look forward to the
financing of these plans because of its present favorable economic position in the world market. In most tropical African countries investment
capital is imported or given as AID; a large part of the returns must
be re-exported, allowing no or little capital accumulation. Ghana and
Nigeria are two of the few exceptions in Africa that can, because of
the fabulous rise in demand and price of cocoa, accumulate capital.
Under these conditions and with careful planning and evaluation of local
and environmental factors it is possible that the ecology of nutrition in
Ghana may have an improved picture in the future.

BIBLIOGRAPHY: GHANA

1. Boateng, E. A., A Geography of Ghana, University Press, Cambridge 1959.

2. Directory of the Republic of Ghana 1961-1962, The Diplomatic Press and
   Publishing Co., London, 1962.

3. Field, M. J., The Agricultural System of the Manya Krobo of the Gold
   Coast, Africa, Vol. 14 (1943-44), pp. 54-65.

4. Food and Agricultural Organization of the United Nations Foods and Nutrition. Report to the Government of Ghana No. 1449, Rome 1962.

5. Food and Agricultural Organization of the United Nations, The State of Food
   and Agriculture 1961 and 1962.

6. Food and Agricultural Organization of the United Nations, Monthly Bulletin
   of Agricultural Economics and Statistics, Vol. 10, No. 10, Oct. 1961, pp.
   17-19.

7. Grant, Faye Woodward, Nutrition and Health of Gold Coast Children, Journal
   American Dietetic Association, Vol. 31, No. 7, Chicago, July 1955, pp. 685-
   702.

8. Jelliffe, D. B., Village Level Feeding of Young Children in Developing Tropical Regions with Especial Reference to Buganda, Journal of the American
   Medical Women's Association, Vol. 17, May 1962, pp. 409-414.

9. Jelliffe, D. B., Infant Nutrition in the Tropics and Subtropics, World Health
   Organization.

10. Johnston, B. F., The Staple Food Economics of Western Tropical Africa,
    Stanford University Press, Stanford, 1958.

11. Jollans, J. C., Meat Preferences of People in the Central Region of Ghana,
    Journal of the West African Science Association, 1959, Vol. 5, No. 1, pp.
    64-78.

12. Jones, William O., Food and Agricultural Economies of Tropical Africa. The Food Research Institute 1961, Reprint Stanford University.

13. Jones, William O., Manioc in Africa, The Food Research Institute, Stanford University, 1959.

14. Kimble, G. H. T., Ghana, Focus, Vol. IX, No. 8, Revised Nov. 1960, A publication of the American Geographical Society.

15. Mayer, J., Ghana, A Challenge to Nutritionists, Nutrition Reviews, Vol. 17, No. 7, July 1959. pp. 193-196.

16. Meyerowitz, Eva L. R., Concepts of the Soul Among the Akan of the Gold Coast, Africa, Vol. 21 (1951), pp. 24-31.

17. Murdock, G. P., Africa, its People and their Culture History, McGraw-Hill, New York, 1959.

18. Murdock, G. P., Staple Subsistence Crops of Africa, Reprint from the Geographical Review, Vol. L, No. 4, 1960, pp. 523-540.

19. National Academy of Sciences, National Research Council, Division of Anthropology and Psychology, Human Environments in Middle Africa, Final Report, Feb. 1961.

20. Phillips, J., Agriculture and Ecology in Africa, Faber and Faber, London.

21. Platt, B. S. and Mayer, J., Report of a Joint FAO/WHO Mission to Ghana, Oct. 27 to Dec. 6, 1958.

22. Poleman, Thomas T., The Food Economies of Urban Middle Africa—The Case of Ghana. Reprint The Food Research Institute, Stanford University, 1961.

23. Purcell, F. M., Diet and Ill Health in the Forest Country of the Gold Coast, H. K. Lewis, London, 1959.

24. Sai, F. T., Introducing New Foods Against Protein Deficiency, Nutrition Reviews, Vol. 18, No. 12, Dec. 1960, pp. 353-355.

25. The Stateman's Yearbook 1962-1963, St. Martin's Press, New York 1962.

26. United Nations Demographic Yearbook, 1961.

GHANA

LIST OF TABLES

TABLE NO.1

Population
Ghana 1960

Regions		Capital	
Eastern	1,579,903	Koforidua	28,261
Western	622,851	Sekondi	34,513
Central	725,993	Cape Coast	41,143
Ashanti	1,108,548	Kumasi	190,323
Brong Ahafo	588,724	Sunyani	12,186
Northern	531,045	Tamale	40,327
Volta	782,574	Ho	14,497
Upper	751,119	Bolgatanga	5,523
Total	6,690,757		

Source: Statesman's Yearbook 1962-1963, p. 514

TABLE NO. 2

Production
Ghana 1948-1962

Items	Area (000) Ha.		Yields (T./Ha.)		Production (1,000 T.)	
	1948/53	1961/62	1948/53	1961/62	1948/53	1961/62
Corn	142	252*	1.1	0.7	168	183*
Millet	175⎫	309*	0.5	0.5	99⎫	154*
Sorghum	134⎭				79⎭	
Rice	20	28	1.1	1.2	23	34
Sweet potatoes	64	--	7.5	--	482	481
Manioc	66	87*	7.7	12.6	512	1,092
Dry peas	16	--	2.0	--	31	--
Groundnuts (in shells)	55	--	0.8	--	43	49

Source: FAO Production Yearbook 1961/1962 Vol. 16

*1959-60

TABLE NO.3

Calories and Proteins
Ghana

Location	Time	Total Calories	Total Proteins in Grams	Percent Animal
Kumasi	March-April	1890	50	56.5
Rural (cocoa growing)	Oct-Dec.	1506	29.8	49.0
Ashanti (cocoa growing)	Oct-March	1741	41	55.2
Forest Zone Village	1932-1935	2195	29	25.9

Source: Platt, B.S. & Mayer, J.M. - Report of a Joint FAO/WHO Mission to
        Ghana FAO/59/3880

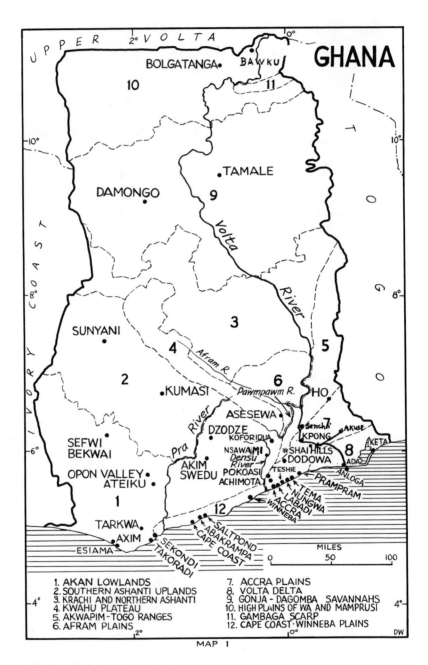

1. AKAN LOWLANDS
2. SOUTHERN ASHANTI UPLANDS
3. KRACHI AND NORTHERN ASHANTI
4. KWAHU PLATEAU
5. AKWAPIM-TOGO RANGES
6. AFRAM PLAINS
7. ACCRA PLAINS
8. VOLTA DELTA
9. GONJA - DAGOMBA SAVANNAHS
10. HIGH PLAINS OF WA AND MAMPRUSI
11. GAMBAGA SCARP
12. CAPE COAST-WINNEBA PLAINS

MAP 1

After E. A. Boateng, "A Geography of
Ghana," Courtesy of Cambridge University Press.

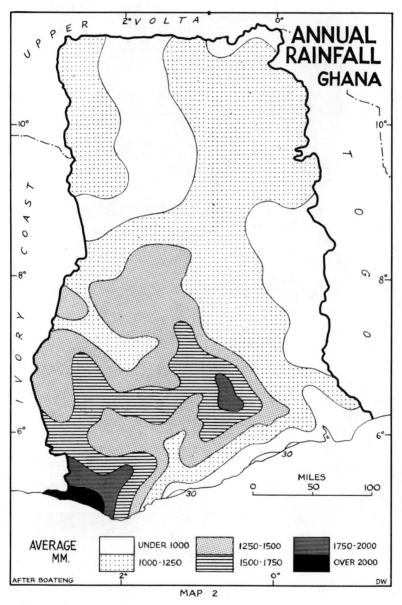

After E. A. Boateng, "A Geography of
Ghana," Courtesy of Cambridge University Press.

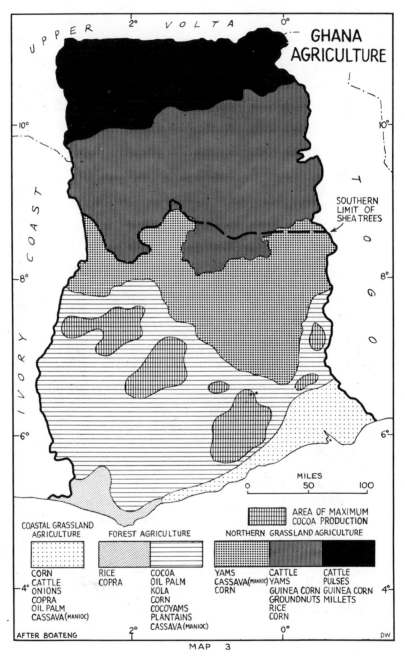

GHANA
AGRICULTURE

SOUTHERN
LIMIT OF
SHEA TREES

MILES
0   50   100

AREA OF MAXIMUM
COCOA PRODUCTION

COASTAL GRASSLAND
AGRICULTURE   FOREST AGRICULTURE   NORTHERN GRASSLAND AGRICULTURE

CORN   RICE   COCOA   YAMS   CATTLE   CATTLE
CATTLE   COPRA   OIL PALM   CASSAVA(MANIOC) YAMS   PULSES
ONIONS   KOLA   CORN   GUINEA CORN   GUINEA CORN
COPRA   CORN   GROUNDNUTS   MILLETS
OIL PALM   COCOYAMS   RICE
CASSAVA(MANIOC)   PLANTAINS   CORN
                              CASSAVA(MANIOC)

AFTER BOATENG

MAP   3

After E. A. Boateng, "A Geography of
Ghana," Courtesy of Cambridge University Press.

NIGERIA

TABLE OF CONTENTS

NIGERIA

Weights and Measures

1 Meter	= 39.370 inches = 3.281 feet
1 Kilometer	= 1,000 meters = 0.621 of a mile
1 Square Kilometer	= 0.386 square miles
1 Hectare	= 2.471 acres
1 Kilogram	= 2.204 lbs.
1 Quintal	= 100 kilograms = 220.4 lbs.
1 Ton	= 1,000 kilograms = 2204.6223 lbs.
1 Nigerian £	= 2.80 U. S. $

Since July 1, 1959 the Nigerian currency has been issued by the Central Bank of Nigeria.

NIGERIA

I

BACKGROUND

A. GEOGRAPHY [3][15][16]

Nigeria is situated on the west coast of Africa on the shores of the Gulf of Guinea between 4° 24' and 13° 40' of northern latitude and between 3° 20' and 14° 25' east of Greenwich. It is bounded on the west by the Republic of Dahomey and on the north by the Republic of the Niger; to the east lies the Republic of Cameroun; its northeast corner constitutes three-fourths of the western shores of Lake Chad.

The total area of the territory is 872,841 sq. km. It extends to 1050 km. at its greatest depth from the coast to the northern border and 1120 km. at its widest point. The country is divided into three unequal portions by the river Niger and its main tributary, the river Benue. To these three portions belong different people, cultures, and agricultures (see Map No. 1).

The Niger is about 4160 km. long, rising in the Futa Jalon Hills of Guinea and crossing Nigeria in a southeasterly direction for the last 1227 km. of its journey to the sea. The Benue, which rises in the Republic of Cameroun, flows westward for 800 km. through Nigeria to its confluence with the Niger at Lokoja, where the two rivers merge to form a mighty stream that empties into the sea through a 320 km.-wide delta.

Along the coast, screened from the sea by wide sandy beaches are lagoons, creeks, and mangrove swamps, forming an intricate system of waterways. Behind this is the forest belt, from 80 to 160 km. deep, gradually thinning out into a bush country characterized by stunted trees lining the banks of the principal rivers. North of the rivers the land rises to form the Jos Plateau, generally 650 meters above sea level; parts of the plateau are as high as 1800 meters. In the extreme north the country merges into the Sahara and slopes gently down toward Lake Chad. In the east the soil rises southward to form the Cameroun Mountains.

The climate of Nigeria is both tropical and subtropical. Rainfall varies considerably within the region and decreases from south to north according to fairly parallel climatic bands. While there is no month without rain along most of the coast and the immediate hinterland, drought prevails during five months from early November through March in the northern third of the country. During this dry winter season most of the rest of the country gets from 125 to 250 mm. of rain, and the delta area gets 500 mm. During the rainy season, from April through October, the northern third receives 500 to 1000 mm., the center 1000 to 1500 mm., and the coast from 2000 mm. to more than 3500 mm. at certain places. There are occasional storms at the outset and at the peak of the rainy season that travel in a southwesterly direction at a speed of over 50 km. an hour and can do great damage to crops, housing, and roads.

Temperatures are moderately high and show little range along the coast. Inland and northward temperatures reflect increasing range, both seasonal and daily, with further variations caused by altitude. Highest temperatures occur in April, lowest in December. Mean maximum temperatures increase from the coast northward while mean minimum temperatures decrease. Lagos has a range of 15°C to 36°C, while Katsina's temperatures extend from 4°C to 45°C. Obviously, these figures do not apply to higher portions of the Jos Plateau. The prevailing winds are from two directions: the southwesterly, maritime winds bring warm, moist air and rain to the area; the northerly, continental or "harmattan" winds are very dry.

The climatic features condition the vegetation zones. The swamp-forest areas that include all the mangrove and coastal vegetation and cover the Niger Delta supply fuel and building material to the coastal villages. The high rain forest next to the coastal forests supplies export woods. The savannas or grasslands of the interior can be subdivided into the "derived" savanna, north of the rain forest; the guinea savanna in the center; the Sudan savanna in the north; and the Sahel savanna in the vicinity of Lake Chad. Each has its specific type of menu and diet.

The agriculture of Nigeria can be generalized as follows: roots are the main food crops of the south, cereals the main food crops of the north, with areas of overlap in between where cattle also are an important agricultural resource.

The Western Region, settled by Yoruba farmers, produces both wet-season crops like yams and dry-season crops like cereals. Good water balances and fertile soil provide for three types of crops: subsistence (yams and manioc), domestic export (Kola nuts) and foreign export (cocoa).

The Northern Region, settled by the stable people of the former Hausa and Fulani Kingdoms, has certain advantages. It is on the trading routes of the Sahara. Its chief crops are cereals, which are harvested once a year. In addition, the absence of flies permits large-scale cattle raising; and adequate soil and water balances favor the cultivation of groundnuts and cotton.

The Eastern Region, settled by a majority of Ibo-speaking people, depends mostly upon its palm oil trees in the southern portion and on cattle in the northern portion. The southeast has reached its population-carrying capacity and presents ecological survival problems that will be studied later.

In both the southwest and the southeast rainfall is concentrated in both time and space, allowing two harvests a year; but soils are eroded and leached in many places.

According to Buchanan, Nigeria can be divided into a number of topographical units as shown on Map No. 2. Their enumeration gives a good condensed general description of the country:

1. Coastal creeks and lagoons
2. The Niger Delta
3. The dissected margins
4. The western plains and ranges
5. The southeast downlands and the Cross River Basin
6. The lower Niger Valley
7. The Niger Trough
8. The Benue Trough
9. The high plains of Hausaland
10. The Jos Plateau
11. The hills and plains of Kerri-Kerri and Gombe
12. The Biu Plateau and plains
13. The Cameroun-Bamende-Adamawa Highlands
14. The Mandara Mountains
15. The Sokoto Plain
16. The Chad Basin

Nigeria became an independent, self-governing nation of the British Commonwealth of Nations on October 1, 1960. It became an independent Republic on October 1, 1963. It is politically divided into three self-governing regions and one federal territory. The regions are called: Eastern Nigeria, Northern Nigeria, Western Nigeria (see Map No. 1), and the Federal Territory, which includes the capital city of Lagos. The federal government, located at Lagos, consists of an executive council of ministers with 22 members and a prime minister. Each region has a bicameral legislature. The following short table gives the size and population of these administrative and political units:

Region	Area (sq. km.)	Population (1961)
Northern Nigeria	688,490	19,514,000
Eastern Nigeria	67,758	8,300,000
Western Nigeria	116,523	7,119,000
Federal Territory	70	364,000
Total	872,841	35,297,000

The most important cities are Ibadan (600,000 people), Lagos (364,000), Kano (130,000), Ogbomosho (140,000).

B. POPULATION [23][26][3][17]

With 15 percent of the total population of intertropical Africa, Nigeria is the most populated country in the continent. Only Egypt and

Ethiopia have populations exceeding that of Northern Nigeria alone. A recent controversial census has placed the total population at 45 million (see "Africa Report" November 1963). Its rate of growth is estimated at 2.5 percent a year.

The non-Nigerians include Britons, Lebanese, Syrians, Indians, French, and Americans and number about 27,000. The majority of the population lives in agricultureal areas, and some 75 percent of the adult labor force, men or women, are engaged in agriculture, forestry, and animal husbandry.

1. Ethnic Groups and Tribes

This population includes about 250 different ethnic and linguistic groups. In Northern Nigeria the most important are the Hausa, numbering $5\frac{1}{2}$ million; the Fulani, 3 million; the Kanuri, 1.4 million; the Tvi, and many others. In Western Nigeria there are the all-important Yoruba, $4\frac{1}{2}$ million; the Edo, 452,000; the Western Ibo, 374,000; and the Urhobo, 346,000. The largest group in Eastern Nigeria is the Ibo, with 5 million. The important minorities include the Ibibio, 750,000; the Annang, 450,000; and the Ijaw, 265,000. Buchanan remarks that "the process of land occupation" is not complete and that tribal migrations still occur. Internal disputes that include the possibility of intertribal warfare, which has been avoided so far, have been feared in recent months (1963). Bitter rivalries exist between the Yoruba and the Ibo in the south, the Ibibio and the Ijaw on the border of Iboland, and the Hausa and the Kanuri in Bornu. Serious trouble erupted in May 1962 in the Western Region and nearly caused the province to splinter off from the rest of the country. Because of hybridizations and cross-marriages, a great variety of physical types are found in the country, ranging from Bantu Negro forest types to the lighter skinned, thin nosed, soft haired Mediterranean Fulani. In the middle of the plateau area a community of Negroes resembling the Pygmies or the Nigrellos of the Congo are found.

2. Religion

Nigeria, like Chad, lies at the crossroads of Caucasian Islam and Negro animism. Islam dominates in Northern Nigeria and has also penetrated Yorubaland to a significant extent. Animism, however, is widespread in the south and governs the majority of Yorubas; according to this set of beliefs, spirits and gods are everywhere, giving supernatural meanings to the objects and circumstances of daily life; each village honors its own god or gods, to which sacrificial offerings are made. They consist of food and the paraphernalia of daily life.

Christianity has also made some inroads due to the tireless work of the missionaries. They have reached some groups among the Yoruba and Ibo, but even after he becomes a Christian, the Nigerian villager preserves some respect for his local gods. The missions have laid the foundations of western education, especially in the southern parts of the country.

3. Language

In the north the main languages are Hausa, Fulani, and Kanuri. In the west Yoruba is understood by the majority, and in Eastern Nigeria there are large Ibo-, Ibibio-, and Efik-speaking areas. English is the official language of the country. The various cultures are so widely intermingled that no systematization can be accurate. It can be said that, of the three major ethnic and linguistic groups, the Hausa occupy the Northern Region, the Yoruba the Western, and the Ibo the Eastern. Yet, only one-third of the population of the north speak Hausa, although the language is spreading among the other two-thirds as a second language. One-fourth of the western population do not speak or understand Yoruba, and one-third of the eastern population do not speak Ibo. In addition, numerous minority groups speak their own languages and live according to their own traditions.

4. Population Distribution

The overall density of the population is 40 per sq. km., but this is unevenly distributed and follows, as elsewhere, the pattern of urban attraction and rural fertility, creating some areas of over-population. There are three major centers of population and culture: Yorubaland, Iboland, and Hausaland. The Yoruba concentration corresponds to the area of cocoa production of the western dry forest zone; the Ibo concentration corresponds to the area of palm-oil production; and the Hausa concentration is related to the cotton-producing zone. There are vast differences between these areas, each fostered by the compelling factors of soil and climate. To a greater extent perhaps than in other parts of Africa, there are large clusters of populations that do not deserve to be called towns because they do not have a town's functional organization and significance. Buchanan estimates that there are over 70 such population concentrations grouping about $2\frac{1}{2}$ million people. Lagos, the capital, is one of the most overcrowded cities of the world, with a population density of approximately 5000 people per sq. km. Percentages of urbanization vary; 35 percent of the population is urban in the Western Region while only 7 percent in the east and 4 percent in the north can be so qualified. The towns and cities of Nigeria can also be classified as European-created, such as Lagos, Kaduna, and Jos, or native-generated, such as Ibadan, Kano, and Enugu. In relation to diet and food, the p r o b l e m of the u r b a n i z e d, slum-dwelling, detribalized African is the same as in the other countries studied in this report.

In the rural areas the round, thatched, mud-and-clay house is common in the south, while in the north the flat-roofed, boxlike dwelling of the dry, hot climates is found.

C. AGRICULTURAL POLICIES [3][7][11]

The purpose of Nigerian economic and agricultural policies is two-fold: to solve the problems posed by the population explosion in rural areas (Iboland and Tvi areas) and in the cities, where food has to be found for the increasing crowds of city immigrants from the country-side, and to produce adequate hard-currency export crops. In pursuance of these goals, the First Development Plan of Nigeria (1962-1968) is based on an investment (federal and regional governments together) of U.S. $1,894,000,000, of which the federal government absorbs the great-est part, $1,155,000,000. In this Plan primary production has been al-lotted $127 million. Modern and traditional techniques are incorporated in this development plan under the guidance of Regional Production Development Boards.

The Niger Dam Project at Kainji, which will benefit agriculture as well as provide increased power, has been allotted $190 million and the Niger Delta Development Board $6.5 million; the Western Nigeria De-velopment Plan aims at diversifying the economy, both within and outside agriculture. Primary production in this province is to absorb 20 percent of the total capital expenditure of $252.8 million. Invest-ments in the development of tree crops will absorb $15.7 million; $5.6 million will be assigned to the development of existing agricultural schemes; $14 million will go for agricultural credit; and $15.7 million will be provided to develop cooperative farm settlements. These sub-stantial investment plans indicate the concern of the government with the problem of feeding a growing population. The expansion of cash and export crops rather than subsistence crops, which was needed to finance political and social development, has resulted in a decline in the duration of fallow periods, a loss in fertility, and in erosion.

II

FOOD RESOURCES [11][9][10][3][1]

A. GENERAL

Nigeria's food and other agricultural resources come from 14,979,000 hectares of arable land and permanently cultivated surfaces, while another 31,960,000 hectares are covered with forests and and 45,438,000 hectares are either built up or otherwise unsuitable for agricultural purposes. Agriculture provides at least 50 percent of the national income and 85 percent of Nigeria's exports. At the present time agricultural products account for about 80 percent of Nigeria's food. The most important food crops are yams, manioc (gari), guinea corn, millet, corn, rice, cocoyams, beans, and cowpeas. North of the rivers Niger and Benue, where grains provide the staple foodstuffs, agricultural production has expanded markedly since the war, and food supplies are generally adequate during the greatest part of the year. South of these rivers the position is not satisfactory; although production has, on the whole, kept pace with the increased population, consumption is generally low and the diet is lacking in protein. There is an overdependence on root crops as staple foods, and the required food crops are being replaced by cash crops.

The seven most important agricultural exports are palm kernels, palm oil, groundnuts, cocoa, cotton, rubber, and bananas. These items make up 96 percent of Nigeria's agricultural exports.

Buchanan recognizes four types of agricultural economy:

1. A basic subsistence economy that occurs throughout the country, either as a sole aspect of agriculture, as in the remote sectors of the middle belt and Cameroun areas, or as a subsidiary economy to cash-crop farming, as in the cocoa belt of Yorubaland.

2. An internal-exchange economy, facilitated in recent years by improvements in the transportation systems. These exchanges involve many basic foodstuffs, such as corn, yams, palm oil and cattle, and luxury or less basic items such as kola nuts, fruit, rice, and sugar. This domestic trade is essential to the support of diets in areas where export crops are grown.

3. A peasant, export-production economy, based on cotton and groundnuts in the north and on palm oil and cocoa in the south.

4. A plantation economy, deemed to be of minor importance and limited to a few plantations producing palm oil and rubber.

B. MEANS OF PRODUCTION

1. Agricultural Labor Force

Although seventy-five percent of the population is engaged in agriculture, an adequate labor force is seldom available for the major agricultural projects. Most Africans avoid outside work. As reported elsewhere in this book, extra money means little to the African farmer unless he has a specific use for it, such as paying a tax, buying a bride, buying food during the hungry season, and so on. In such cases heads of households may send the junior men to work for short periods for a salary on any available project. Whenever such jobs coincide with the dry season, when there is little to do on his own farm, the Nigerian is willing to hire out but not at other times. Manpower availability is therefore dependent on coincidence between need for labor on large enterprises and lack of work on subsistence farms. This situation results in considerable irregularity and inadequacy of labor, because manpower is often available when it is not needed but scarce when work is crying to be done. African labor is very difficult to handle; it is unreliable and choosey; field work has a low appeal, tractor driving a high one. On the occasion of the Mokwa Agricultural Project it was discovered that labor was, on the whole, scarce, unsatisfactory, and generally limited. According to an old tradition, work-seeking laborers move from the northern to the southern provinces after the millet, groundnut, and sorghum harvests have been brought in;

they seek employment in the southern cocoa farms; then they trek back home by March to sow their own crops before the rains, often trading in kola nuts on the way.

2. Farms

Farms vary in size according to the quality of the soil, the manpower in the family, and the crop. While household units were large in the past, they have a tendency to become smaller as the younger generation leaves the villages to try its luck in the cities. As elsewhere in Africa, there are subsistence farms, cash-crop farms, plantations, and scientific developmental farms.

Most subsistence farms in Nigeria operate under the shifting cultivation system that has been defined by Buchanan as an economy in which rotation of fields, rather than rotation of crops, occurs; clearing is done by fire; digging is done by hoe rather than plow; power originates in people rather than in animals; occupancy periods are short and fallow periods long. The area under cultivation on such farms varies considerably. It can be as small as 0.6 acres in the south and as large as 15 acres in the north. Weeding is seldom done more than once. Crops are harvested two or three years in succession, and then the area is abandoned. The advantages of this system under African circumstances have been discussed in another chapter and are now generally recognized, but in a land of rapid population expansion the pressure on the soil is such that the system may break down. In the root belt farms are concerned with yams, manioc, and corn. Fallow periods vary from three to four years in Iboland to eight to fourteen years in Yoruba country.

In the north, farms are concerned with cereals of the millet type, guinea corn (sorghum), and groundnuts, the last sometimes being sold on the world market when prices are high or being integrated into domestic diets when other foods are scarce; groundnuts are therefore grown here as a subsidiary crop. Some farmers allow adequate restorative fallow periods, others cannot afford it. Farms are often large, covering up to 15 acres, of which one-half may be planted to sorghum and one-half planted to cotton.

Another type of subsistence farming is to be found at the outskirts of the Jos Plateau. There the barren hills have been settled by tribes chased from the more fertile plains by aggressors. These areas include the Mandara Mountains and parts of the Northern Cameroun. Terrace farming is based on the use of organic waste, rotation of crops, and planting of protective trees. (Buchanan.)

Permanent cultivation is also found in the north around Kano and other large towns where animal manure is available and a ready market can be found in the nearby cities. These suburban farms are usually small, three to four acres. Over half of the land is sown with food cereals, one-third or less with groundnuts, the balance with roots. Other farms in the north grow tobacco or sugar cane on "fadama" (flooded land).

Irrigation is not well developed because in the north, where it is needed, there is little water available.

Livestock in the area at migration time (see below) supply some milk, milk products, and occasionally some meat. Goats provide manure and hides but are seldom milked; sheep are migratory like cattle but do not yield any wool and are used for meat on festive occasions; chickens and eggs are for sale in towns but are not consumed locally. On the farm labor is supplied by women. What they do is governed by their age and physiological condition (unmarried, child-bearing, and so on), by the composition of the household, and by the status of the husband. The land is held in trust by the headman of the village; the farmer has only the use of it until he moves to another plot, according to traditional rules. Work on the farm coincides with the rainy season and extends from April through November. This is the time when there is a demand for labor, male or female, the latter mainly on the subsistence plots. According to a recent FAO study, 65 percent of the females of the household work in the fields; the balance may work indoors at weaving or at other work. Very young and very old women plant the seeds; the others do the hard work. Among the Jos Plateau tribes a curious habit is reported: the females of the family have a plot of their own; four days a week they work on the husband's land and three days a week on their own. Crops on the women's land are used to feed the family during the hungry season and, as such, constitute some kind of reserve. Some of this reserve is used to brew beer, and some is for sale.

The most important cash crops in Nigeria are cocoa, palm oil, and groundnuts, followed by cotton and bananas. Cocoa was introduced by native chiefs in or around 1874 and has been almost exclusively developed by Nigerian farmers. Almost one-seventh of the world production originates in Nigerian individual farms, most of which are located in the western province around Ibadan, where, according to Buchanan, they bring in three-fifths of the regional income through exports and support approximately 1 million people. Cocoa farms are sometimes solely devoted to this cash crop; sometimes mixed farming is practiced. When there is mixed farming, nutrition crops are sown between the cocoa trees, at least during the four or five years of their early growth, after which they produce so much shade that nutrition crops wither. The average farm in this region is only 1.6 hectares (4 acres), but some are as much as 4 hectares. Where the soil is good, more and more of it is used for cocoa, and the area becomes a food-deficit area. Plant diseases such as "swollen shoot," black pod, etc. have recently plagued the cocoa industry. Spraying could have at least partially controlled them, but such measures are not well accepted by the farmers.

Nigeria is the world's largest exporter of palm kernels and palm oil, and a considerable amount is also consumed locally. The farms or palm groves are all located in the south and almost all in the Eastern Region, where they represent four-fifths of the export business.

The soil has to be moist but well-drained. The trees represent a natural vegetation and can be considered wild or semiwild. They are owned individually by the farmers; if they grow in groups, they are the property of the community. Almost every part of the tree is used: the stalks for building, the leaves for roofing, the juice for drinking, the oil for cooking, and the pressed kernel for feeding livestock. Most of the work of extracting is done by hand, although some mills and presses have been introduced in recent years over the staunch opposition of the labor force.

Groundnuts were first grown as a food crop but have become an export item with the development of the railroads. Northern Nigeria claims to be the world's leading exporter of this crop. The extension of the Bornu Line to Maiduguri will result in increased development of groundnut farms in that area. Most of the groundnut-exporting farms are found in and around Kano and Katsina, where there is the light soil the crop needs and where the summer rainfall is an adequate 600 to 900 mm. In the groundnut belt farms are small, covering about one acre; it is estimated that two-fifths of the Northern Region's population depends on this crop for their livelihoods; many other farmers in Nigeria plant groundnuts as a food crop. The government has developed a plan for the creation of more groundnut mills in the Northern Region.

Other cash crops include cotton, which is a useful substitute for goundnuts when prospects for the latter are poor. Cotton fits into the farm schedule well because it is harvested after the food crops are in. Cotton farms are found in the northwest along the railroad from Jos to Kaura Namoda.

Plantations are of secondary importance in Nigeria. According to Buchanan, this is due to a reluctance of the government to encourage a system alien to the local family and tribal way of life. Such thinking is quite unusual in new nations. It is, therefore, not surprising that an opposite attitude has been adopted by some Regional Production Development Boards. The plantation system occurs almost exclusively in Cameroun territories (Cameroun Development Corporation) and in the Sapele and Calabar areas under the United Africa Company.

Resettlement projects very similar to the paysannat system developed in French Equatorial Africa also exist in Nigeria and have encountered similar difficulties. Buchanan summarizes them aptly by saying that one has a choice between two methods: a minimal one in which the bare necessities are offered the settler (a road, a hut, and one year of food and water); and a maximal one in which cleared land, a whole village, farming tools, animals, and cash advances are given. The results, as would be expected, are opposite. In the first system progress is slow but reasonably sure; in the second most of the settlers take what is given and return to their casualness and indifference as soon as support is withdrawn.

Finally, experimental and scientific farms are also found in Nigeria, in some instances combined with settlement projects such as the Niger Agricultural Project. Experimental schemes are found at Sokoto, Wuya-Edozhigi, Shemankar (rice), Ijebu, Udi, Ishiagu, Calaro (farming and palm oil), Santa (coffee), Bonny (coconut), Oban (rubber), Obudu and Ogim (cattle).

3. Fertilizers

Some farmers object to fertilizing the fields because it increases weed growth and causes more work. Those farmers also think that if fertilizer increases yields, it should be used to reduce the acreage under cultivation so as to get the same result with less work. Here again the African attitude of adjusting his needs to a minimum of work is in evidence. However, where the absence of the tsetse fly allows cattle raising and hence availability of animal manure, some farmers understand its value and use it.

In the overpopulated parts of Iboland, where the soil is very poor, the problem of restoring fertility is acute, and green manure through tephrosia and acoia grasses are the only resource until trypanosome-resistant cattle have been developed. In most subsistence farms soil restoration comes from ashes of the burned shrubs and leaves. In the groundnut belt some fertility is retained through the nitrogen-fixing property of the crop. In the Agricultural Development Project grass fallows and imported chemical fertilizers are used. Some phosphates and superphosphates may be expected from fields in Abeokuta once they are in full development; so far the use of imported fertilizers is limited by its cost. Nigeria's consumption of commercial fertilizer in recent years is shown in metric tons below:

Kind of Fertilizer	1958-59	1959-60	1960-61
Nitrogenous	1,800	900	1,000
Phosphate	1,200	600	800
Potash	1,700	900	1,900

4. Mechanical Equipment

Remarks made on this subject in other chapters of this book apply also to Nigeria. Mechanical agriculture poses considerable problems in tropical Africa. Social and economic factors are involved. Mechanization requires some disruption of family life and can be applied only on large holdings; this means a choice between granting land to foreign enterprise and increasing further socialization—sometimes both are necessary. For these reasons mechanical agriculture is limited to the few larger projects in which modern treatment of agricultural problems have met with mixed successes. The successful use of mechanical equipment on the subsistence farms is closely linked to economic and social changes of considerable magnitude, including consolidation of land tenure and acquisition of large amounts of fertilizers to maintain and increase soil fertility. The following table shows the availability of tractors in Nigeria:

Kind of Equipment	1959	1960
Crawlers	49	41
Wheels	170	182

C. PRODUCTION

The production of agriculture in Nigeria can be roughly represented by a grain belt in the north and a root belt in the south, overlapping in the middle tier of the country. Yams, roots, and manioc are found almost everywhere up to the tenth parallel north, while grains occur as far south as the seventh parallel. In the north the main cereals are sorghum and millet, with rice in the Sokoto Valley where its culture is mechanized. Rice is the main cereal grown in the south (see Map No. 3).

1. Cereals

No recent reliable figures are available on corn acreages and production, but averages for 1948 through 1953 gave an acreage of 808,000 hectares and 755,000 tons, of which 270,000 tons were produced in Western Nigeria alone. In the same years millet and sorghum were reported at 4,108,000 hectares and 2,688,000 tons, while rice was sown on 171,000 hectares and gave a crop of 250,000 tons. Poor-soil types of millet, called acha and tamba, are also found in many areas. In 1962 unofficial figures indicated an increased acreage in the Eastern Region of 50 percent over these figures, and it was believed that coastal swamps might lend themselves to rice cultivation and thus play an important role in the country's food supplies.

2. Roots and Tubers

No recent reliable figures for the production of these foods are available, and older figures have to be considered estimates. The average between 1948 and 1953 gave the acreage planted in yams as 1,308,000 hectares with an annual production of 9,998,000 tons. Some of this production goes into domestic trading channels. Eighty-five percent of commercial yams carried over the railroads come from the Middle Belt stations and are shipped to the food deficit areas of the Jos Plateau and the cocoa centers of Western Nigeria. There are two types of yams: zinji, or superior, and all others. Zinji is used in ceremonies, sacrifices, displays, and, as a prestige food, is stored except in case of acute needs. All other forms of yams are eaten. Zinji bulbs are tied to a pole, about thirty side by side, and can be seen at prominent places in the markets.

Manioc was introduced into Nigeria about 1900. Prior to its introduction the months of June to August were periods of great food scarcity in the south. It is said that 683,000 hectares were in production in 1958-59, a drop from the 999,000 hectare average sown during 1948-1953. This drop is probably caused by the increased acreage in cocoa. Production of manioc dropped from 10,722,000 tons in 1948-1953 to 8,575,000 in 1958-59.

3. Other Crops

Other crops of nutritional significance include cowpeas, of which two improved strains have recently been developed. They are suitable for cultivation in the northwestern Nigerian climate, but at present they are mainly grown in Northern Nigeria. This region ships considerable quantities of these pulses to food-deficit areas to help make up protein deficiencies. Groundnuts cover an acreage of 630,000 hectares, mostly in the Kano, Bornu, and East Sokoto areas. Yearly production was 1,150,000 tons in 1960-61 and in the three preceding years had averaged 1 million tons a year, of which about one-third was exported. Sesame oil seeds are grown on 61,000 hectares in the Middle Belt, in the area inhabited by the Tivs. This crop has steadily improved since its beginnings in the early 1930's; the production was 13,000 tons per year from 1948 to 1953 and grew to 28,000 tons in 1960-1961; it supplies cash and cooking fats for all the Tiv population.

Palm kernels and palm oils originate from a fairly stable 430,000 hectares that produce around 430,000 metric tons of kernels and oil every year. In 1960-61 Nigeria produced 6800 tons of copra, a drop from 8800 in 1959-60 but an increase over the 2500 ton average of the 1948-1953 period.

Cocoa, the queen of Nigeria's cash crops and the mainstay of its economy, grew from a production of 108,000 tons per year from 1948 to 1953 to 195,000 tons in 1960-61, 85 percent of which came from the provinces of Ibadan, Abeokuta, and Ondo.

Other crops include ginger in south Zaria, soya beans in the Benue area, and kola nuts in the Ibadan, Abeokuta, Ilaro, and Lagos areas. Nigeria is not self-supporting in sugar, and imports have risen to 5000 tons, or one-third of the need in 1961. There are plans for the development of 8000 hectares of marshy land that would be suitable for sugar-cane plantations. This is a North Region crop, grown near Zaria, Kano, Katsina, and in the eastern part of Sokoto Province. There are also plans to develop such crops as rubber, cashew nuts, coffee, and tea.

4. Sources of Animal Protein[3][7][26][31]

There is a general shortage of meat in Nigerian diets except in the north and among the wealthier classes in the towns.

Cattle. The presence of the tsetse fly in the Southern and Middle Belts has confined cattle resources to the north. However, trypanosome-resistant breeds of cattle are being acclimatized. A small number (160,000) are reported to exist in Eastern Nigeria. These are chiefly the dwarf Muturu cattle, which seem to be doing well but provide little meat and milk. A small herd of these animals is under the control of the East Nigerian Development Board on an experimental basis. In Western Nigeria, some ranchers raise a cross between muturu and zebu, but the total herd in the region does not exceed 70,000 head. Most of the cattle, goats, sheep, and pigs are in the north in the provinces of Kano, Sokoto, and Bornu, as shown in the table below. Ninety-

five percent of these animals are in the hands of the Fulani people. As
in Chad, water and pasture problems are of great concern. They govern
a northward migration away from tsetse-breeding sites during the rainy
season; on the Jos Plateau, for instance, it is estimated that the herds,
at that time of year, increase three hundred percent. The trend is reversed at the beginning of the dry season when the herds move to the
meat-hungry south.* They feed on the stems and residue of crops on
their way and help fertilize the soil with their manure. Buchanan and
other experts believe that in spite of this occasional and temporary
integration of agriculture and pastoral economies the settlement of
nomadic Fulanis is not to be expected in the near future, because
drastic changes in cultures rarely occur. The divorce between animal
husbandry and agriculture is one of the most serious problems to be
faced in a country whose diet lacks animal protein, whose fields lack
fertilizers, and whose cattle, all concentrated in the hands of a single
ethnic nomadic group, lack water and pasture. As a result, except in
the extreme north and among the wealthier classes in the towns, there
is a general shortage of meat.

Distribution of Livestock in Nigeria (1962)

Region	Cattle	Goats	Sheep	Pigs
Northern Nigeria	6,000,000	11,000,000	3,000,000	150,000
Western Nigeria	70,000	650,000	300,000	110,000
Eastern Nigeria	160,000	1,370,000	800,000	20,000
Total	6,230,000	13,020,000	4,100,000	280,000

These figures, however, are tentative. They are based on the
jangali or cattle tax and, for obvious reasons, must be low; best guesses
would place them 15 percent higher. It is thought that approximately
700,000 cattle are slaughtered each year in the Northern Region, 180,000
in the Western Region, 80,000 in the Eastern Region and 35,000 to
40,000 in Lagos. Considerable quantities of dried meat from Northern
Nigeria are sent to the south, particularly to Ibadan and Western
Nigeria. About 50,000 pigs are also consumed annually. A program to
develop the cattle industry in the northern grassland areas of Western
Nigeria is being developed. It was announced that an appropriation of

---

*The loss of cattle that can occur as a result of migration through the tsetse
belt has been proved to be considerable; even resistant strains become susceptible when their resistance is lowered. From 700,000 to 800,000 injections of
trypanocides are given yearly to cattle, while clearings and insecticide operations are undertaken against G. morsitans in Bauchi, Kaduna, and Zaria.

$8.4 million would be made. The program is intended to lower the price of meat and eggs in order to bring them within the reach of the population. A large number of cattle and some sheep and camels are brought into Nigeria each year from neighboring countries, especially from Chad. A program of development of new veterinary clinics is afoot.

The bulk of the goat and sheep population is also found in Northern Nigeria, but some are raised in Eastern and Western Nigeria. It is estimated that approximately 5 million goats and 700,000 sheep are slaughtered annually. Of them, all except about 100,000 goats and 100,000 sheep are killed in Northern Nigeria. With American aid, plans to expand animal husbandry in Northern Nigeria are being carried out. Overall, the livestock population of Nigeria and the numbers slaughtered are thought to be increasing slowly.

Milk and Dairy Products. The development of a dairy industry on the Jos Plateau is a significant achievement. Unfortunately, its benefits are limited to the wealthier groups in the cities and to the Fulanis who sell their products. Milk is absent from the diet of more than three-fourths of the population. Production of butter, cheese, and clarified butter depends on the rainfall. Peaks of both production and rain are reached in June, July, and August, when the rainy season brings grass. The output of milk drops nearly to zero between November and February.

Fisheries. Fish and prawns (large shrimps) are an important source of food and protein in Nigerian diets, but no reliable estimates are available of the quantities consumed each year. However, urban consumer price surveys suggest that more than $78 million is spent on fish annually. This would indicate a consumption of approximately 50,000 tons of fish caught in local waters as compared with 35,000 tons of imported dried and canned fish. This means a little over 2 kilos per capita per year or five and one-half grams a day. Of the imported fish, about two-thirds are consumed in Eastern Nigeria, one-third in Lagos and Western Nigeria, and practically none in Northern Nigeria where meat is available. Lake Chad in Northern Nigeria is an important source of dried fish for Eastern Nigeria. The importance of increasing local fish supplies is fully recognized. Introduction of nylon, the use of mechanized fishing gear, additional and improved fishing vessels, the development of inland fisheries by construction of fish ponds, and the training of staff in fish culture are all measures now being taken. In Northern Nigeria the Panyam Fish Farm, which is situated some 60 miles from Jos, is contributing to the raising of the dietary standards of the people of the Plateau. Carp, which is a quick-maturing fish, is being sold with success, and yearly consumption by the people of the Plateau is said to be more than 50,000 lbs. Experiments are being carried out in the artificial production of two indigenous fishes, giwanruwa and heterotis. Preliminary indications are that both of these fishes can be produced under inland conditions. In the past, almost 90 percent of the total tonnage of fish imports were air-dried cod and similar fishes from Iceland and Norway. In order to increase the proportion of protein foods in Eastern Nigeria, the government of the area allocated the sum of $305,000 to fisheries in its four-year development plan that ended in 1962. The ultimate goal of the government is to provide one pound of fish per week per capita or about 168,000 tons of fish annually. This sounds quite ambitious since it amounts to twice the catch and import of fish in the whole of Nigeria at present. Yet, among the masses living inland, fish is much too expensive to be a regular item of diet. When caught, river fish are sold (rather than eaten) because of their high value.

D. FOOD SUPPLIES [3][4][30][23]

There is very little information about storage capacity and food stocks in Nigeria.

The country has two kinds of food markets: the large food stores of the urban areas, which are supplied almost entirely by import trade controlled by foreigners and recently a few Nigerians, and the African markets.

Imported food is strictly for city dwellers. The African markets are supplied from neighboring villages and from the limited domestic cash crops. They are run by women who squat beside their wares spread out on woven trays.

At the family level there is little storage space. As elsewhere in Africa, men store the grain after the harvest in large mud huts, from which they take two or three days supply at a time to give to the women, who keep it in their own huts or in the cooking hut. In these very primitive granaries the millet and other cereals soon become contaminated and spoiled. In the root belt the crops are often left in the ground for over a year and the soil serves as a storehouse.

In Nigeria, as in other countries of Africa, markets are the center of commercial as well as social activities. Two of the markets at Kano and Onitsha are outstanding in size and permanence; and they are probably the largest food supply for the mass of the population. Permanent smaller markets are found in almost every town or village; they are open on special days at regular intervals—often every four days. Most of what has been said about African markets in the chapter on Ghana is true of Nigeria.

Regional food supplies stand at very different levels throughout the country and throughout the year. As elsewhere, the hungry season in the northern tier of the country is the end of the dry season; and almost every year, in some places, the balance of last year's crop is exhausted too soon. In the north pyramids of groundnuts in bags ready for the export trade are seen in many places, especially around Kano, Nguru, and Kaura Namoda. Grains are stored in an unknown number of granaries, but no scheme of compulsory saving of food is at present in operation. In the south some roots and tubers are found piled in the huts, but no significant reserves are available.

Transportation. Railroads, rivers, roads, and caravan trails play an important role in food distribution. The Nigerian Railway has a mileage of 1950 km. All lines originate from Lagos and Port Harcourt and distribute the imported goods up-country. The Western Line runs from Lagos through Ibadan to Kano; branch lines connect the main line to Kaura Namoda, which serves as a railhead for cotton and groundnuts, and to Nguru, which is an important center for groundnuts. Fairly large supplies of foodstuffs are carried through the railroads to the domestic markets.

The total mileage of the roads in Nigeria has increased by more than 50 percent since the war, and there are now approximately 37,000 miles of roads altogether, of which over 4000 miles are asphalt; the rest are gravel or dirt. In view of the size of the country, this gives a ratio of road-length per sq. km. of about 0.06, which is far too small, and it is believed that this should be increased by another 50 percent.

Airways also are important to transportation and communication in Nigeria. Apart from the national airports, there are customs airports at Benin, Enugu, Bussa, Ibadan, Jos, Kaduna, Makurdi, Port Harcourt, Sokoto, Yola, and Zaria. Ten other airports are used for charter flights, and 23 additional landing strips are also used by light aircraft.

In case of localized food shortages or famines, the transportation system, especially in view of the air facilities, would probably be adequate to supply even distant and remote parts of the country.

E. FOOD INDUSTRIES [7][3][23]

Food processing is the most important industry, as would be expected in an agricultural country. The industry includes the processing of the roots and tubers, grains, fats, meats, and dairy products that have been discussed in the previous paragraphs. Manioc is pounded into gari, as in most of tropical Africa. This is done by hand in the family or tribe. Rice is milled on a small scale in fourteen different rice-producing centers, but rice consumers do their own milling in most parts of the country. Other cereals, such as millet, acha, and tampa, are also milled by hand. A new flour mill, completed at Apapa in 1962, will use imported wheat. It is expected that wheat-growing experiments such as are being undertaken in Northern Nigeria will reduce Nigeria's reliance on imports (see below). Imports benefit only the urban and suburban better-off people. There are 110 bakeries employing ten or more people each in the various urban centers of the country. Two biscuit factories, one at Apapa and the other at Ikega (Lagos), are now being built (1963).

Vegetable fats are processed in various fashions from different original sources and with different degrees of mechanization. Throughout most of the country palm oil is still produced by hand. Simple presses have, however, come into their own, especially since World War II. Their number remains very small, but the government is pushing industrialization along this line. The pioneer oil-mill program has a capacity of 50,000 tons annually. A large mill exists at Apoje in Western Nigeria. At Funtua and Kaura Namoda groundnut presses can each produce 250 tons of oil and 350 tons of cake. Shea nuts are an important source of fats. They are mostly processed at home, but there is one new processing factory at Zaria, and a factory at Apapa is said to have a manufacturing capacity sufficient to meet the present margarine requirements of the country.

Almost all of Nigeria's tea is now imported, but blending and packaging is undertaken in a new factory at Apapa. Small-scale production of ground and liquid coffee is carried out at Lagos. Baby food with a groundnut flour base is also manufactured at Apapa. There are breweries at Lagos and Aba that have a total annual capacity of approximately six million gallons. A third brewery is being established at Kaduna. Soft drinks are manufactured in more than 60 factories throughout the country.

There is the beginning of a meat industry based on the large cattle capital of the Northern Region. There is a meat-canning factory at Kano, which, apart from meeting the local demand, exports corned beef to neighboring Ghana, Liberia, Sierra Leone, and to the West Indies. This export reached a value of $140,000 in 1960. The cannery at Kano has recently been enlarged, and the production of corned beef and beef extract may be doubled. There are also two well established pig farms: one at Kano, claimed to be the largest in the world, and the other at Minna in Northern Nigeria. Both of these meet all present Nigerian demands for processed pork and find a ready export market. The manufacture of pork products is undertaken at factories at Apapa, near Lagos, and at Port Harcourt. Butter, cheese, and clarified butter-fats are also produced. The production of butter and cheese at Vom was suspended during 1960, but exports of clarified butter-fat valued at $112,000, were continued. The dairy at Vom also produces dried milk powder, which, with groundnut flour added, is distributed by the medical authorities to children. A factory at Mashim uses imported dried milk powder to produce reconstituted milk, yogurt, and cream. Three other factories at Kano produce toffee, boiled sweets, sugar-coated nuts, and peppermints.

There were plans (1959) to establish a sugar refinery capable of producing 40,000 tons a year at Jebba and to grow sugar cane on 5500 acres at Bacita in the province of Ilorin (1962?). The government of Western Nigeria has a Five Year Plan (1960-1965) to invest over $190 million in agriculture and industry. Considerable attention is being paid to the development of food industries in that region.

United States investments in Nigeria were estimated at $25 million in 1962 but were expected to increase by $10 million in 1963. Direct economic aid under the foreign aid program stood at $43.6 million as of July 1, 1962. In November 1963, a pledge of $224 million was reported to have been made by the United States in loans and grants.

Other countries and institutions have also pledged assistance. All pledges combined, which include loans and grants from the World Bank ($120 million), Britain ($25 million), West Germany, etc, fall short of about $675 million of the 1960-1965 Plan's needs.

Foreign investments in the country amount to $70 million a year. The gross national product grows by 4 percent every year.

F. IMPORT-EXPORT [28][29][7][27]

Nigeria's imports of food do little, if anything, to help the general level of nutrition. The percentage of people that use significant amounts of imported foods is very small. Yet year after year food imports increase, a fact which can be taken as a token of prosperity and of higher standards of living among certain people, if not among the masses. Imports of fresh, chilled, and frozen meats have increased from $741,000 in 1959 to $1,028,000 in 1960. Imports of wheat flour have risen from $7,393,000 to $8,830,000 during the same year and total food imports from $58,370,000 to $66,953,000 (see Table No. 1 for the total imports of food in Nigeria in recent years). It is to be noted that the import of beer increased in value by 10 percent in recent years, as did the import of alcoholic spirits.

Most of the trade, as would be expected, is with the Commonwealth. Among other customers are Japan, West Germany, the Netherlands, the United States, Italy, France, Belgium, East Germany, and Czechoslovakia. Exports consist chiefly of food. This means that farmers must raise crops for export, as well as food for themselves. As elsewhere, the lure of export crops reduces the level of domestic food production and creates a critical situation for the Africans who neglect their manioc for profits from cocoa. The reverse also occurs.

Nigeria has been unable to maintain its exports of palm oil because of increased consumption at home and because of labor competition from other sectors of the economy. Export of palm oil dropped from 205,000 tons in 1960 to 185,000 tons in 1961, and figures for the first quarter of 1962 indicated a continuance of this trend. (See Table No. 2 for export values in recent years.)

III

DIET TYPES

A. GENERAL

Malnutrition is as common in Nigeria as elsewhere in Africa, but it is not universal; it occurs in certain places, at certain times, and among certain people. It is caused chiefly by lack of proteins and certain vitamins. Malnutrition bordering on starvation occurs in the north during the hungry season of the pre-harvest months, but malnutrition, rather than actual starvation, is more common in most of the country.

With a wide variety of foods available, the diets are astonishingly monotonous and self-limited. The same porridge that is the basic food of every tropical African, made with cereal in the north with some manioc added, or with manioc products in the south with some grains and cereals added, fills the stomachs of Nigerians. Soups made of green leaves, manioc leaves, salt, pepper, and onion are found everywhere with the addition in the south of red palm oil, rich in Vitamin A, and of groundnut oil in the north. Meat is so scarce as to be considered a luxury; fish, as we have stated, is available on the coast and along the rivers but is usually very expensive. Dried fish from the Chad region is also eaten in some places in the east but is also highly priced. It is surprising that little fruit is consumed, because it is available in many places.

Fats, in spite of their availability, are not intensively consumed; groundnuts, palm oil, shea butter and egusi (melon seeds), in that order, are the most commonly eaten, seldom accounting for more than one-third of the fat that is needed in a satisfactory diet.

According to FAO, water in the north comes from wells in a large percentage of cases; these are often found on the farm; if not, arrangements with a family that possesses a well must be made. In most of the rest of the country, water comes from streams; it is kept in earthenware jars, covered or open, which often serve as a breeding place for mosquitoes, especially when continued usage and lack of scrubbing add organic deposits to the water.

B. NUTRITIONAL LEVELS [3][15][19][20][21][10][2][12][5][6]

The average yearly per capita income of the Nigerian people has been variously estimated at $80 a year, but, as elsewhere, the figure is inflated by the inclusion of the large income of the very few. This confines the food resources of the masses to what can be grown or locally bartered.

Nutritional levels vary with the people and with the season. In-between meals, consumed by about 30 percent of the people investigated, make evaluations difficult.

Northern people, except in the hungry season, enjoy in general a better diet than those living in the cocoa belt. There deficiencies in caloric and protein intake are more common, resulting in shortages of elements such as methionine, crystine, and tryptophane. The mortality rate for children under five years of age reaches almost 50 percent, allegedly due to dietary deficiencies.

According to Nicol, who made individual dietary surveys of children among Kanuri, Shuwa, Otukwan, Camberri, Ibo, and Yoruba samples of populations, caloric intake varied greatly with age and with the occupation of the parents. In farmers' children, aged four to six, intake ranged from 910 to 1380 calories per day, aged ten to twelve, from 1770 to 1970, while the children of Ibo and Yoruba clerks consumed as much as 2730 calories a day. Ascorbic acid intake was studied in two groups of forty Nigerian children; less than 16 mg. per day was eaten after cooking losses. During the mango season, however, intake rose to 170 mg. a day. The study indicated that when given ascorbic acid supplements, the growth of these children was improved.

It was also found that the milk of lactating mothers is low in calcium and phosphorus, but the ratio of calcium to phosphorus, which together provide the bone-building material, is normal and comparable to that found in similar surveys in Europe and the United States.

Except in urban areas 90 percent of the women breast feed their babies up to two years, then shift them abruptly from breast to pap, made of corn. The whole grain is soaked overnight; then the water is drained off. Milling is done by pounding, either at home or at a mechanical center near the village. Finally, the corn meal is soaked again in water for two to three days with occasional changes of the water; the soluble nitrogen fraction is thus lost; the residual starches are made into pap (ogi) and/or pudding (eko).

After three years the baby is given adult food without meat. If he has a chronic ulcer somewhere on his body, he will be forbidden to eat beans.

In the north the same system prevails, except that the pap is made of guinea-corn (sorghum), which is a better source of protein; a mixed adult diet, including occasionally some fowl, is introduced earlier than in the south.

The classical cycle of protein deficiencies in the mothers and of kwashiorkor in the children is present. Women's diets are normally restricted because of their status as women. During pregnancy, when development of the fetus drains their bodies of nourishment, they become more debilitated. Their undernourishment is further increased by various taboos against such foods as eggs, mutton, chicken, insects, cowpeas, and so on.

The child is breast-fed for a long period and is weaned abruptly when the next child needs the breast. The older one is then shifted to a diet of manioc. These practices create the conditions of kwashiorkor in childhood and liver cirrhosis in adolescence.

Nigerian Cooking, Dishes and Food Habits. Women cook in the courtyard or in a kitchen separate from the hut.

The kitchen is often shared by wives of the same husband and by other women of the same social group. Cooking is done in clay pots, set on stones over a fire. Fuel is a problem. In the north firewood is used, but it is scarce; stalks of corn are used when available. Some people use dried animal dung that would be better used for fertilizer.

Mortar and pestle are the most important cooking utensils and often consist of a hollowed large stone and a wooden stick. Cereals are pounded into meal or yams crushed into dough (fufu). From the bases, porridge is made with addition of water and spices.

Manioc is treated, as elsewhere, by drying and grating; it is often fried. Corn is widely eaten throughout Nigeria, and in the north it is sometimes served with milk and sugar. Kola nuts are used like candy and are offered to visitors. They are also used in many religious and familial ceremonies as bases for oaths. In addition to dishes already described in other chapters of this work, certain dishes are typical. One such dish is the tuwon dawa of the Makarfi* district of Northern Nigeria, populated by Hausa, Fulani, and pagan peoples. It involves the following steps:

1) Threshing the guinea-corn. This is done out in the compound using wooden sticks.
2) Winnowing.
3) Soaking the grain in a small amount of water in the mortar.
4) Pounding to loosen the husk.
5) Washing the kernels and drying them in the sun for one or two hours.
6) Thoroughly pounding the kernels in the mortar to produce a course flour.
7) Grinding the flour using a small and a large grinding stone.
8) Sieving the flour to remove lumps.
9) Repeat grinding and sieving until flour is an even fine texture.
10) A small amount of this flour is added to boiling water and is stirred until the mixture thickens.
11) The food is covered and when it boils the remaining dry flour is added and is cooked for five to seven minutes.

The soup served with tuwon dawa may or may not contain meat. It always contains ground locust bean cakes (a source of vegetable protein), palm oil (a potent source of Vitamin A), salt, and pepper. It is thickened with one of several ingredients, including dried baobob leaves, dried okra, or powdered melon seed. Vegetables are added to the soup if and when available. These include spinach, "bitter leaves" or "water leaf," tomatoes, and onions.

Other foods prepared in Northern Nigeria include hura, based on a mixture of sorghum and millet; koko or kunu, in which these cereals are cooked and presented as a porridge but in which the proportions of the cereals vary. Rice, manioc, (pounded, boiled, or roasted), and yams are more and more commonly eaten in the north. Beans (cowpeas) and locust beans are served fried in groundnut oil (kosai) or baked with palm oil (alele). Groundnuts are fried or used as cakes (kuli kuli). The corn cobs are strung dried before being stored and can be eaten in several ways—roasted, ground, pounded, or boiled. Vegetables are always boiled for a long time and the resulting gruel is seasoned with pepper, palm oil, and chili. Milk, when available, is either allowed to

---

*Near Funtua.

sour or made into cottage cheese. Wild game is not an important part
of the diet; most small game has already been exterminated, and there
are no firearms to kill the big beasts. Small animals and insects, including rodents, reptiles, grasshoppers, and so on are killed with clubs
for food; and many are killed when fire is used to clear the jungle; they
are roasted, fried, or boiled immediately after being caught.

It is reported that Nigerian tribes are more free of animal taboos
than other tropical Africans, although this cannot be statistically confirmed. It is believed, however, that oranges and mangoes cause jaun-
dice; and eggs are taboo to girls because it is believed that they cause
sterility. Common practice is to have one meal a day, usually in the
evening, although occasionally there are two; a bowl of thin porridge is
sometimes eaten in the morning. Workers of both sexes have a snack
during their work in the fields that consists of cold vegetables brought
from home wrapped in a leaf or bought from itinerant vendors. There
can be long hours of fasting during any 24-hour period. Children, when
either going to school or working in the fields, often wait a long time
before getting their first meal of the day.

Infants in rural areas are mostly breast-fed until the mother's milk
runs dry or until another child displaces the baby. In the cities, especially Lagos, breast-feeding is going out of fashion and bottle-feeding
is becoming more common. This ill-advised imitation of Western practices in a social environment that lacks sterile water, refrigeration,
and aseptic bottles leads to a remarkable increase in infant diarrheal
syndromes, often severe. This situation is found not only in Lagos but
in all African cities and is one of many consequences of what could be
called "dysculturation."

In the home, like everywhere else in Africa, the head of the family
is served first and is given the choicest morsels. He may eat alone,
or take his bowl out to eat with friends, or eat with other senior members of the household. Very seldom are old women included and more
seldom very young infants. Yet there is a general respect for seniority,
especially in the north among the Hausa. The wives and children are
usually served only with leftover food, as is the custom in most African
cultures; this results in malnutrition or even in starvation. Other members of the household imitate the senior male and either eat with their
peers or alone when they choose to carry their bowls of food outdoors.
Beer is often used to wash down the food; palm wine is a luxury and is
drunk only on festive occasions.

A study of the food consumption of small samples of communities
living in the different vegetation zones of Nigeria was undertaken by
Nicol and published in 1959 (see Map No. 4). Table No. 3 gives the
daily intake of these various population groups in grams over a period
of one year and, among other things, illustrates the switch from cereal
in the north (Tangaza and Jarawaji) to yams and other roots in the
south (Mbanege and Bero-Okuta) while groups living in the center were
having both.

Caloric intake ranged from 2980 for Jarawaji men and 2920 for Bunga men to 2060 for Bero-Okuta men and from 2650 for Jarawaji women to 1520 for Tangaza women. Table No. 4 gives the details of these intakes (after Nicol) and shows animal protein deficiencies in all except the Jarawaji and Langai men. Fat consumption is low everywhere in all people. Calcium intake is inadequate in Tangaza and Bero-Okuta people and in practically all children. Vitamin B intake is poor in the north and in Bero-Okuta but rises to a satisfactory level in palm oil areas; ascorbic acid intakes are low in all areas.

Nicol notes that at Tangaza the year of the study coincided with a poor harvest, the drought having partially dried out the millet crop, but that in other areas the crops had been average. He also pointed out that in Bero-Okuta a new automobile road made it possible for the farmers to sell their yams to cocoa-growing farmers in the south. Such sales deplete their own food supplies without bringing cash enough to buy necessary supplements—malnutrition results. This situation is not uncommon in "developing" Africa and is alluded to elsewhere in this book. The table also shows that meat was eaten in Tungan Maidubu and Langai and fish in Jarawaji and Bunga, while in Bero-Okuta and Mbanege very small amounts of animal foods were consumed. Parasitic infestation was heavy in all areas with malaria parasites, and hookworms were present in all areas.

Keeping in mind that caloric requirements of people are in part determined by their energy output, the caloric intake of the Jarawaji and Bunga men seems to exceed the "n o r m a l" requirements recommended by FAO under similar physical, environmental, and body-weight conditions. Yet these populations of cattlemen and farmers are very active, so it can be cautiously concluded that "agreement between dietary calories and caloric requirements was obtained for men and women over twelve years of age in those communities whose way of life was not associated with considerable physical exertion, provided food supplies were not short."

Considering pregnant and lactating women, the authors found it almost impossible to identify samples that could be compared to controls satisfactorily. Their studies, however, suggested that "food was shared among adult women in such a way as to prevent any marked loss of weight during lactation. . . and to allow a reasonable gain of weight in the last trimester of pregnancy."

Other Nigerian villages were studied recently by Collis, Dema, and Omululu. Studies were carried out in various agricultural zones of the Ilesha Division of the Western Region, to which a gold-digging settlement of Hausa people at Sabo-Igun and a sample of local police families were added. The results of this study are found in Tables No. 5 and 6. Table No. 5 shows the usual difference between the cereal-eating Hausa (in Sabo-Igun settlement) and the tuber-eating Y o r u b a in the other village.

Certain dietary habits make for malnutrition. The Yoruba, for example, have the habit of washing the powdered grain so that the protein

is removed and only the starch remains. Very few fresh fruits and
vegetables are eaten. Consumption of pulses and animal foods is low.
The study also revealed that alcohol is seldom used by the Moslem
Hausa.

Table No. 6 shows the seasonal variations in caloric and protein
intake and shows a low average caloric consumption of 1550 calories
in the hillside village of Oka Ila in August, with a maximum of 1830
calories at the best season in February. Even when caloric requirements were met at the most plentiful time of the year, there was still
a general imbalance in protein intake. The cocoa villages (Igun, Ijana-
Itarna) were the worst off. Cash crops bring in money only once a
year; when it is spent, starvation is unavoidable, especially when all
the land is used for cocoa trees. Where mixed farming occurs
(Abebeyun), the situation is better. At the end of the dry season and
beginning of the rains, the people fall back on the poorer starchy foods
with the most inadequate protein content, such as plantain and manioc.
The ratio of protein calories to total calories is nowhere near requirements. Unfortunately the food is scarcest when the work is
heaviest at the beginning of the rainy season, and becomes more abundant when the crop is harvested after all the hard work is done.

Table No. 7 shows the percentage of calorie and protein requirements that are consumed in the various villages of the study. Age and
sex composition of the samples have been taken into account. The table
shows that, with the exception of the Abebeyun people from November
to February and of the "local group" (police force), nowhere are the
requirements in calories met. The protein requirements are never
met.

In control villages eighty to ninety miles west of Ibadan, it was also
found that people do not have enough to eat and that the protein intake
is extremely low. Another control was made in the Pankshin division
of Northern Nigeria where cereals such as sorghum and acka (Digi-
taria exilis) are basic in the diet; Hausas add milk and meat; Suras
and Aujas add beer. Caloric and protein requirements are met, yet
children mortality is high (54 percent under age 5); this shows that,
once an individual has survived the dangers of childhood, he or she
may become a reasonably healthy adult if he or she had a reasonable
amount of protein in early years. This is in contrast with the situation
found in the south where lack of protein in early years often leads to
liver cirrhosis in adolescence and adulthood.

As soon as one rises in the social scale, the food situation improves. The Community Grammar School in Awo Omomma in Iboland
feeds its students three meals a day as follows:

        Breakfast   Porridge (pap)
                               Bean bread

Luncheon	Beans (cowpeas) with rice
	Vegetable stew with palm oil, green
	tomatoes, onions, and chili peppers
Snack	Orange
Dinner	Garri (ground manioc)
	Soup made of goat meat, crayfish,
	palm oil, onions, chili peppers, ogili,
	hausa (fermented locust bean seed
	cake) and equisi (pounded seeds)

Such a menu is still short of the required protein supply and of ribo-flavin, but energy requirements for this type of sedentary work are almost met and other nutrients are in satisfactory amounts (Table No. 8).

IV

ADEQUACY OF FOOD RESOURCES [25][3][1]

In a country as diversified in geography and cultural patterns as Nigeria, there are many reasons for an inadequate diet. The two most important reasons, however, are the expansion of cash crops over the most fertile lands and the population increase. The expansion of cash crops has become mandatory because of a growing urban population (25 percent) that has become more and more dependent on store-provided imported food, and because of the ambitious social development programs. The imports and development projects have to be paid for with the earnings of the export trade, which in turn depends on world prices. Although the emphasis on cash crops for exports must be deplored, little can be done about it as long as no other s o u r c e of foreign-currency earnings is available. The Nigerian exports are vegetable oils and cocoa; year in and year out, these cash crops represent four-fifths of the total income, amounting to approximately U.S. $364 million. While the import-export balance was favorable every year up to 1954, it has been unfavorable every year since, in spite of an expansion of the cash crops. This expansion carries its own built-in limitations. It brings about a decline of world market prices in the very commodities it produces, and it diminishes the amount of land cultivated in subsistence crops. Prospects for increasing food resources are reasonably encouraging because there is no overall shortage of land; but such a development would be based on the use of improved seeds, artificial fertilizers, insecticides, and better methods of storage, all of which are costly: the financing of these programs may prove more difficult than expected. Some expect that the increasing urban population and

rising standards of living will provide the farmer with the incentive to
adopt the techniques necessary to increase production; but this, so
far, is nothing more than a hope.

The population explosion makes itself felt mainly in two or three
areas. Most important and already alluded to in the beginning of this
study are the areas found in Owerri Province of Eastern Nigeria, in the
Tiv-inhabited districts south of the Benue, and in some areas around
Kano. In Iboland the population densities average 158 per sq. km., but
concentrations of 293 per sq. km. are found around Orlu. Unfortunately,
the soil is poor and eroded; the transfer of population, a very risky
operation at best, cannot be encouraged under local circumstances. Replenishment of the soil with imported fertilizer is possible but costly,
and mixed farming is difficult because of the presence of tsetse vectors.

In the Tiv area south of the Benue town of Makurdi, population densities are not excessive, but the traditional system of agriculture demands too much land and too short fallow periods. Cash cropping has
further reduced the amount of subsistence land available for the growing population. Here again further resettlement of the people is unac-
ceptable for cultural reasons, illustrating the diversity of the ecology
of malnutrition. Adequacy of food resources in the north around Kano
is also threatened by the growing population. As in Chad, the Central
African Republic, and Ghana, the improvident character of the African
is partly responsible for this situation.

Confronted by these multiple threats to the adequacy of food resources, the governments of Nigeria, both under the Colonial Development and Welfare Act and under the Regional Production Development
Boards, have established a number of projects intended to offset the
nutritional consequences of agricultural instability. Buchanan distin-
guishes seven types of plans designed to improve nutrition: resettlement; large-scale mechanization of agriculture; cooperative farming
with mechanization; integrated rural development; livestock production;
plantation development; and irrigation. In short, some of these schemes
are designed to move people when they exceed the carrying capacity of
the land, others to increase productivity by scientific methods, and
others to develop livestock for meat and manure.

Some of these schemes have been discussed in the previous pages.
All have run into difficulties. There are basic ecologic laws that en-
force a slow pace for changes intended to control the habitat. For
examples of resettlement projects, a number can be cited. Usually
mentioned are the Shendham Agricultural Development and Resettlement Scheme, the Kontagora Native Authority Land Settlement Scheme,
and the Bamenda Cross River Calabar Scheme. There are others.
While some of these projects have met with limited success, none has
provided an overall solution to the problem of resettlement. It is
doubtful that a solution is possible. Increased production was expected
from such vast projects as the Niger Agricultural Project at Mokwa
(the failure of which has been thoroughly explored and explained by

Baldwin); and from cooperative projects such as the Eruwa Mechanized Farming Scheme.

Rural-development projects, intended to give power to a whole area in imitation of the United States TVA Authority, are also being developed (such as the Ogun River Project). Irrigation schemes and plantation developments have also received attention.

Livestock development has received high priority, as in the Obudu P r o j e c t where an attempt is being made to develop and establish trypanosoma-resistant breeds of cattle.

In times of stress due to such causes as racial tension, intertribal warfare, or external wars, all possible in Nigeria in spite of a rather promising start, there is no doubt that the food economy of the country, already precarious, will become serious. Famine situations such as exist at present in the former Belgian Congo would soon arise, especially in the cities. Such food crises would develop in direct proportion to the industrialization and development of the area. The most advanced groups would suffer most; those nearest to primitive agriculture would suffer least.

V

NUTRITIONAL DISEASE PATTERNS[15][8][5][6]

Throughout the country, with some notable exceptions, people are underweight, especially children. Hemoglobin rates vary between 60 percent and 75 percent; 100 percent is never observed. From 20 percent to 80 percent of the population, depending upon the area, show some signs of anemia. Kwashiorkor is present and was diagnosed 450 times during a two-year period at the Nutrition Clinic of the University College Hospital at Ibadan; and 350 cases were seen at the Wesley Guild Hospital at Ilesha in a period of fifteen months in 1960 and 1961. Many people do not realize its connection with malnutrition and consider it only another childhood disease.

Children's development is slow in the rural areas for which data are available, and considerable differences (up to 15 cm.-6 inches) in height are found at age $4\frac{1}{2}$ between rural children and those of urban professional people. Signs of vitamin deficiencies are constantly found; dry, scaly skins exist in 50 percent of the patients observed; 4 percent have pellagra; 20 percent have stomatitis and glossy redness of the tongue; all have gingival and dental sepsis; 6 percent to 8 percent of the patients have tropical ulcers. More serious disturbances include kwashiorkor, partial kwashiorkor, and occasionally marasmus, beriberi, and rickets. In towns dirty bottle-feeding of infants with inadequately boiled milk or water causes severe diarrheal syndromes. The most common vitamin deficiency seems to be in the Vitamin B Complex. Vitamin A deficiencies are frequently found except in the palm-oil belt.

VI

CONCLUSIONS

Because of its very prosperity, the nutritional equilibrium in Nigeria is probably more threatened than in other tropical African countries. This apparent paradox may, however, be explained. This prosperity has caused a population explosion that is not found to the same extent in neighboring lands. The economy is based on two export crops that, more and more, take the soil needed by subsistence crops. While the riches produced after the war have allowed some social progress, the masses are still uneducated and resistant to modern technology. There are many signs indicating that the people will not catch up, in the near future, with the demands of a modern Western industrial state. Agricultural progress also seems problematic. The soil of Nigeria does not have the natural fertility required to support a growing population. It does not, as yet, produce the resources that would allow the purchase of much-needed fertilizers. It has created a population pattern that includes overpopulation, overfarming, and overgrazing in certain areas; and the reverse in other areas where tsetse vectors have reinvaded lands previously settled by men. A new reclamation of these lands with modern scientific and mechanical implements is needed, but there is no evidence that the country can afford such an expenditure. Nigeria is an example of a country in which the jet age has come too soon while the country has not emerged from the hand-and-hoe level of agriculture. There is a dangerous gap between the capabilities of the soil and people and the program devised for their development.

BIBLIOGRAPHY: NIGERIA

1. Baldwin, K. D. S., The Niger Agricultural Project, Harvard University Press, Cambridge, Mass., 1957.

2. Bassir, O., Nutritional Studies on Breast Milk of Nigerian Women During the First Year of Lactation, Journal of Tropical Medicine & Hygiene, June 1956, Vol. 59, No. 6, pp. 138-144.

3. Buchanan, K. M. & Pugh, J. C., Land and People in Nigeria, University of London Press, Ltd., 1962.

4. Business Week, Lagos Thrives as Hub of African Market, March 3, 1962.

5. Collis, W. R. F., Dema, J. and Omololu, A.: On the Ecology of Child Health and Nutrition in Nigerian Villages, I. Environment, Population and Resources, Tropical Geographical Medicine, No. 14, pp. 140-163, June 1962.

6. Collis, W. R. F., Dema, J. and Omololu, A.: On the Ecology of Child Nutrition and Health in Nigerian Villages, II. Dietary and Medical Surveys, Tropical Geographical Medicine, No. 14, pp. 201-229, September 1962.

7. Directory of the Federation of Nigeria, 1962, The Diplomatic Press and Publishing Co., London.

8. Fleming, R. A., Cause, Pathologic Aspects and Treatment of Phagedenic Ulcer in West Africa, Journal of the International College of Surgeons, Vol. 38, August 1962, p. 120.

9. Food & Agriculture Organization of the United Nations Production Yearbook, 1961, Vol. 15.

10. Food & Agriculture Organization of the United Nations, Report to the Government of Nigeria, No. 1531, Rome, 1962.

11. Food & Agriculture Organization of the United Nations, State of Food and Agriculture, 1962.

12. Hauck, H. M., Dietary Study in a Nigerian Secondary School, Journal American Dietary Association, No. 39, pp. 467-472, November 1961.

13. Hills, M., Protein Malnutrition in Western Nigeria, Thesis, Sheffield, 1960.

14. Howe, R., Rough and Tumble Nigerian Politics Still Go by the Book, The Washington Post, Nov. 18, 1962.

15. Jelliffe, D. B., Culture, Social Change and Infant Feeding, Current Trends in Tropical Regions, The American Journal of Clinical Nutrition, Vol. 10, No. 1, pp. 19-45, 1962.

16. Kenworthy, L. S., Profile of Nigeria, Doubleday and Co., Garden City, N.Y., 1960.

17. Mitchel, N. C., Nigeria, Focus, Vol. IV, No. 7, March 1954.

18. Nicol, B. M., The Calorie Requirements of Nigerian Peasant Farmers, British Journal of Nutrition, No. 13, pp. 293-306, 1959.

19. Nicol, B. M., The Nutrition of Nigerian Children with Particular Reference to their Energy Requirements, British Journal of Nutrition, 1956, Vol. 10, No. 3, pp. 181-197.

20. Nicol, B. M., The Nutrition of Nigerian Children with Particular Reference to their Ascorbic Acid Requirements, British Journal of Nutrition, 1956, Vol. 10, No. 4, pp. 275-285.

21. Nicol, D., A Pilot Survey in Nigeria, West African Medical Journal, 1953, July-Aug-Sept., Vol. 2, No. 3, pp. 123-128.

22. Nigeria Yearbook, 1962.

23. Reed, D., Nigeria, Black Africa's Brightest Hope, Reader's Digest, March 1963, p. 186.

24. Skinner, S.W., Africa Firsthand vs. Secondhand, U. S. Department of Agriculture, Vol. XXVI, No. 5, May 1962.

25. Staniforth, A. R., Report of Duty Tour April 25-May 27, 1962, FAO/UNICEF Extension Nutrition Project No. P/L 81.

26. Statesman's Yearbook, Macmillan and Co., London, 1962-63.

27. Time Magazine, Vol. LXXXI, No. 13, March 29, 1963.

28. U. S. Department of Agriculture, World's Palm Oil Trade Shows Signs of Levelling Foreign Agriculture, Vol. XXVI, No. 10, Oct. 1962, p. 14.

29. U. S. Department of Commerce - World Trade Information Service, Economic Developments in Africa and the Near East, 1959, Part I, No. 60-10.

30. Wenmohs, J.R., Markets Old and New in Nigeria, U. S. Department of Agriculture, Foreign Agriculture, Vol. XXVI, No. 1, Jan. 1962.

31. World Health Organization, Technical Bulletin 247, Expert Committee on Trypanosomiasis, Geneva, 1963.

NIGERIA

LIST OF TABLES

TABLE NO. 1

Imports

Nigeria 1939-1961
in 1,000£ (1£ = 2.80 U.S. $)

	1939	1958	1959	1960	April 1961
Sugar	80	3,351	3,185	3,786	1,247
Confectionery	11	427	505	476	149
Salt	239	1,797	1,772	1,864	746
Wheaten flour	37	2,117	2,640	3,153	1,083
Fish	240	7,482	8,717	7,935	2,817
Milk	30	1,079	1,340	1,192	553
Ale, beer, stout, porter	65	3,319	3,602	3,898	1,381

Source: Nigeria Yearbook 1962

TABLE NO. 2

Exports

Nigeria 1939-1960
(in £ 1,000)

Commodity	1939	1957	1958	1959	1960
Cocoa	1,776	26,036	26,668	38,298	35,056
Palm Kernels	1,873	17,959	20,450	25,925	25,097
Palm Oil	930	13,810	12,663	13,757	11,064
Groundnuts	1,048	20,139	26,948	27,519	21,955
Benne seed	117	1,366	890	1,157	1,832
Columbite	—	761	457	1,125	2,120
Tin Ore	2,368	1,301	1,526	2,085	6,044
Coal	42	472	466	352	127
Timber (sawn)	40	915	1,209	1,182	1,117
Timber (logs)	85	3,323	4,123	4,877	5,918
Plywood & veneers	—	747	909	950	1,097
Bananas	314	2,799	3,264	2,608	2,606
Goat skins	456	1,031	3,937	4,214	1,985
Cattle hides	191	1,145	1,084	1,549	1,622
Cotton (raw)	191	6,507	7,845	7,301	5,181

To countries of the Commonwealth

	1939	1954	1956	1957	1958	1959	1960
United Kingdom	6,288	106,341	85,268	77,751	74,943	82,025	77,551
Canada	13	252	280	789	4	321	1,166
Ghana	180	628	706	1,065	810	787	872
South Africa	24	194	136	49	171	216	111
Others	33	874	554	583	792	856	1,138

To Foreign Countries

	1939	1954	1956	1957	1958	1959	1960
United States	1,990	15,725	12,585	7,607	8,609	11,842	15,597
Belgium	47	1,111	1,839	1,887	1,178	4,124	3,129
Czechoslovakia	23	134	261	288	430	543	630
France	687	2,306	1,002	5,426	1,956	1,925	6,351
Germany	1,191	4,551	5,784	5,692	11,105	13,257	12,465
Netherlands	669	9,603	13,357	12,478	18,224	25,943	20,718
Norway	43	547	706	342	489	584	992
Others	177	3,637	5,676	5,600	5,184	10,666	21,390

Source: Nigeria Yearbook, 1962

TABLE NO. 3

Summary of the Mean Daily Food Intakes (g) Over Periods of
1 Year of the Men and Women Over 12 Years of Age in the Population
Groups Investigated in Rural Nigeria

Foodstuff	Jarawaji		Tangaza		Bunga	
	Male	Fem.	Male	Fem.	Male	Fem.
Sorghum and bulrush and finger millets	712	621	502	420	568	583
Maize	0	0	0	0	95	78
Rice	0	0	78	35	0	0
Digitaria spp.	0	0	0	0	0	0
Yams and yam flour	0	0	0	0	17	67
Sweet potatoes	0	0	0	0	0	0
Cassava (fresh flour and gari) and locally prepared starches, bananas and plaintains	11	0	15	25	167	113
Other roots	0	0	0	0	23	2
Groundnuts, whole, cake and oil	11	1	6	5	7	6
Other oilseeds and nuts	5	17	21	11	9	6
Legumes, mainly Vigna spp. and Parkia spp.	13	14	15	16	8	7
Red palm oil	0	0	0	0	0	0
Fresh and dried green and red leaves and veg.	31	34	17	10	41	38
Other fruit and vegetables	13	21	4	5	222*	145[†]
Meat, poultry and reptiles	15	12	2	1	5	3
Fish, fresh and dried	62	43	2	1	37	27
Offals of various sorts	2	3	1	1	0	0
Milk, butter and cheese	109	226	34	37	81	40
Beer (sorghum and millet)(ml)	0	0	0	0	0	0
Honey	1	1	0	0	0	0
Palm wine (ml)	0	0	0	0	0	0
Edible earths	0	0	2	2	1	1
Imported salt	12	12	6	4	5	4
Sugar-cane for chewing	0	0	0	0	3	1
Cube sugar	3	0	0	0	0	0
Larvae	1	1	0	0	0	0
Fish oil	4	4	0	0	0	0

* Includes 142 g pumpkin flesh
[†] Includes 108 g pumpkin flesh

Source: Nicol, B. M. - British Journal of Nutrition, Vol. 13, pp. 293-306, 1959.

TABLE NO. 3 (Continued)

Tungan Maidubu		Langai		Bero-Okuta		Mbanege	
Male	Fem.	Male	Fem.	Male	Fem.	Male	Fem.
628	508	275	212	81	58	0	0
4	8	3	6	24	48	1	1
0	0	8	4	0	0	6	2
0	0	161	108	0	0	0	0
6	8	89	79	1417	1008	1641	1205
0	50	58	59	0	0	3	2
0	0	17	11	21	26	24	20
0	0	39	42	2	2	0	0
1	1	14	25	3	2	10	13
10	6	17	13	17	22	17	15
160	173	25	18	4	3	29	31
0	0	4	3	0	0	14	16
15	10	58	52	43	51	46	50
3	27	20	29	24	19	38	49
74	39	61	47	4	3	9	8
0	0	0	0	0	0	2	2
3	2	7	10	0	0	1	3
0	0	81	15	2	1	0	0
0	0	592	670	0	0	20	17
6	9	3	3	0	0	0	0
0	0	0	0	0	0	674	276
12	6	0	0	0	0	1	1
9	8	7	6	8	6	6	4
3	6	0	0	2	0	0	0
0	0	0	0	0	0	1	1
0	0	0	0	0	0	2	2
0	0	0	0	0	0	0	0

TABLE NO. 4

Nutrient Composition of the Average Daily Diets of
Rural Nigerian Peasant Farmers in Seven Different Areas of the Country

Village	Sex and age (years) group	Calories (kcal)	Protein Animal (g)	Protein Vegetable (g)	Fat (g)	Calcium (mg)	Iron (mg)	Vitamin A (i.u.)	Thiamine (mg)	Riboflavin (mg)	Nicotinic acid (mg)	Ascorbic acid On the raw basis (mg)	Ascorbic acid With allowance for cooking losses (mg)
Jarawaji	Men over 12	2980	29	83	37	1400	56	900	3.6	1.1	27	13	0
	Women over 12	2650	24	68	33	1100	49	1200	3.2	1.1	22	16	12
	Children: 4-6	1380	22	34	23	1100	26	1000	1.6	0.6	13	12	6
Tangaza	Men over 12	2250	2	71	29	300	24	1400	2.2	0.9	19	7	3
	Women over 12	1520	1.5	46	19	260	16	1200	1.5	0.6	13	12	5
	Children: 7-9	1390	1	42	21	230	16	900	1.5	0.6	13	8	4
	4-6	1180	1	35	16	200	13	800	1.2	0.5	11	8	4
Bunga	Men over 12	2920	11	83	40	880	37	4200	2.9	1.4	24	133	44
	Women over 12	2120	8	62	28	720	26	4000	2.1	1.0	17	65	30
	Children: 10-12	1880	6.5	62	28	550	22	3400	2.0	0.9	14	68	17
	7-9	1790	5	52	26	490	21	3700	1.7	0.8	14	85	23
	4-6	1480	4	43	21	380	16	3000	1.5	0.7	11	57	17
Tungan Maidubu	Men over 12	2910	16	106	34	560	43	2800	4.1	1.5	31	18	6
	Women over 12	2520	8	96	26	470	36	2750	3.9	1.3	27	39	22
	Children: 10-12	1820	6	72	18	360	28	2000	3.0	0.9	20	30	16
	4-6	1110	3	47	11	280	16	1000	1.8	0.5	10	22	9
Langai	Men over 12	2550	15	77	45	610	29	4100	2.2	1.3	24	43	14
	Women over 12	2110	10	72	40	560	25	3200	1.9	1.0	22	52	21
	Children: 10-12	2120	15	61	43	530	26	3900	1.9	1.1	21	53	19
	7-9	1440	15	36	36	340	18	2700	1.8	0.7	15	42	14
	4-6	1180	8	33	24	360	15	2700	1.1	0.7	11	25	9
Bero-Okuta	Men over 12	2060	1.5	50	14	460	19	1600	1.7	0.7	12	160	35
	Women over 12	1680	1.5	40	12	350	15	1500	1.4	0.5	9	122	31
	Children: 7-9	1400	1	34	15	280	13	1500	1.2	0.5	9	101	25
Mbanege	Men over 12	2390	3	59	31	640	23	11880	2.1	1.0	17	216	54
	Women over 12	1950	2.5	51	28	540	22	13000	1.7	0.8	17	178	45
	Children: 7-9	1520	1	38	22	370	15	7100	1.3	0.5	10	144	37
	4-6	1210	1	28	10	250	10	3300	0.8	0.3	6	90	22

Source: Nicol, B. M. - British Journal of Nutrition, Vol. 13, pp. 293-306, 1959.

TABLE NO. 5

Mean Composition of Diets Obtained from Six Ilesha Communities
During the Period August, 1960, to July, 1961

Foodstuff	Ijana-Itarua	Igun	Sabo-Igun	Oke-Ila	Abebeyun	Local Police[a]
Yams: fresh tuber	595	581	91	867	700	52
: dry flour	1	—	—	—	—	131
Cassava: dry gari	115	92	42	78	104	75
: boiled root	—	—	8	—	15	—
Plantain: boiled fruit	26	53	3	21	32	1
: dry flour	16	26	1	8	52	4
Taro: boiled corn	31	—	—	122	14	—
Maize: dry starch	49	55	26	10	35	95
: cooked grain	50	35	—	68	73	3
: whole meal, dry (minus bran)	—	—	185	—	—	—
Rice: dry grain	6	16	68	1	6	24
Wheat: bread	2	3	5	1	2	7
Cowpeas: dry beans	61	48	28	19	45	121
Locust beans: fermented sp.	9	11	19	9	10	5
Melon seeds: dry	3	3	5	3	3	3
Okra fruits: fresh	21	19	39	27	19	16
Leafy vegetables: fresh	34	26	50	17	17	53
Juice fruits:	4	4	1	6	5	9
Chillies: fresh	49	30	32	16	23	36
Onions: fresh	2	1	10	1	5	14
Meat and bone scraps: fresh	20	14	20	7	12	50
: dry	3	11	—	1	11	2
Cow hide: boiled in potash	1	1	—	—	2	3
Fish with bones: dry	1	4	20	1	9	8
Milk: evaporated	—	1	1	—	1	1
Snails: fresh	2	1	—	1	—	1
Red palm oil	17	19	40	20	30	38
Kola seeds: fresh	3	4	3	1	2	1
Awusa seeds[b]: boiled	1	8	—	3	1	—
Palm wine and cereal beer	123	175	13	124	153	51
Tea drink	—	1	16	—	6	5
Sugar: refined	—	1	10	—	1	1
Cooking salt	3	3	9	4	4	4

Notes: The diets in each group were recorded for seven consecutive days at
quarterly intervals and the quantities expressed as grams edible portion/head/
day. Local items: Sabo-Igun only, Pennisetum, dry flour, 4; Sorghum, id., 11;
groundnuts, boiled, 1; groundnut oil, 5; Igun: mushrooms, fresh, 1; Oke-Ila,
Abebeyun, caterpillars, fresh, 2 and 1 resp. Juicy fruits: tomatoes, paw paw,
orange juice.

a. Mean of records collected in May and July, 1961.
b. Awusa seeds: Tetracarpidium sp.

Source: Ecology of Child Nutrition and Health in Nigerian Villages. Collis,
W.R.F. et al., Tropical Geographical Medicine, Vol. 14, pp. 201-
229, 1962.

TABLE NO.6

Seasonal Variations in Calorie and Protein Intakes by Five Ilesha
Communities Between April, 1960 and July, 1961

Locality	Total calorie intake/head/day	Crude protein intake (grams per head/day)	Protein calories (percent total calories)
Ijana-Itarua			
min.	April 1640	April 35	8.2
max.	Feb. 2050	Feb. 51	10.4
Igun			
min.	Aug. 1760	Aug. 36	8.2
max.	Feb. 2100	Feb. 60	11.4
Sabo-Igun			
min.	July 1740	Aug. 48	9.2
max.	Nov. 2360	Feb. 69	12.7
Oke-Ila			
min.	Aug. 1550	July 27	6.5
max.	Feb. 1830	Feb. 37	8.3
Abebeyun			
min.	Aug. 2000	July 44	8.5
max.	Nov. 2490	Feb. 57	10.3

Source: Ecology of Child Nutrition and Health in Nigerian Villages - Collis,
W.R.F. et al., Tropical Geographical Medicine, Vol. 14, pp. 201-
229, 1962.

TABLE NO. 7

Protein and Calorie Intake; Percentage of Requirements

	Protein						Calorie					
	April 1960	Aug. 1960	Nov. 1960	Feb. 1961	May 1961	July 1961	April 1960	Aug. 1960	Nov. 1960	Feb. 1961	May 1961	July 1961
Ijana-Itarua	49	57	74	70	36	57	75	78	83	92	78	81
Igun		52	78	96	76	69		82	86	95	87	80
Sabo-Igun		67	70	69	91	61		77	99	92	88	69
Oke-Ila		32	28	31	35	33		70	79	83	79	75
Abebeyun		65	77	91	75	74		88	116	102	85	91
Local Group (Abebeyun Police force)					92	99					105	103

Source: Ecology of Child Nutrition and Health in Nigerian Villages - Collis, W. R. F. et al., Tropical Geographical Medicine, Vol. 14, pp. 201-229, 1962.

TABLE NO. 8

Estimates of Calories and Certain Nutrients Per
Person Per Day at Nigerian Secondary School

	DATE OF SURVEY	
NUTRIENT	November 1959	May 1960
Protein		
Total (gm.)	55	67
Animal (gm.)	10	14
Calcium (mg.)	407	619
Iron (mg.)	13	16.1
Vitamin A (I.U.)	6380	6687
Thiamine (mg.)	1.59	1.89
Riboflavin (mg.)	0.41	0.52
Niacin (mg.)	12	12.2
Ascorbic acid (mg.)	73	39
Calories	2500+	2200+

Source: Hauck, H.M., Dietary Study in a Nigerian Secondary School, Journal
American Diet. Association, Vol. 39, pp. 467-472, Nov. 1961.

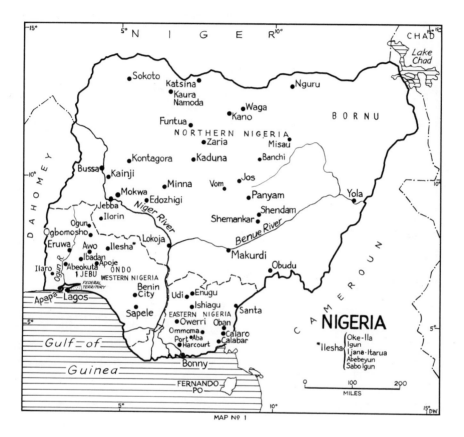

MAP Nº 1

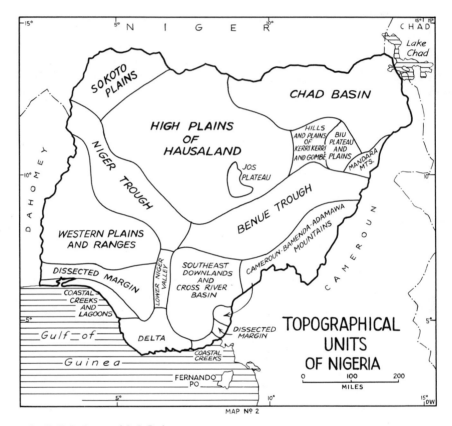

After K. M. Buchanan and J. C. Pugh
from "Land and People in Nigeria,"
Courtesy of Publisher, University of
London Press Ltd.

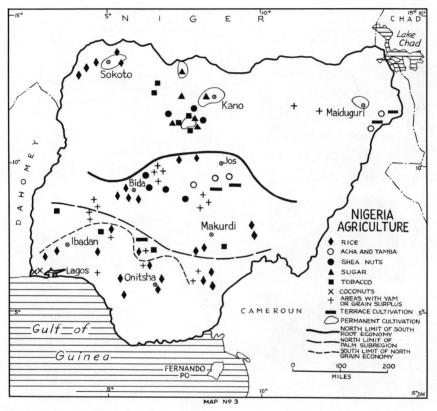

MAP N⁰ 3

After K. M. Buchanan and J. C. Pugh
from "Land and People in Nigeria,"
Courtesy of Publisher, University of
London Press Ltd.

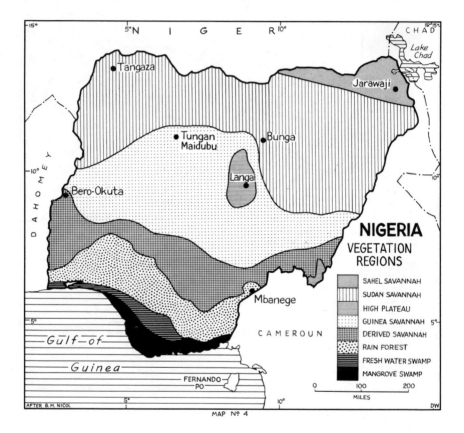

MAP Nº 4

REPUBLIC OF THE CONGO (LEOPOLDVILLE)

TABLE OF CONTENTS

REPUBLIC OF THE CONGO (LEOPOLDVILLE)

Weights and Measures

1 Meter	= 39.370 inches = 3.281 feet
1 Kilometer	= 1,000 meters = 0.621 of a mile
1 Square Kilometer	= 0.386 square miles
1 Hectare	= 2.471 acres
1 Kilogram	= 2.204 lbs.
1 Quintal	= 100 kilograms = 220.4 lbs.
1 Ton	= 1,000 kilograms = 2204.6223 lbs.
1 Congolese franc	= $0,0055
1 U. S. $	= 180 Congolese francs (1964)
	= 65 Congolese francs (1960)
	= 50 Congolese francs (1958)

REPUBLIC OF THE CONGO (LEOPOLDVILLE)

I

BACKGROUND

A. GEOGRAPHY [2][5][14][28]

Topography and climate

The former Belgian Congo, now called Republic of the Congo (Leopoldville), is located in the center of tropical Africa astride the equator between 5°30' North and 14°South. Two-thirds of its land area thus lies in the Southern Hemisphere. In breadth, it extends from 12°9' to 31°18' East. The territory's boundaries were defined by the Neutrality Declaration of August 1885 and December 1894, further modified and acknowledged by treaties with Germany, Great Britain, France, and Portugal. The territory was declared a free state at the Berlin Conference of 1884-1885 with Leopold II of Belgium as its Head of State; it became a Belgian colony in November 1907 and achieved independence on June 30, 1960.

The Republic is bounded on the west and north by two of the Republics of Former French Equatorial Africa, the Congo (Brazzaville) and the Central African Republic. The Republic of the Sudan lies to the northeast. Uganda, (a Sovereign State*), the Republic of Rwanda, the Kingdom of Burundi, and the State of Tanganyika are on the eastern border. Northern Rhodesia and the Portuguese colony of Angola lie on the south. Angola and the Atlantic Ocean limit the country on the south and west.

The country enjoys considerable geographic unity as it includes almost all of the land drained by the Congo Basin south of the Ubangi. It covers approximately 905,062 square miles or 2,344,116 square kilometers. It is almost completely landlocked with the exception of a small coastline, 40 kilometers (25 miles) long, north of the mouth of the Congo River on the Atlantic Ocean, where the port of Matadi lies. The country can be compared to a saucer, with a rim of hills and mountains in the northeast, the east, and the south, sloping toward the center. In the northern half of the country a thick equatorial forest discourages agricultural expansion, which, however, has succeeded in various places (see Map No. 2). On the surrounding hills the country looks like wooded savannas, bush, and grasslands.

---

*Neither Republic nor Kingdom.

The relief consists of several mountain ranges. The Crystal Mountains between Leopoldville and Matadi in the west continue into the Katanga Mountains in the south, and the Central Graben that separate the Zambezi River Basin from the sources of the Nile include the Albert, Edward, Kivu, and Tanganyika chain of lakes. The altitudes increases along the chains from an average of 650 meters in the west to the high Ruwenzori Mountains in the east with peaks rising up to 5500 meters. The floor of the saucer is flat with a gradient of about 150 mm. every $1\frac{1}{2}$ km., or 1 to 10,000, between the Stanley Falls and Leopoldville. This causes the wide rivers to rampage outside their beds frequently. The physical features govern the identification of the geographic regions to which certain types of vegetation, culture, and population belong.

The climate is hot and humid in the center of the country, becoming cooler and drier toward the mountainous rim. Meigs recognizes eight climatic regions in Africa, four of which can be found in the Congo: a temperate highland climate in the southern province of Katanga, where temperatures range from 18°C to 24°C at Elizabethville and annual rainfall averages 1850 mm.; a tropical highland climate associated with the highlands of southern Kasai, where temperatures range from 24°C to 26°C (at Luluabourg) and where the average annual rainfall is 1200 mm.; a tropical wet-dry climate south of the equator in the lowlands of Kasai and along the western sections of the lower Congo Basin, where temperatures range from 22°C to 27°C (at Leopoldville) and annual rainfall amounts to 1000 mm.; and the equatorial wet climate of the northern districts, except for small strips of land in the extreme north, where wet-dry conditions prevail. Along most of the equatorial zone temperatures range from 25°C to 27°C and total annual rainfall reaches 1650 mm. (Stanleyville). At Coquilhatville temperatures range from 24°C to 26°C and total annual rainfall amounts to 1475 mm. Thus, moving away from the equator, the available moisture diminishes, and conditions become gradually less favorable for agriculture. The geography and climate create the ideal habitat for the tsetse flies, vectors of sleeping sickness.

All rivers of importance drain into the Congo or its tributaries, which include the mighty Ubangi. The eastern chain of lakes includes the western shore of Lake Tanganyika, the western shore of Lake Kivu, the western two-thirds of Lake Edward, and the northwestern shore of Lake Albert, all offering some navigable routes and fish resources but also a convenient habitat for various mollusks, vectors of schistosomiasis.

The Congo, with a course of 2900 miles or 4640 km., is the sixth longest river in the world and the third longest in Africa (after the Nile and the Niger). Its width extends over two and one-half miles between the capital cities of Leopoldville and Brazzaville. The Ubangi forms the northern boundary of the country and has 644 navigable km.; the Kasai with 864 km. and some forty other rivers total approximately 15,000 km. of navigable waterways.

B. POPULATION [5][14][17]

1. General

The population of the Congo include both indigenous and non-indigenous groups. The indigenous p o p u l a t i o n comprises five recognizable ethnic groups, each of them divided into a varying number of tribes. These groups are the Bantus, the Sudanese, the Nilotics, the Hamites, and the Pygmies and Pygmoids. The Bantus are the most important, comprising fifty-four different tribes or groups. They are found in all provinces* (see Map No. 1). The Sudanese are found in the north and northeast; they include fourteen tribes or groups. The Nilotic people are found only in the East; they include the Alur people. The Hamites are found in the Kivu area with one tribe, the Tutsi. The Pygmies are found in the northeast and northwest with four groups, the Mbuti, the Efe, the Aka, and the Tschwa.

The names of these tribal groups are confusing. While the International African Institute advocates the use of the root word only, the people themselves always use the prefix "Ba," the people, when mentioning themselves or others. Thus, the Kongo people become the Bakongo, the Boa may be called the Bua, Babua, or Abbabua; the Lunda call themselves the Balunda; the Pygmies of Moyen Congo and Ubangi provinces call themselves the Batwa or Bachwa while scientists call them Twa or Tschwa. Table No. 2 gives the names of the major tribes by provinces as they were known in 1960.

Generalizing somewhat, it can be said that the Bantus are essentially agriculturists; the Hamites, Sudanese, and Nilotic groups have a major interest in cattle; and the Pygmies still belong to a picking and gathering jungle culture.

As of January 1, 1959, the A f r i c a n population amounted to 13,540,182 with a rate of growth estimated by various sources at 1.27 percent, 2 percent or even 2.5 percent. This means that this figure should be raised to 14,399,983, at least, as of January 1, 1964.

The non-African group on January 1, 1959, comprised 88,913 Belgians or 75.36 percent of the nonindigenous group. There were also 5166 Portuguese, 3635 Italians, 3316 Greeks, 2315 British, 2378 French, 1912 Americans, and 10,348 others, including the half-castes and mulattoes. Since that date an estimated 40,000 Belgians** have left the country. Table No. 3 gives the numerical data concerning population groups in 1959.

2. Languages and Religion

The most important native languages are Kiswahili or Kingwana in the east and northeast, Lingala along the Congo River between Stanleyville and Leopoldville, Kikongo in the lower Congo area, and Kiluba or Tschiluba in the south. The majority of the population is

---

*Four territories are under referendum; two more provinces than are listed in Table No. 1 may result.
**As of April 1964 the return of some Belgian technicians is reported.

animist and fetishist. Their beliefs include a varied set of taboos, pe-
culiar to each tribe, that influence nutrition, especially that of the most
vulnerable groups, women and children.

Missionary work has been active in the Congo. At the beginning
of 1959 there were 10,284 missionaries, of whom 7436 were Roman
Catholics; these included 1532 Africans. Protestant missionaries numbered 2848, of whom 1195 were Africans. On January 1, 1962, the
Congolese massacred twenty-two priests in Nord Katanga. Yet the
number of converts is large. There were an estimated 4,546,160
Catholics, 825,625 Protestants, and 150,000 Moslems at the beginning
of 1959.

3. Demography

The structure of the African population shows a majority of
women—8.5 percent up to age 45,* after which the proportion is gradually reversed. Children under age fourteen represent 40 percent of
the population, so in 1970 the procreating population will have increased
from 30 percent in the 1950's to 35 percent.

The urban population living in towns of over 10,000 inhabitants
on January 1, 1959, amounted to 1,178,861 people or 8.6 percent of the
total population leaving 91.4 percent to live on the land. The population
density varies considerably, as shown in Table No. 3 where the population data is summarized.** The overall density is 5.83 per sq. km.
or approximately 15 per sq. mile. Densities by provinces vary from
8.88 in Kivu and 8.96 in Leopoldville to 3.40 in Katanga and 4.5 in
Equateur. Higher densities are found in the clusters of periurban populations around the big centers and in the industrial and mining areas
of Katanga and Kasai.

Birth rates and death rates vary considerably in different regions of the country. The birth rate is highest in the industrial areas
of Katanga and lowest in the rural part of Leopoldville Province, while
death rates are highest in rural areas and lowest in the urban and industrial areas of the country. During the last few years the trend has
been for the birth rate to rise and for the death rate to fall. In the urban
area of Leopoldville, for instance, the birth rate has risen from 38.74
percent in 1955 to 51.92 percent in 1959 while the death rate during the
same period dropped from 9.71 percent in 1955 to 7.62 percent in 1959.
Infantile mortality in the urban and suburban areas has fallen fairly
rapidly in the last decade, and it is estimated by the World Health Organization that this is probably true for the rural areas as well. No
reliable statistical data, however, are available for the rural population
as a rule. Infantile mortality in the urban area of Leopoldville, however, has dropped from 154.5 per 1,000 live births in 1955 to 62.8 in
1959. Main causes of infantile mortality in the area were: pneumonia

*For every 200 men there are 217 women.
**By 1964 the urban percentage of the population had notably increased; ac-
curate figures are not available.

and broncho-pneumonia, 7.1 percent; anemia and malnutrition, 7.1 percent; upper respiratory diseases, 5.6 percent; gastroenteritis, 4.1 percent; tetanus neonatorum, 2.1 percent; measles, 1.9 percent; external causes, 1.9 percent; prematurity, 1.8 percent; diseases of the heart, 1.5 percent; and congenital malformations, 1.2 percent.

4. Detribalization [33][51]

The most important feature of this African population is its gradual detribalization in the urban areas. Table No. 4 gives the numerical facts of this situation. Extensive psychological studies have been made of this phenomenon; its dynamism originates in a strong desire to imitate the Western world in an image of wealth, power, and security. The younger generation, comparing life in the city (with its activity, its lights, its permanent markets and stores) to the dreariness of the village (its hard and fast tribal and family rules, its poverty, its mud, and its dangers) hardly hesitates. The dangers of the changeover are not so obvious as its apparent advantages, but they are nonetheless considerable. In Stanleyville, for instance, it was found that the earnings of the unskilled immigrants from the bush are insufficient to support life in an urban area if at the same time tribal ties are maintained as most of them desire. Many of these city dwellers go back to the bush occasionally to take care of their tribal obligations in obvious search of security; two-thirds of the detribalized marry within the tribe, binding them to a family rather than just to one girl. This creates an additional burden because when relatives come to town seeking hospitality, they stay in the urbanized African's room until they find work. This period may last indefinitely, putting further stress on salary and other resources. On the other hand, the African who leaves the traditional life and thus sheds his duties to tribe and relatives loses the security it affords against destitution. He has to face suddenly increased needs with an inadequate salary. As a tribal African, he very seldom had to buy food; this was grown, picked, gathered, hunted for, and occasionally purchased by the chief when bartering goods or money were available; in the city he is suddenly confronted with the unforgiving demands of the money economy, and this has a considerable demoralizing effect on the detribalized African.

There is also the problem of sex and domestic life for men who leave their women back in the village. Many young men turn to alcohol, which is cheaper than a belly full of manioc or porridge at city prices. The resulting demoralization of the young men creates an ugly situation. This problem existed prior to independence. The Belgian government had tried to encourage the preservation of tribal ties by imposing stiff educational demands for those who sought urbanization and westernization. Under present conditions, without funds for schools and social services, it is feared that chaos may result from an uncontrolled, too hasty detribalization.

5. Habitat [14]

Housing. Among the Congolese a village is formed by a clan or
a tribal group. It is subdivided into hamlets, which are formed by a
number of families, usually related to each other, and in sections each
formed by one family. The huts are very often round with a conic roof,
especially among the Banda, Azandi, Mongatu, and some others, but
also among some of the Bantu tribes. Occasionally the huts may have a
square base and a four-sloped roof (Bateke and Pygmies), or they may
have a rectangular base and a roof that resembles the carapace of a
tortoise. The material for the roof is thatch or palm leaves, depending
on the resources available. The walls are made of wood occasionally
but more often of reeds woven together like baskets or of latan leaves
or even grass, sometimes even of mud. In most cases the huts are built
on a pedestal of clay and have some underground foundation. Riverine
tribes often build their homes on stilts. Very often these huts are
adorned with sculpture or paintings on the walls themselves when the
building material lends itself to decorations. There are few or no win-
dows. The ventilation is poor, and the mud floor is polluted by the feces
of children and pets. A man may own several huts in a compound around
a well, which provides separate housing for women and children.

The type of housing described above favors the spread of tick-
borne infections and rodent-borne diseases such as plague because
ticks live in crevasses in the wall and rats nest under the thatched
roof. The crowding inside the hut favors the transmission of many
air-borne and droplet-borne infections, while the free defecation in
and around the compound is an inexhaustible source of hookworm eggs
and larvae.

Other types of housing are found in the richer villages or in the
cities where some of the évolués (westernized natives) live. There
bricks are used because fuel for baking them is available. A corrugated
iron roof replaces the thatch. The pressure of the detribalized groups
has brought about the development of centres extra coutumiers (detribalized centers) in the suburbs of the main cities. These centers
were created by the cooperation of the government, the city, and the
men who need the shelter. They may not be entirely satisfactory, but
at least they have water and electricity. Such centers exist at Leopoldville, Elizabethville, and other places. In these cities before independence there were schools, dispensaries, and social work. To solve the
housing problem, an Office of African Cities had been created in Brussels, which planned a ten-year program for the construction of 40,000
houses, half of which were to be built in the city of Leopoldville. This
office provided guidance and plans for twenty-two types of houses; unfortunately only three of them conformed to the standards set by the
Institute of Hygiene.

Finally, in the large cities there are houses as well built and
beautiful as any in the warmer climates of Europe and the United States.

C. AGRICULTURAL POLICIES [26][28][20][41][17][17]

The present government of Leopoldville, like most African governments, lays great stress on the advantages and feasibility of promoting individual ownership in place of the traditional collective ownership that is still the general situation in Africa. The change to individual tenure was begun under the Belgians with the paysannat farms.

Unfortunately, this system runs counter to many customs and psychological attitudes of the people. A Nigerian chief is often quoted as having said, "Land, and the right to cultivate it belong to a vast family, of which many are dead, a few are living, and countless numbers are still unborn." This illustrates well the attitude of the people toward land tenure. Also, there is no denying that the traditional system, as noted elsewhere in these reports, yields maximum production with maximum protection of fixed assets. As long as fertilizer is practically unavailable to the common villager, the shifting of cultivation and the burning of bushes do provide some safeguard against exhaustion of land and do afford some security against erosion. As population increases, however, the pressure on fixed amounts of arable land is a factor that weighs against the traditional system. Scientific methods that provide greater yields for the same amount of land create problems that lead to the development of agricultural units larger than those that could be allotted to one family.

There is therefore a trend to cooperatives, of which the paysannat is a form. Following earlier failures in adapting Western agriculture to Congolese conditions, the Belgian government, before independence, had tried to evolve a modern version of "Bantu agriculture," which was characterized by a long period of fallow and natural regrowth. These policies were compulsory in the paysannats. Emphasis had been placed on rotation and scientifically organized mixed crops, on adding organic matter and returning the land to the forest whenever possible. In addition, the paysannat groups used selected seeds, timed their operations carefully, and controlled insects and pests. The policies also included compulsory acreage quotas in food crops, to insure sufficient food production for the local farmer as well as reserves for the growing urban population. Mechanization and intensive fertilization were part of a second phase that never had time to develop.

There is no doubt but that the present government favors continuing these policies. It established a Ministry of Land in May 1963; cadastral operations were begun by the staking of all private individual and collective properties.

All the above policies were made possible by the availability of Belgian and Belgian-educated technicians. There were in 1958, 1351 schools for teachers in agriculture; 244 schools for agricultural assistants; 35 fishery schools; 227 schools for garden culture; 11 schools for veterinary attendants; 48 schools for veterinary assistants; 24 schools for farming; and 18 agronomical institutes giving university degrees.

Most important of these institutes was the National Institute for Agronomic Studies in the Belgian Congo (INEAC).* This had an agronomical
research station at Yangambi, comprising twelve sections devoted to
the region and the factors of production in the central basin of the
Congo River, five sections devoted to plant improvement and rural
technical methods, and two sections devoted to the problem of stock
raising and pisciculture. Other stations similarly organized existed in
the lower Congo, in the north, in the south, in Katanga, in the Kivu, and
in the Ituri regions. The results of the scientific research of these institutes were widely circulated among the native rural population
through the Government Agricultural Services. Noteworthy among these
were the stations for local adaptation and the centers for the improvement of native livestock.

What remains of these institutions and what efficiency they have retained is difficult to assess; the lack of educated personnel has, without
doubt, drastically curtailed their operation. Yet the new government is
fully aware of the need for continuing education in order to keep the
level of production as high as possible. To effect this it requested
American aid to further agricultural education by establishing a new
school to train Congolese farmers in modern agricultural methods.
Such a school was inaugurated in November 1962 at Vanga, about 100
miles from Leopoldville, by the Agency for International Development.
The school was planned by the Congolese Polytechnical Institute and
constructed by Congolese workers with the help of American experts.
The Vanga school is the third of its kind to receive United States aid.

The United Nations Civilian Mission in the Congo included agricultural experts who, in cooperation with the new government of the Congo,
are taking steps to reactivate an agricultural program. Their policies
can be summed up in the following way:

1. Salvage what can be salvaged from past achievements with the
hope of priming the economy again.

2. Prepare for the future, essentially by encouraging the training
and education of agricultural technicians.

The first concrete implementation of these policies was to assist
in the production of cotton, both by selling stocked-up reserves from
previous years and by distributing 200 tons of insecticides to protect
the 1963 crop. Little could be done to assist the production of coffee.
This was hit by a general slump in world prices. The pyrethrum industry, having ceased to receive its raw material from Rwanda and
Burundi after these two countries gained their independence, was beyond assistance also. However, sugar-cane factories, especially in
the Kivu, were helped. An effort is being made to re-establish a marketing structure; marketing experts advise on the channeling of food
grants from the United States and also recommend policies to provide
for the import of spare parts needed to restore to use the agricultural
machines, idle since independence. These experts also recommend

---

*Institut National des Études Agronomiques au Congo.

the import of breeding animals and incentive goods (trinkets, bicycles, cooking utensils) to encourage the people to return to work and to take their produce to the markets.

In keeping with the policy of rehabilitation and the safeguarding of the existing assets, veterinary experts, armed with large quantities of vaccine, have aided in the control of rinderpest, which had broken out in dangerous fashion in the former Orientale and Kivu Provinces. In addition, the United Nations Civilian Operations has given assistance to protect and rehabilitate the famous Botanical Garden at Kisantu and to restore the Albert National Park. Assistance was also given by small farmers in the form of supplies of vegetable seeds, insecticides, and fertilizers and to the market gardeners around Leopoldville in order to relieve the threat of famine in that city. Worthy of note is the assistance given to the largest of the vegetable projects to be found around the city at N'djili, where 400 families have formed an agricultural cooperative.

In line with the policy of preparing for the future, the training of Congolese personnel has been given top priority by the United Nations Mission. A Farm Mechanics Training Center, organized for the dual purpose of training Congolese to handle farm machinery and of saving valuable equipment lying abandoned on thousands of farms, has so far (October 1963) had four sessions. One hundred thirty-eight Congolese farm mechanics have been trained; the best students in each course have been kept on as demonstrators. In March 1962 the FAO Mission established an experimental station for horticultural training at Mikondo on the outskirts of Leopoldville. In addition, twelve students have entered their first year of the two and one-half year diploma course set up at Lovanium University with the assistance of the United Nations Civilian Mission. Up to the end of 1962 a total of 14 experts from ten countries were engaged in undertaking agricultural assistance in the Congo. Forty fellowships had been granted under United Nations auspices for perfecting agricultural training abroad. Laboratory equipment was furnished, especially for the diploma course at Lovanium University. The cost of the equipment plus the cost of three tractors purchased for the Farm Mechanics Training Center and other equipment totalled $30,000 at the end of 1962. Technical assistance to agriculture within the Civilian Operations Program has been financed solely by the United Nations Fund for the Congo and amounted at the end of 1962 to $711,480, with a balance of unspent funds ready to be dispersed during the year 1963. In addition, a Food and Agricultural Organization Program for 1963, to cost $741,000, will include advisory services by 37 experts, two courses for farm-mechanics training, an accelerated course for agricultural assistance, a poultry-farming training center, and a number of veterinary courses at Lovanium University.

II

FOOD RESOURCES

A. GENERAL [17][19]

Under the present conditions of flux and transition, an estimation
of the food resources is difficult unless it is based on previous records.
Prior to independence agriculture accounted for 40 percent of all resources of the economy. In 1959 the total land area was estimated at
234,493,000 hectares. This area was roughly divided into: arable land
under permanent crops, 48,995,000 hectares; permanent meadows and
pastures, 2,435,000 hectares; forests, 100 million hectares; built-up
areas or unusable land, 83,063,000 hectares. This land produced the
food resources of the country in both cash crops (coffee, palm oil,
cocoa, cotton seeds, etc.) and food crops (manioc, sweet potatoes,
plantain, etc.). These crops were produced by both European enterprises and Congolese farms. Among the latter, some were gradually
being westernized while others were still run along traditional lines.
Some of the food crops thus produced got into commercial channels
while some remained within the circle of the village, the tribe, or the
family. As of 1958 there was a total of 2,762,042 hectares of land that
had been conceded to private individuals or private and government-
sponsored enterprises. They amounted to 1.16 percent of the country's
total area but to 5.6 percent of its arable land. The same year 1,969,356
hectares had been sold outright rather than conceded to private individuals or to private and government-sponsored enterprises. As a result,
a total of 4,731,398 hectares representing almost 10 percent of the total
arable land and 7.7 percent of the forest and agricultural land had been
alienated in favor of Europeans or Western-oriented enterprises.

B. MEANS OF PRODUCTION

1. Agricultural Labor Force [46][12]

Before independence some 85 percent of the working population
was engaged in agricultural enterprises. Some worked as laborers on
foreign-owned plantation; most produced food on a subsistence basis
on their own or tribally-owned land. In 1957 the number employed as
hired agricultural laborers was estimated at 300,000. Since 1960 disruption of work on the plantations has displaced many laborers, who
have returned to their villages or migrated to the cities. As a result,
the statistics for agricultural labor today are nonexistent or misleading.
It is clear, however, that there is considerable unemployment and that
a system of public works is necessary to absorb the unemployed. In
July 1963 Prime Minister Adoula was urging the unemployed in the
cities to return to the villages and cultivate the land.

2. Farms [20][26][28][5][7]

The Congolese farm system is basically similar to those discussed in various other countries of Africa. There are large European plantations. African farms run along Western lines (paysannat), and private, tribally-owned subsistence farms, traditionally run.

European Agriculture. No credible record of what is left of European agriculture to date is available. While figures of acreages might be procured, the efficiency with which they are run—under the present conditions of no skilled labor and no machinery—is impossible to assess. The problem of European-owned plantations is highly confused. Ownership has not been decided, and both managers and laborers leave and return, depending on the current political circumstances. The extent to which the efficiency of production has been impaired is indicated by the drop in exports, shown in Table No. 9. European enterprises were and still are largely concerned with cash crops. Under the Belgians those crops existed mainly on the large plantations and consisted of coffee, palm oil, rubber, cocoa, and pyrethrum (see Table No. 7 for acreages and production in 1959). Cash-crop production was at first little affected by the events of 1960. Later, especially in 1961, production dropped sharply, due to the abandonment of some of the plantations in the eastern part of the country.

Congolese Agriculture. In 1954 the Belgian government started establishing cooperative farms, the paysannats, with the purpose of trying to tie the population to the land. These farms covered 1.6 million hectares and provided a good living for about 166,000 inhabitants. By 1960 the paysannats had increased to over two million hectares and supported well over a million people. These farms, more than 200,000 of them in 1960, were scattered all over the country where land and conditions were suitable. It was anticipated that by 1965 one-sixth of the population or 450,000 families would be established on cooperative farms. The policy was to concentrate on crops yielding high cash returns in order to improve the standard of living of the farmers, while food crops were planned to raise their dietary levels. Farmers living on the paysannat farms received guidance as to what to plant and how. The government reserved the right to impose certain crops; this was called the "Educational Agricultural Program;" in fact, the purpose was to assure a satisfactory level of production for the increasing population, especially in the cities. Cash crops were sold for the benefit of the people through a system that eliminated the middleman and thus tended to give the farmer a stable return for his work. Some success is indicated by the fact that the per capita income on the paysannat farms rose from about $5 per year prior to World War II, to $300 per year in 1960, one of the highest African-owned individual or familial farm incomes in the country. In addition, the government provided community services, such as schools, hospitals, and extension services.

The effects of the 1960 mutinies that followed independence and the attendant disruption of law and order during the years 1960-1961 were disastrous. More than 500 government agricultural engineers and their Congolese assistants left their guidance work on the paysannats and deterioration began. Machinery rusted in the fields without maintenance, lack of foreign currency prevented purchase of replacement parts, and technicians were not available. If the trend is not stopped, it is likely that those farms that represented a reasonable transition between the past and the future will eventually return to traditional work, with or without tribal support and assistance. However, a number of these paysannats did survive, especially in the area of Thysville.*

Subsistence Farms. Subsistence farms, tribally owned, and worked to a great degree by the women of the family, still represent most of the food-producing agriculture in the Congo in terms of manpower, land cultivated, and tonnage produced. This production is not included in the pre-independence figures given in Table No. 6 and is difficult to compute now. The problems regulating production—in a subsistence, nonmonetary economy—are common to most families of the African tropical belt and have already been alluded to in these reports. The traditional methods of agriculture result in the alternation of periods of plenty and periods of starvation as a result of the vagaries of climate and of the improvident frame of mind of the African. Equalization of supply, even if it were acceptable to the local psychology, is difficult to achieve. To avoid alternate "feast and famine," it is necessary to build up reserves, and that requires cultivation of large fields to increase production. That does not fit in with the tribal land-tenure system and the slash-and-burn technique, otherwise so useful and imposed by the nature of the soil. While the "landman," whose job is to allot fields to the tribe's families, is usually chosen with care, he is only human and may allot lands for the year to his friends. This is no inducement for anyone to work harder to improve a field that may be allotted to another man next year. Even if it were possible to harvest more than is immediately needed, the surplus could not profitably be sold, precisely because in a surplus year there is no demand for it; neither can it easily be stored because of rodents, pests, humidity, and the perishability of most crops. Finally, the successful farmer who moves into the money economy and enriches himself may be envied, ostracized, or even accused of succeeding through witchcraft. To these problems, inherent in the system at all times, the present situation has added its own difficulties. It is reported that insecure farmers produce barely what they need; when they produce more, they cannot move the products because of bad conditions of the roads and insecurity. Congo-Presse revealed in May 1963 that the government had complained about some food being available in Central Congo provinces that could not be moved from the villages because of insecurity, bad roads, and lack of trucks.

---

*Personal communication, J. King Gordon.

3. Fertilizers [19]

The greatest problem in Congolese agriculture, as in other areas of Africa, is the procurement of cheap fertilizer. Most of the Congo land is poor, except in the Kivu area, because of heavy tropical rains and poor farming methods. Fertilizers are lacking because of the absence of animal manure and the lack of integration between animal husbandry and agriculture. The normal increase in population will soon increase the problem of food inadequacy, especially if the present unsettled conditions continue. Even in times of peace and security there was a shortage of fertilizers. A report of FAO in 1958 noted that Congolese farms, including those of Ruanda-Urandi,* used only 1200 tons of nitrogen fertilizer, 0.7 tons of phosphate fertilizer, and 0.7 tons of potash fertilizer.

4. Mechanical Equipment [18]

In 1962 FAO estimated the number of all-purpose tractors available in the Congo at 2000 units. In 1964 the number of Congolese technicians qualified to run this valuable machinery efficiently or to replace repatriated European technicians was far too low. As a result, machinery valued at some U.S. $15 million is rapidly deteriorating on plantations and paysannats. There are too few Congolese able to make precise requisitions for spare parts, and even when the correct parts are ordered their procurement takes a long time. FAO technicians feel that it would be unwise to import tractors and machinery as long as there is not a sufficient number of qualified Congolese technicians to maintain them. This is another reason why a high priority has been given to the training of Congolese technicians. The depreciation of the present machinery in the hands of nonqualified men has been evaluated at U.S. $2.5 million per year. The loss of production due to this state of affairs is also considerable. To operate the 2000 tractors that are at present available, although in dire need of repairs, some 2500 to 3000 drivers, mechanics, and storekeepers are required. This means that, estimating the service period of a trained man at about 15 years, each year 160 to 200 Congolese should be trained. For this purpose a center has been established at N'djili, 20 km. south of Leopoldville.

C. PRODUCTION

1. Sources of Carbohydrates [19][26]

The index of per capita food production dropped to 72 in 1960-1961 from a level of 100 in 1954. Between 1940 and 1959 the acreage in the hands of Africans devoted to food crops had risen from 480,000 hectares to 2,700,000 hectares. The area devoted to cash crops had risen from 150,000 to 450,000 hectares. These figures of course include the paysannat farms and refer only to food crops that were moved through commercial channels. The food crops, as separate from the

*Now Rwanda and Burundi.

cash crops, include such items as cereals (wheat,* corn, millet, sorghum, and rice), tubers (manioc, sweet potatoes, yams, and European potatoes), pulses (essentially dry beans and voandzia peas), and fruit (especially bananas and plantain bananas). The pattern of this cultivation and the results of production were, as elsewhere, governed by a large variety of factors: soil, climate, tradition, skill, and especially, in subsistence agriculture, the highest possible return in food value, measured in terms of hunger satisfaction per hour of work. Many studies in food economics have explored this problem and we can agree with Johnston that the following list of crops represents a decreasing order of yield: manioc, plantain, yams and sweet potatoes, wet rice, corn, dry rice, sorghum and millet. The emphasis placed on these different crops in the Congo reflects almost exactly the list of preference given above.

Tables No. 5 and 6 give the acreage known to be planted to these various food crops and the reported production moved through commercial channels in 1961 and 1962.

Manioc from 633,000 hectares produced a crop of 7,212,000 tons in 1961. The crop of plantain bananas, another staple food in certain areas, came from 224,000 hectares and produced 1,956,040 tons of fruit in 1958. Sweet potatoes from 56,000 hectares yielded 316,000 tons in 1961. Corn from 358,000 hectares in 1960 yielded 333,000 tons. Corn is mainly a savannah crop, and its culture has been promoted, and even enforced, prior to independence, to insure the feeding of the growing population of the industrialized towns. Rice came from 153,000 hectares and yielded 164,000 tons also in 1960. The production of rice had increased fourfold in twenty years.

2. Sources of Fats[19][26]

Groundnuts are the chief source of fat. Cottonseed and sesame are considered cash crops, although there has been an effort in the Congo, under the Belgians, to use cottonseed cakes as a protein supplement to the rations of school children. Peanuts and groundnuts were grown on 280,000 hectares in 1960-1961; the crop was 175,000 tons. In 1962 this production had dropped to 130,000 tons. Tables No. 5 and 6 give the acreage and production levels of a few other food items.

The figures given in the two previous paragraphs do not give the total of the food grown in the Congo. They report only the food produced and sold for which records are available. It is known, however, that the sale of food for local use has increased noticeably in recent years. A report of the Central Bank of the Belgian Congo in Rwanda and Burundi indicated that between the years 1948 and 1955 sales of the major staples of domestic diets (manioc, plantain, corn, and rice) rose from 10 percent to 20 percent of total consumption. It is likely that this

---

*The consumption of wheat by Africans is said to have increased five times between 1948 and 1955. It must be assumed that this will continue, in view of the accelerated pace of migration from the villages into the cities where wheat is the staple cereal.

trend has continued between 1955 and 1963, but no official figures can be found. Rice topped the list of foods grown for commercial sale on the domestic market; 65 percent of all rice consumed came from domestic sources through these channels.

Thus, in order to compute the total food resources of the country, it is necessary to add estimates of the unreported food grown in the villages to the official figures.

Cash Crops. [5][19]   Cash crops, as already stated, were and are mostly in the hands of Europeans. They include coffee (both robusta and arabica varieties), rubber, palm oil, palm nuts, sesame, cottonseed, sisal, tobacco, sugar cane, cocoa, pyrethrum, tea, cinchona, and perfume plants. Tables No. 5 and 7 give the area sown and the production in selected years between 1948 and 1962 for some of these crops (see also Map No. 4).

The top money-maker in 1958 was coffee, covering 95,702 hectares, producing 59,322 tons, and earning 2,401,800,000 francs ($48 million). This represented approximately 40.9 percent of all commercialized agricultural production in 1958. Approximately 16 percent of this was produced by A f r i c a n s. In 1961-62 this production dropped to 54,000 tons.

The second money-maker was palm oil, was planted on 179,009 hectares, producing 407,671 tons and bringing into the Congo economy 1,202,400,000 francs or U.S. $24,048,000. This represented approximately 20 percent of all commercial agriculture, the largest share of it was produced by Africans. In 1961 the production dropped markedly to 223,500 tons.

Almost on par with the palm oil and palm nut was rubber production; the crop was planted on 58,000 hectares, producing approximately 41,293 tons and bringing to the Congo 848,200,000 francs, or U.S. $17,000,000. This type of agriculture represented 15.6 percent of commercial agriculture, with the native production approximately five times that of the Europeans. In 1962 the production dropped to 37,700 tons.

Cottonseed, an almost entirely native crop that supplies fats as well as protein in certain diets, covered 339,692 hectares and produced 157,163 tons of product in 1958. Earnings amounted to 874 million francs, or U.S. $17,500,000 and represented 16 percent of the cash-crop economy. In 1961-62 the area covered had dropped to 121,000 hectares and the production to 40,000 tons. While these drops in cash-crop exports lower the earnings of foreign exchange so badly needed for the restoration of communications and a g r i c u l t u r a l equipment, they threaten the food economy only indirectly. Far worse in direct consequences is the drastic drop in the actual production of food crops, creating real famine in some areas (Kasai) and threatening more starvation in others.

3. Sources of Animal Proteins [5][17]

Livestock. The Belgian government had made considerable efforts to improve livestock production by reducing the areas where
tsetse flies breed and by introducing resistant breeds of cattle. Most of
the livestock is concentrated in Katanga, in the Kibali-Ituri Province,
and in North Kivu. At the beginning of 1959 the total number of cattle in
the hands of European husbandrymen was 467,781. Swine numbered
45,890, sheep 20,464, goats 3,998, and there were some horses, donkeys, and mules.

In the hands of native husbandrymen, cattle amounted to 536,980,
swine to 307,619, sheep to 720,254 and goats to 1,900,513. While most
of the population got their animal protein from fishing and occasional
hunting, the production of meat as a result of the slaughtering of
139,000 cattle, 125,000 pigs, 62,000 sheep, and 186,000 goats amounted
to three kg. per capita per year.

Fresh milk produced in the Belgian Congo in 1958 amounted to
12,417 tons; in addition, 1300 tons were imported. Five hundred tons
of butter were produced locally; 2500 additional tons were imported;
150 tons of cheese were domestically produced and 1500 were imported;
most of the animal proteins from these sources were used for the
European and évolué population; very little of it went to the native
market.

There were in 1958 41 centers for the improvement of native
livestock distributed throughout the provinces; 20 of them were in the
eastern provinces. The National Institute for Agronomic Studies in the
Belgian Congo had a number of divisions and experimental stations established trhoughout the country in order to improve agriculture (see
above).

Fisheries. Fish represents an important source of animal protein in the Congo. Only part of the catch is recorded every year. In 1958
fish of various kinds were available to the population in the amount of
146,445 tons. These supplies included 98,000 tons of fresh water fish;
8494 tons of dried and salted fish; 7156 tons of smoked fish; 5511 tons
of salt water fish. In addition, 26,708 tons of salted and smoked fish and
576 tons of frozen fish were imported. Divided among all the inhabitants
and assuming no loss in transportation and preparation, this would provide 36 grams of fish per capita per day. A considerable effort was
made by the government to improve and to develop fish pond culture;
ponds were progressively increased in the last decade from 15,174
units in 1948 to over 122,000 units in 1958. They covered 4500 hectares
and yielded 500 kilos of fish per hectare in 1959.

D. FOOD SUPPLY [26][51][41][21][48]

At the time of this writing, there are no food reserves in the Congo.
According to local observers, the breakdown of the western sector of
the Congolese economy is principally responsible for this situation.

The resources that are still available are those of the native sector of the subsistence economy. And, even this minimum has been seriously threatened at certain times and places. However, external resources of western origin have been mobilized; air transportation and even air-drops have been organized. Such measures have alleviated to a certain degree an otherwise tragic situation. There was a famine in 1960 in South Kasai and sporadic famines in other places. In February 1963 a shortage of food in Leopoldville resulted in sudden and uncontrollable inflation of food prices. Appeals were launched at that time to all Congo provinces to send supplies from their reserves, if any.

The following foods are, theoretically, available in the various regions (see Map No. 3):

Manioc is the dominating food crop in most areas. Certain provinces, however, stand as exceptions to the general rule. In North Kivu the main crop is sweet potatoes, which cover an area twice as large as that of manioc; yams and cocoyams come next.

Plantain is as important as manioc in three areas, the Uele Province, the Haut Congo, and the Nord Kivu, and it is a close second in Kibali-Ituri, Maniema, Ubangi, Moyen Kongo, and Kongo Central. Elsewhere, plantain seems to fill whatever space there is that is not occupied by manioc.

Corn is as important as manioc in Ubangi and in the Kapinda Savanna area of the Lomami Province. It is also found in Uele, Kongo Central, Maniema, and Sankuru Provinces.

Rice and manioc are equally important in Sankuru, Maniema, and Haut Congo. Rice is grown also in Ubangi, Moyen Kongo, Uele, Cuvette Centrale, and Kibali-Ituri.

Millets and sorghum occupy a relatively small area, which is surprising. These cereals are found in Kibali-Ituri, Kivu, and in Katanga Orientale.

There are numerous reasons for the regional distribution of food crops. Johnston believes that climate and soil conditions are relatively unimportant and considers that social, economic, and historical circumstances are decisive. He cites in support of this opinion the influence of a powerful Baluba chief in introducing manioc into a nonmanioc-eating area; the people became known as the Bena Kalundwe (people of manioc). Other reasons for the popularity of manioc are discussed in the chapter on Nigeria; among them is the fact that it is available at the end of the dry hunger season.

The prices of both cereals and tubers vary widely. Plantain bananas are highly priced in Katanga and Leopoldville; and, in general, all foods fetch higher prices in the areas of concentrated urban and suburban population and in industrial areas.

Food Supply of Leopoldville. The problem of feeding Leopoldville is a major one. The resources of the immediate suburban areas are not sufficient to feed the million Africans living in the city now. The main sources of food are the regions of Madimba and Thysville, both located at more than 100 km. from the city. The first is the granary of Leopoldville while the second is its vegetable garden.

Rice is grown mostly for Leopoldville in parts of former Equateur Province (see Table 1). More and more, as stated above, the native inhabitants of the city are asking for bread, but its production has been a monopoly of European bakers, few of whom have chosen to remain in the area. In the immediate vicinity of Leopoldville there are a number of gardens, where most of the European vegetables and local fruits are found. These local fruits include papaya, avocados, mangoes, pineapples, oranges, tangerines, and bananas.

In normal times the supply of fish comes from the coast or from the Congo River. The fresh-water fish is said to be the best, but it is much more expensive than seafood, which therefore enjoys increasing popularity; but the seafood has to come from the sea, and the railroad has often broken down in recent years. Smoked fish come from Equateur Province and from Lac Leopold II Province or, according to one source, from Lake Tanganyika, while dried fish is imported from Angola. Meat comes by plane from Chad or from Angola.

It was estimated in 1958 that Leopoldville needed at least 20,000 tons of rice, 16,500 tons of manioc flour, 15,000 tons of chickwangue, 5000 tons of beans, 2400 tons of bread, 2500 tons of dried fish, 1900 tons of smoked fish, 1750 tons of fresh fish, 700 tons of meat, 2500 tons of palm oil, 1500 tons of groundnuts, 1000 tons of sugar, 800 tons of salt, 4500 tons of bananas, 2000 tons of tomatoes, and 2000 tons of vegetables per year. This was when L e o p o l d v i l l e had a population of at most 360,000 inhabitants. Now that the population has more than trebled and communications are disturbed, the question of avoiding famine in the big city is one of primary importance and difficulty.

All the foods listed above are sold in the various markets of the city. There are six main markets, four of which are permanent and protected against the weather by covered galleries. In addition, there are a number of small markets in different parts of town. They open in the morning and continue late at night under the light of candles. At the end of 1958 there were 5300 people working and trading in the six major markets. The number is said to have multiplied five-fold by 1963. No special licensing is required except the payment of a daily tax.* The official prices are posted at the e n t r a n c e of the markets, a n d the traders are supposed to abide by these regulations. However, frauds such as overcharging and underweight are common, and often the victim, fearful of malefic charms and the evil eye, does not dare to make a complaint. In July 1963 it had been estimated that the cost of food had increased in Leopoldville by 50 percent over that in 1962.

The problem of supplying food for other industrial areas, such as the Katanga copper belt, has always been a difficult one. The growth of industrial activities and the development of urban areas in several

---

*In 1958 these taxes were: 1 or 2 francs for indigenous products, 3 francs for European products, 5 francs for poultry and fish, and 6 francs for other imported products. They have increased ten-fold following the various devaluations.

provinces, as in Leopoldville, have created a demand that the regional agriculture cannot easily meet. Just before independence two-thirds of the 38,000 tons of corn needed in Elizabethville and Jadotville came from Kasai, 350 miles away. With the breakdown of transportation and of agricultural production in Kasai since 1960, the food supply of these two cities, as well as of other lesser industrial centers, rests almost entirely on imports from afar, often carried by air.

E. FOOD INDUSTRIES, REFRIGERATION [4] [5]

In 1959 there were in operation 435 bakeries, 80 cold storage warehouses, 48 lemonade and soda water plants, 31 artificial ice factories, 12 breweries, 11 confectioneries and chocolate plants, 6 biscuit factories, 3 jam factories, 557 coffee-processing plants, 49 coffee-roasting plants, 625 flour mills, 168 rice mills, 74 cocoa-processing plants, 12 distilleries and oil refineries, 16 tea factories, 2 sugar refineries, and 1 macaroni factory; in addition, there were 1104 fish-processing plants, 52 smoked-meat plants, and 192 dairy plants producing butter and cheese. Little is known about the fate of these industries under present circumstances. In July 1963 there were long lines of people waiting at bakeries in Leopoldville. The rice ration was only 16 kilos per capita for any single purchase.

Food sanitation is unsatisfactory. Under the Belgians control of foodstuffs was carried out by the Institute of Hygiene. It was limited to the inspection of sanitary conditions in establishments frequented mostly by the European population. Monthly visits were paid to 15 hotels, 23 restaurants, 9 bars, 15 butchers, and 39 bakeries. The situation in the Congolese native markets was very unsatisfactory. Only 50 percent of the city markets had water-closet facilities; only a few had water taps in the vicinity; and still fewer had hard-surfaced floors. After independence there was complete interruption of the activities of the Institute of Hygiene. The World Health Organization, up to 1963, had sent four sanitary engineers to the Congo in the hope of improving the situation.

F. IMPORTS-EXPORTS [6] [16]

Exports of agricultural products were, up to 1962, an important source of revenue that helped pay for imported food. Trade in agricultural products has considerably lessened in recent years. Table No. 9 indicates the fate of agricultural exports during the years 1960, 1961, and 1962, compared with 1959. Coffee exports have dropped by about 48 percent, but tea exports increased from 3495 tons in 1959 to 3962 tons in 1962. Cocoa exports have increased. Palm oil has dropped about 15 percent, as has palm kernel oil. The groundnut and cottonseed oils, which were mainly in the hands of the Africans, have completely disappeared from the export market. Manioc export production has dropped from 49,000 tons to 2000; bananas have dropped from 31,000 to 28,000 tons; other items suffered much the same fate. Corn exports dropped from 8863 tons in 1959 to 1407 in 1960 and to none in 1961 and 1962.

The persistent reduction in export tonnages is becoming more and more alarming; imports of food and machinery have to be increased when there is no foreign currency to pay for them. The reasons for this situation are many: lack of security, weakness of the transportation system, lack of tradespeople and marketing organizations are among the most important.

Up to 1960 plantation production was handled by private enterprises that specialized in oil (Congopalm) or in coffee (Cafecongo or Cafekivu). Government intervention was limited to the control of quality. Farmers' production was moved through intermediaries, both on the domestic and on the export markets. After 1960 the Congo government eliminated the intermediaries and replaced them by a government agency—The Office of Agricultural Products—whose duty it was to serve the farmers' and the plantations' production as well as to handle the marketing of their products.

Farmers' output was curtailed by the cancellation of compulsory sowings in the paysannats, while plantation output was reduced by inadequate marketing and insecurity. The cash-crop economy was caught between the old system and the new, and imports of consumer's goods were reduced by the failure of the cash crops to earn enough foreign exchange. The lack of consumer's goods in turn resulted in farmers' indifference to production of subsistence foods beyond their immediate needs.

This situation, coupled with disruption of transports, soon resulted in a glut in certain areas and in scarcity in others. It is now believed that the problem of restoring agricultural production is not a technical one but a social one, dependent on the establishment of law, order, and security, as well as on the rehabilitation of the transportation system. It also depends on the availability of the consumer's goods needed to provide incentive to the farmers. In certain areas farmers collect palm kernels only if there is something to buy in the stores for the money they can get from their sale. This availability of consumer's goods in turn depends on the earning of foreign exchange to pay for them and import them. This is linked to production. It can only be hoped that enlightened foreign assistance will help the government to break into this vicious circle.

G. TRANSPORT AND COMMUNICATIONS [5][46][39]

One of the chief obstacles to economic development in the Congo, as in all other countries of Central Tropical Africa, is the difficulty and inadequacy of transportation. There are in the Congo a total of 144,376 km. of roads, about one-fourth are considered main roads, one-half local roads, and a small mileage is private. Maintenance of these roads, as in other areas, has broken down. Many roads are said to be impassable, and even the streets of Leopoldville are full of holes. On the eve of independence there were 35,000 automobiles in the Congo, 9179 light trucks, 12,679 trucks, 489 busses, and 783,575 bicycles. There were a number of major public carriers, all owned by the Belgians. There is little information as to how many of these have survived the independence turmoil, but there is no doubt that most of them are in need of parts that cannot be produced and repairs that cannot be made.

The Congo River with its tributaries and the other rivers provide a widespread and relatively inexpensive mode of transportation; they also link railways and roads to most parts of the country. However, river transport is interrupted in various places by cataracts, so that goods must be t r a n s p o r t e d over the interim s p a c e by railway or highway.

Transportation costs are obviously high because of the great distances involved. The total waterways network, including rivers and lakes, amounts to 9965 miles, of which 956 miles are on lakes.

There is a commercial flotilla of barges, freight boats, tugboats, and cargo commercial shipping—barges, freight boats, tugboats and cargo-passenger boats—in 1959 totalled 1349 units, with a total power capacity of 71,133 h.p. and a loading capacity of 351,760 tons.

There are two major seaports, Matadi and Boma, with 317,708 sq. feet and 31,538 sq. feet of warehouse space respectively. Major inland ports are Leopoldville, Stanleyville, and Coquilhatville. The port of Matadi in 1959 handled 700 ships, exported almost 900,000 t o n s of goods, and imported over 700,000 tons of goods.

There were a total of 5142 km. of railroads linking the various waterways, which still form the backbone of the Congo's transportation system. Some of the railways connect with contiguous lines in neighboring countries. The most important of the domestic railroads is the link between the seaport of Matadi and Leopoldville, which is a single-track railroad. The rolling stock consisted of 482 locomotives, 245 passenger coaches, 8931 freight cars, and 5 Diesel rail cars.

Air transportation is the most commonly employed method of transportation because of the long distances involved. The breakdown of surface transportation has increased its importance, and on many occasions the larger cities have received some of their food by air.

H. FOREIGN AID [23][37]

Foreign aid to the Congo is considerable. It is usually channelled through the United Nations Fund, which was established by a General Assembly Resolution for the purpose of restoring the economic life of the Congo and carrying on its public services. Contributions to the Fund come from a variety of sources: voluntary donations from U.N.

members; donations from any specialized agency that helps administer the programs; and unconditional gifts from nongovernmental sources if the Secretary General approves.

In 1962 United States foreign aid to the Congo rose to $66,900,000, and as of March 1963 approximately U. S. $81 million had been committed, through the United Nations, to pay for imports; agricultural commodities, in the amount of $42.8 million, were sold in the Congo for local currency. The amount of currency placed at the disposal of the provinces for their needs is established by the Monetary Council every month but no control of the disbursements at provincial levels existed as of March 1962. In addition to these financial contributions, in 1962 1149 internationally recruited specialists in a dozen different fields were occupied full time in the Congo working toward the rehabilitation of its infrastructure and economy. There seems to be no doubt at the present time that the future of the whole country depends upon the continuation of this aid in funds and personnel.

III

DIET TYPES

A. GENERAL [17][38][12][8]

Prior to discussing diets, past, present, and future, it must be remembered that the per capita yearly income of the average Congolese is between $70 and $100 a year. This official figure, however, is misleading. It includes export statistics, which inflate the totals. Export trade was and still is controlled by foreigners; the actual yearly per capita income of the Congolese is unquestionably lower than the official figures.

In rural areas, relatively little cash changes hands, and among the urban detribalized dwellers poverty is widespread. Part of these city immigrants try their luck at petty commerce. They are always on the verge of bankruptcy. The most educated are absorbed by an evergrowing body of idle civil servants. The food and nutrition problems of the Congo were thoroughly studied before independence. In 1949 a vast research program was initiated by the "Institut pour la Recherche Scientifique en Afrique Centrale (IRSAC)" under the leadership of Van den Berghe. Its original terms of reference included detection of undernutrition in the population; study of physical growth and development; investigation of the problems of metabolism in the African; exploration of sources of proteins and their nutritive values; description and mapping of deficiency diseases; exploration of fat metabolism in the African; and compilation of a list of African foods. A competent staff of scientists and a network of laboratories were assigned to these tasks; the two most important were located at Lwiro and Feshi. These studies resulted in the publication of over 50 important papers, which provided a fairly good body of knowledge regarding nutrition in the Congo.

These scientific institutions, or rather what is left of them, are now partially supported and safeguarded by UNESCO. While the present emergency superimposes its pressures, the basic findings of the Belgian teams remain generally true and are not likely to change in the near future except for the trend of migration into the cities and the attendant consequences. Over 80 percent of the population depends on its own cultivation of the soil for its subsistence. The Congo is thus confronted with the same problems as all the other countries of Central Africa. There is a shortage of quality proteins and an abundance of starchy foods. The staple foods are, as elsewhere in the tropical belt, manioc, corn, plantain, rice in certain provinces (especially in the Kivu), millets to a small degree in certain parts of the savannah, and beans in the east.

In the forests the diet is often diversified because of the possibility of picking wild berries and occasionally catching small game. In the savannah, however, the diet is very often restricted to one or two items. When manioc is the sole basic food, malnutrition results because its proteins are of poor quality.

B. NUTRITIONAL LEVELS [45][44][8][13][17][1][15][22][8][9][32][34][22a]

In 1947 one source estimated that the Congolese had 3000 to 3500 calories per person per day; but other sources found in 1953 that this had dropped to 2370 calories. All sources agree that carbohydrates supply 85 percent of the calories generated (see Table No. 10). In 1959 a new evaluation reported an intake of 2600 calories. As expected, there are seasonal and regional variations, as in the rest of Africa. These variations are greatest in the preharvest season in the savannahs and in the Kivu highlands. Carbohydrate intake comes mainly from manioc and other roots and tubers, or, in certain areas, from plantain and sweet potatoes. The protein intake comes primarily from vegetables, with a very little animal proteins provided by fish, insects (such as caterpillars), and game. The fat intake comes chiefly from palm oil and varies with the vegetation of the region. It is particularly low in the Kivu highlands, where it represents only 9 percent of the total intake.

In most of the Congo the average intake of vegetable protein is said to be 40 grams per day except in the Kivu highlands, where beans are the staple food and where the vegetable protein diet amounts to 80 grams a day. In 1949 it was estimated that animal proteins were supplied in the amount of 4.4 grams a day. This estimate was raised to 7.7 grams in 1957 and to 8.4 grams in 1959. Many efforts have been made to raise this level of animal protein in the African diet. Milk and powdered milk have been distributed in some places. Substitutes for animal proteins have been explored. Among these, such protein-rich foods as cottonseed cakes, soya bean cakes and fish flour seem to hold hope for the future.

The inadequate food base has caused a number of unsatisfactory diets, especially among infants after weaning and young children.

Since it is generally accepted by the Africans that the fetus in the womb partakes of the solid foods eaten by the mother (which, of course, is true), they believe that the sooner after birth the child absorbs the manioc porridge that everybody else eats, the better it will be for the child's nourishment. Thus, there is a tendency to deprive the baby of the only animal protein (mother's milk) he can get. Of course, there are other reasons for the sudden weaning of children, such as the displacement of nurslings from the breast by a new arrival.

A trend toward shortening the breast-feeding period in imitation of European practice is noticeable, as elsewhere. As a result, the manioc diet has a chance to be started at an earlier date. Holemans, who has carried out investigations in the traditional environment of the Kwango area, confirms that the diet there is based on manioc with various supplements, such as voandzia (pulses), millet, corn, beans, caterpillars, spiders, and dried fish. Samplings show that 89 percent of the caloric intake comes from the manioc, 6.3 percent from vegetables, 2.6 percent from animal sources, and 1.4 percent from palm oil. The same type of fare is found in the Kasai, Katanga, and in the forested areas. In the north, in former Equateur and Orientale Provinces, bananas and corn are eaten, often washed down by the fermented banana wine brewed in the villages or bought at the tavern in the nearest town. In the east, along the frontier with Burundi and Rwanda, cereals, peas, and millets make up the basic diet, while rice is eaten in some areas in Kivu. There basic foods are arranged in a variety of diets that depend upon the environment, the geographical location, and the traditional attitude of the various tribes. It is a challenging question to find out what is the most influential factor in determining the choice of diet; several examples could be given of neighboring tribes having a very different standard of living in an almost identical environment.

1. Some tribal diets

The Kuba. Between the rivers Kasai and Sankuru, a group of 80,000 to 100,000 people, the Kuba, live one of the best lives of any tribal population of the Congo. Their production goes beyond their subsistence needs and serves their culture, which pays tribute to wealth and prestige. They are mostly agriculturists; their diet is based on corn, manioc, beans, groundnuts, and voandzia peas. Their animal proteins come from insects (ants, caterpillars) or from mollusks, fish, and game. They make salt from plants treated by hot water (see below). Products that they have in excess, contrary to what happens in most other parts of the Congo, are sold on the market. Placed by order of decreasing popularity, these products include roasted groundnuts, bananas, sugar cane, palm oil, gourds, manioc and banana bread, caterpillars, manioc leaves, dried groundnuts, imported salt, beans, leaves of the bean plants, tobacco, pineapple, eggplants, yams, voandzia, fish, local salt, spices, prawns, palm wines, and mushrooms. In addition, they know how to melt iron ores and make tools, which they use efficiently for fishing and hunting and, generally speaking, for controlling their environment.

The Lele. In contrast to the Kuba, the Lele (in the territory between the Kasai River and the Loanga River) live a very mediocre existence. The soil on which they survive is so poor that it can support only a bush-like vegetation despite a rainfall of 1800 mm. a year. Their basic food is corn, in addition to which, like the Kuba, they grow voandzia peas, manioc, and plantain. They eat all these foods seasoned with pepper. They have some sugar cane and occasionally pineapple. During the last years of Belgian rule, agricultural officers of the government tried to teach the Lele to do more agriculture and less hunting and to sow their corn twice and harvest it both in November and April. The tribesmen succeeded in getting manioc grown in the grasslands instead of in forest clearings; they have begun to grow groundnuts and rice, which they use as cash crops to make tax money.

There seems to be no doubt, however, that, left to themselves, the Lele would soon dispense with the agricultural duties that had been imposed upon them and return to a more meager diet, enriched only occasionally with a feast due to success in hunting. They hunt in the most simple manner, without nets and without pit traps. They are also poor fishermen; while their country abounds in streams and rivers, their catch is low. The women do the fishing, blocking a slow-moving stream and letting it overflow into a marsh where they catch the smaller fish. At other times of the year they use poison, which they spread over the surface of the waters, and scoop the poisoned fish out by hand or in baskets. The Lele are known to work only about six weeks at the height of the dry season. They are not in the habit of sleeping in their fields to chase away predators, (a custom elsewhere), which leads to the belief that they are not interested in their crops and are poor agriculturists. On the whole, their diet is unsatisfactory and is probably one of the lowest in the whole tribal system of the Congo.

The Suku. Farther to the southwest, in the vicinity of Feshi, live the Sukus on soil that is even poorer than that of the Lele. They grow manioc. They are said to lead a very wretched existence.

The Pende. Still further south, the Pende live on soil that is almost as poor as that of the Lele and Suku tribes. Because of their considerable energy and industry, however, they grow millet (especially around Gungu). This provides a slightly higher standard of living.

It is notable that in a relatively small area three different peoples grow three different staple crops: (millet, manioc, and corn) and have different standards of living. Such diversity encourages speculation on the relationship that may exist between soil, culture, and genetic makeup.

The Bushong. On the eastern side of the Kasai River, occupying the territory up to the Sankuru River are the Bushong. The Bushong seem to be, on the whole, much better off than the Lele. They have a far more active and diversified life. In May they harvest their crops of beans, corn, and yams and then prepare the ground for the next crop. During this season they also engage in hunting and fishing. They do home work like weaving and repairing huts. In July they harvest bananas and pineapples. They continue to fish and hunt until mid-August; then they begin to plant sugar cane and bananas. At the end of August the rainy season begins and, with it, the time to collect their groundnuts. In September they prepare the soil and plant corn. During this season termites come out in the forest and are collected and processed for food. The wet season then gets too intense, and little work is done during October, November, and December. The little dry season begins early in January, and agricultural work consists of sowing corn and voandzia peas. At the beginning of February a short wet season begins again, during which groundnuts are collected, beans are sown, and termites and other insects are gathered. At the end of February corn is harvested, and the next crop of beans, sweet potatoes, and manioc is .planted. From April to the middle of May, beans and voandzia peas are harvested and tobacco is planted. Compared to the working schedule of the Lele, the Bushong appear to work about twice as hard, yet they do not have a satisfactory diet any more than do their less ambitious neighbors, the Suku or the Pende.

In the Coquilhatville Area. According to Chinn, four types of diets can be recognized among the various tribes living in the former Coquilhatville Province:* (1) the diet of the fishermen, (2) the diet of the hunters, (3) the diet of the tribes that exchange their products and live on a mixed diet of meat and fish, and (4) the diet of those who neither hunt nor fish but subsist on mushrooms and caterpillars.

The fishermen's diet applies to such tribes as the Tshupais, the Monias (who live on the banks of the Ngiri), the Libinsas (who fish in the Congo), and the Sango (who draw their food from the Ubangi River). These people live on smoked fish, because fresh fish is available only during the dry season when the catches are plentiful in the shallow waters. At times caterpillars are eaten instead of fish. The caterpillar season lasts approximately 60 days a year. The diet is completed by the usual porridge and some vegetable fat. Fish and meatless days occur about twice a week. For 100 days a year the diet is purely vegetarian. The total amount of food eaten per day amounts to approximately 2000 to 2300 calories.

The Mogandoes, the Yokote, and the Mbole are hunters; they feed on buffalo, antelope, wild pigs, and elephants. They alternate vegetarian days with meat days and eat caterpillars occasionally. The caloric value of their diet varies between 2040 calories on a vegetarian day and 2768 calories on a meat day. There are approximately 160 days of meat, 25 days of fish, 30 days of caterpillars, and 150 days of vegetables in a year.

---

*Now Cuvette Centrale and Moyen Congo.

People feeding on mixed diets are typified by the Akulas who live near the Mongala River. They barter their fish for the game killed by their neighbors, the Ngwandi and the Mgambi, who live in the Ubangi savannah. These people have smoked fish three times a week and vegetables one day a week; they use caterpillars in July and August and get meat three times a week if they can. The caloric values of these various meals ranges between 2240 calories on a vegetarian day and to 2710 calories on a meat day.

The Bolendas, who live 30 miles away from the Wima River, neither fish nor hunt; caterpillars are their main source of animal protein. In that area the caterpillar season lasts three months, but it can be extended longer for those who have the foresight to smoke some caterpillars in advance. The rest of the time they feed on mushrooms, green leaves, roots, and oil.

The caloric yield of a mushroom meal is 752 calories; if caterpillars are added, it rises to 2200 calories. The gathering of mushrooms is quite a feature in the life of the Bolendas. After the rains the men stake a claim on a piece of land where they expect a good crop of mushrooms and try to fence it in. After that they rush back to their homes to get help for the actual gathering. When they return the claim has frequently been invaded and fights result that may lead to manslaughter.

The Pygmies. The diets of the Pygmies consist primarily of plantain and fruit. They also hunt and get some animal protein this way. Occasionally Pygmies stray from their original habitat and can be seen near the Bantu plantations clearing land for sweet potatoes and peanuts. Rice is available in December and January; plantain all year; manioc in November and March; sweet potatoes in March; honey all year; mangoes, pineapple, wild apricots, loquat, and latex fruit all year; and peanuts in June and July. The fishing season is from December to March, but the hunting season, which may bring elephants, antelopes, small birds, and reptiles, as well as insects, is open all year round. Eggs are sometimes found; the Pygmies do not ferment their beverages.

One of the most interesting characteristics of the Pygmies is, of course, their small stature. Their average height is 1 meter, 42 cm., compared to the average Caucasian height of 1 meter, 72 cm. Their average weight is 37.3 kilos compared to 64.7 for Caucasians. It is, of course, not known whether the small stature of the Pygmy is the result of nurture or nature. There are strong indications that it is probably the result of nature, and it seems to be a Darwinian trait of natural selection, since it is easier to live in the forest when one has a small stature and a considerable amount of energy to expend over it. There is no evidence that Pygmy children raised in a non-Pygmy environment and given a different diet have improved in stature.

2. Detribalized Diets

Some of the most inadequate diets of the Congo are found in the detribalized centers around the cities. There an increasing population tries to imitate the European diet, and alcohol plays a growing role. In the industrial areas of Southern Katanga around Elizabethville and Jadotville the African population has become urbanized and industrialized. The area is not self-sufficient in food. Although this population has a higher per capita purchasing power than most other Congolese, malnutrition occurs because of lack of food availability, especially in times of stress (see above). The introduction of a money economy in that area is recent; it did not exist prior to the establishment of European industry. Markets are held every day, and sellers are known to fix prices among themselves. Only vegetables, fuel, and some manioc are locally produced; the rest of the foodstuffs on the market are imported. Fish comes from 150 miles away; wheat, rice, and beans travel 150 to 200 miles; most of the poultry and eggs travel 400 miles. Two-thirds of the corn, most of the manioc, and all of the oil comes 500 miles or more. During the recent emergency the transportation of these goods has been frequently disrupted, increasing the danger of famine and pushing prices sky high. Prior to independence all these commodities were marketed through European or Asian intermediaries who bought from the farmers; this marketing system has now broken down and is replaced by occasional operators. Perishable goods, which include all animal proteins, were formerly brought to town by rail in dry ice; the losses were minimal. Now this transportation is done by trucks that frequently break down, resulting sometimes in a total loss of the cargo, especially since there are no technicians and mechanics able to repair the trucks before the goods deteriorate. When the goods eventually reach the market, the prices they fetch reflect these difficulties. Caterpillars, collected during the rainy season when they are cheap, are stored until the dry season when the prices rise.

Manioc and manioc products, as well as all forms of corn, millets, rice, potatoes, bread, plantain, oils, and condiments, are mainly sold by women. Men specialize in selling tomatoes, onions, cabbage, fish, and meat. Both sexes sell groundnuts, peas, chilis, and beans.

3. Diets by Regions

In the former Leopoldville Province manioc remains the most important food. During the rainy season, October to December, when it is impossible to dry the dough, corn and bananas take the place of manioc.

In the former Orientale Province the diet is more varied. In the Stanleyville district, on the banks of the river from Ponthierville to Basoko, bananas are the most important food; northward, corn becomes progressively more important. In the west manioc takes first place. Bananas are cooked in ashes, fried, or boiled in water to make a dough; they are rarely eaten raw.

In the Ituri region the basic food is the sweet potato, eaten boiled in water with meat, when available, and beans. Millet and sorghum are losing favor. In the higher Uele the two basic foods are bananas and manioc. Sesamum is eaten in small quantities as a spice. Beans are eaten all year round and rice occasionally when it is harvested in December.

In the former Equateur Province, in the loop of the Ubangi, manioc loses its importance to corn. In the east bananas are the basic food while in the south manioc remains the daily staple; during the rainy season sweet potatoes, breadfruit, and/or corn take the place of manioc. Bananas form about 20 percent of the diets in this area.

Between the Congo and the Ubangi corn is the most important food. Corn is eaten fresh at harvest time; but later on the corn ears are stored under the roof of the house, and a fire is kept burning to dry them thoroughly. The woman picks up what she needs from this reserve. Corn is prepared by soaking in water, then drying and crushing with a pestle until a fine flour is formed; it is then cooked in boiling water to form a thick dough.

Some people of the area, the Banza, prefer bananas and corn and use manioc only when they have nothing else; rice, however, is gaining in importance as a substitute for other foods.

In Kivu the staple foods are more numerous. Bananas, sweet potatoes, millet, corn, manioc, sorghum, and even polished rice are eaten. All of these are served with peas, which the Kivu people relish.

In Kasai manioc and corn are combined in the favorite dish pidia. After manioc is exhausted, millet is mixed up with corn; when nothing else is available, sweet potatoes are eaten.

4. Congolese Dishes [1][9]

Adriaens has given us some Congolese recipes collected in the Kwango area. Meat dishes are usually based on the products of hunting or on the capture of rats and insects. The meat is cooked in water, spiced with chili, salt, and a number of other condiments. Rats are prepared in a different way: the entrails are removed and reserved for the children. Among the Bapelende rats are boiled, or grilled. The animal is first washed with lukewarm water and then laid down to rest on hot palm oil doused with water. The meat and the sauce that result are eaten with luku.* The rat dish is commonly prepared by the de-tribalized people who cannot get game. Caterpillars are usually grilled and eaten with a soup made of pumpkin seeds crushed with groundnuts, or occasionally with mushrooms.

Vegetable dishes are numerous. Saka saka is a purée made with leaves and young shoots of manioc. The leaves are heated on a metal plate over charcoal and regularly doused with water. Then they are crushed in a wooden mortar. The resulting mixture is then put in a kettle and cooked at length with water, salt, and peppers. If available, a small amount of palm oil will be added before the saka saka is eaten.

*Nonfermented manioc paste.

Matango is also a purée of leaves, but it is made with a variety of plants. The leaves are usually cut into small shreds and thrown into boiling water; after a long cooking, a small amount of oil is added, if available.

Dimbula is a purée made with the plant Gnetum africanum combined with crushed groundnuts or with mushrooms, shrimps, and flying ants that have been first passed under the grille, or locusts. When available, fish is added.

Spices and condiments are very important in African diets. Without them the food boiled in water would be tasteless. A number of plants are used as spices, including the leaves of Aeolanthus petastus or Cymbopogan densiflora. The large leaves of the latter are useful in meat dishes. The leaves of Tagetes patula are especially good with fish, while those of Piper guineense are either eaten raw or cooked with meat dishes. Red pepper, found almost everywhere around the huts in the villages, is also very popular.

The natives are also very fond of salted fluids that they prepare from salt-containing leaves. They feel that this vegetable salt increases and enhances the action of the mineral salt. Vegetable salts are produced from salt-containing plants such as Scleria spp. (called makassi or marvodi) and from a number of aquatic vegetables such as lotus and nymphaes. Leaves from such plants are heated until charred; the resulting ash is placed in a special filter and water is poured over it. The resulting fluid is salty; it is called mikeni or mukedi.

Mushrooms are usually cooked in oil and eaten with cooked groundnuts and pumpkin seeds. The waters used for the cooking of all pulses, mushrooms, and even meat, is thrown away.

5. Congolese Beverages

Palm wine is one of the most popular beverages. It is the sap of the palm tree after it has spontaneously fermented. Sometimes fermentation is hastened by the addition of a few vegetable products. The word malafu, followed by a specific name, indicates any one of all natural juices that can be gotten in the jungle after fermentation. All the populations of the Congo prepare malafu; they collect it in calabashes or even in bottles that can be seen hanging from the palm trees in and around most villages. It is believed that the addition of vegetable products to the sap will help kill the worms it contains before it is fermented; leaves of Oxanthus speciosus give the brew its special flavor. In order to expedite fermentation and increase the alcoholic content, several devices are used; either a little bit of the fruit of elaeis or a little bit of the bark of Garcinia kola or Burkea africana is added to the brew. The malafu, thus improved, is filtered through a bundle of dry grass jammed into a leaf, rolled like a cigar and stuck into the bottle-neck of a small calabash.

After the fluid has been collected, it is relatively clear and free of ferment. It is either sold or used immediately. Several fermented beverages are prepared from pineapple, either based on the sap at the beginning of the year or using the juice of the fruit after it has been crushed. Sugar-cane wine is prepared in a similar manner from crushed sugar cane. Kibuku is a native beer made from manioc flour; it is usually cloudy and its taste is tart. The beverage is popular, especially in the detribalized centers.

Although most of the cooking is done with oil, the amount of fats supplied by these diets, including the groundnuts and pumpkin seeds, does not seem to be very high. The amount of pumpkin seeds introduced in the food seldom exceeds 100 grams per family per day, and since the vegetables are always shared by several people of the family, the final amount of lipids absorbed by one single individual is very small.

IV

ADEQUACY OF FOOD RESOURCES [37] [39] [5]

IN NORMAL TIMES

The future adequacy of the food resources of a country like the Congo is difficult to assess; the estimate has to be based on the resources that existed in the last years of peace and order and an estimate of what these resources could become under different and presumably improved conditions. A number of assumptions have to be made. It must be assumed that the circumstances under which the food of 1959 was produced were the best that could be hoped for.

In evaluating the future, we must assume a reasonable degree of social and economic improvement, the re-establishment of peace and order, and the availability of foreign guidance and financial assistance.

It seems that the 1959 resources were the result of an adequate use of the soil. The largest crop was manioc (see Table No. 11), followed by plantain bananas and corn. The cereals cover only a fraction of the total food crops. The yields in manioc, yams, rice, corn, and plantain appear to be higher in the Congo than in most other African areas. The assumption can therefore be made that the choice of these crops for this kind of land, climate, and culture has been good. On the other hand, the area in millet and sorghum is small and the yields are poor. This may mean only that millet and sorghum have been sown in unsuitable areas. We may assume that the dominant role given to manioc was deliberate and wise in view of its very real advantages. Its longer growth period, six to eight months, against three to six months for the millets, is a disadvantage; but this is of little importance where land is abundant and is more than compensated for by the fact that the planting and harvesting of manioc can be staggered, an advantage which millets do not have. Under the circumstances prevailing in 1958 and 1959, it can be estimated that the starchy staple foods known to have been produced in the Congo supplied a total of over 12 thousand billion calories (see Table No. 11), which if evenly distributed throughout the population, would have assured each Congolese of approximately 2200 calories per day. This estimate is consistent with those of most samples for that period. We must keep in mind that the figure is based on production, not consumption, and it does not include consideration of other food resources, either grown or imported.

A similar computation made with figures available for the United States and concerned with the basic American carbohydrates, cereals, and potatoes, would give 8900 calories per capita per day for each citizen of the United States. At this point it must be remembered that the starchy foods represent 85 percent of all calories yielded by local diets in the Congo, while in the United States starchy foods represent only 24.6 percent of the total amount consumed. Thus, in 1959 Americans produced 8900 calories of carbohydrates per capita per day and this represented 24.6 percent of their diet, while Congolese produced 2200 calories per capita per day and this represented 85 percent of their diets. Making allowances for the probable shortcomings of such a computation, it is still an indication that in normal times before independence the food resources of the Congo were marginal at best and did not allow the creation of reserves, even if the technique for storage, preservation, and transportation had been adequate. A considerable effort is needed to lift the country above levels of sporadic malnutrition and give it a minimum amount of food security.

Can we assume that a reasonable degree of social and economic improvement, foreign guidance, and foreign aid will be forthcoming? The answer here is twofold: guidance and aid will certainly be available, but the degree of social and economic improvement they will provide is uncertain in spite of all the good will in the world. To help our discussion, let us assume that the general lines of the Belgian policies for the paysannats will be followed in whatever system will evolve in their stead and that the most will be made of available assets. The Belgian policies were simple: compatibility of culture to land, use of selected seeds, good agricultural practices, and sound rotations and associations. Under these conditions, if the yields of the seven staple crops all over the subsistence acreage were equal to the best the pre-independence paysannats could do, a total of over 52 thousand billion calories would be produced (see Table No. 11). If evenly distributed among the 20 million people to be expected by 1974, when the agricultural improvements stated above will reach their peak, 52 thousand billion calories would provide each Congolese with 7200 calories per day. This would represent some improvement; yet this improvement would be qualified because of (a) the difference between production figures and actual consumption and (b) because of the dependence of the Congolese on starchy foods for most of their diet.

IN TIMES OF STRESS

The situation that has prevailed in the Congo since 1960 illustrates, without the need for speculation, the collapse of food resources under stress. As expected, it is the westernized sector of the Congo culture and civilization that has broken down first. The migration to the cities—caused by insecurity, the search for jobs, and the vain hope that centers of distribution would be better in the cities than in the rest of the country—has resulted in almost unmanageable population densities, especially in Leopoldville, where a million people (instead of 360,000) have concentrated.

Toward the end of 1960 widespread famine among the Baluba refugees in South Kasai was causing more than 200 deaths a day. The U. N. Congo Famine Fund was used to finance relief, and for three months food was airlifted from points of purchase to Bakwanga until sea shipments arrived that could be distributed over land. The Congo Famine Fund was established by the United Nations, which holds in trust cash contributions voluntarily made in response to appeals for aid made by FAO. The Fund is limited to disbursements for the alleviation of famine conditions. Seventy tons of food a day were flown in, thanks to this Fund, and were distributed at points inland, and 500 tons of seeds were brought in to help the refugees start the cycle of food production again. Refugees from Angola, who started coming into the Congo early in 1961, offered another example of the kind of stress that can result in famine. These people numbered over 200,000, while emigrants from Rwanda numbered 100,000. Food had to be given to them by the United Nations to help them subsist. The breakdown of communications, the lack of maintenance, and the roadblocks established by the gendarmerie or by the population cut off a number of sections of the country from food suppliers, causing starvation even though food was plentiful at other points. Low production in the rural areas was also a cause of scarcity in the cities; cut off from city markets, the farmers had no incentive to produce more than what they themselves could use.

On the plantations, at cash-crop levels, lack of production caused a sharp drop in exports, which in turn caused a lack of foreign currency with which to buy imports. This vicious circle of low production, lack of transportation, lack of purchasing power, could be broken only by international assistance. It is clear, as shown by experience, that left to its own resources most of the Congo cannot provide the food needed by the population under circumstances of stress.

In the traditional sector of the economy the situation is better in some places. Some districts even have a glut of food, due to the lack of transportation to the urban centers. In other places insecurity and flight for safety have resulted in outright starvation and in the cessation of any effort to control the environment. When security is threatened, a large part of the population takes refuge in the forest; many people did so during the most hectic days following the mutiny in order to avoid being caught between warring tribal groups and/or murdered by juvenile delinquents. Half of these refugee groups were said to have returned to the villages by the end of March 1963, but many have taken to the jungle again. No agricultural work can be resumed under these circumstances; in August of 1963 famine was continuing. The problems are many. In the former Equateur Province smallpox has broken out on several occasions in many villages. The available grain supply has been converted into alcohol. There is a lack not only of meat and canned goods, but also of all the staple foods that are normally produced in the area. This situation occurs also in the whole of the Kwango Province. Manioc, which is the staple food there, is practically nonexistent. The small quantity that can be found is sold at prices that the mass of the population cannot afford. In addition, no cultivated fields are visible in the countryside, a sure forecast of impending famine. Thus, in the traditional sector as well as in the westernized sector of the Congo culture the fabric of organized life has broken down; only foreign aid can bring relief for this tragic situation. Unfortunately, procurement of parts for machines and transportation equipment is likely to absorb the greatest part of the dwindling foreign-currency reserves, including those supplied by foreign aid. It is also to be feared that much of the 3 billion Congolese francs that have been generated between 1960 and 1962 through the sale of agricultural commodities imported from various countries will be used to increase the purchasing power in the larger cities where prices will rise and thus will divert the imports from the starving rural areas.

V

NUTRITIONAL DISEASE
PATTERNS [10][11][13][3][25][15][31][32][29][34][49][50]

In the Congo diseases caused by nutritional deficiencies are second only to communicable diseases. They constitute a public-health problem of the highest magnitude. In 1959, 54,450 cases of nutritional deficiencies were reported, of which 20 percent were cases of kwashiorkor requiring hospitalization. The number of persons dying from nutritional diseases was given as 1387. Since these statistics relate only to people living within the area of Western culture, it must be assumed that there are many unreported cases in the area of traditional living.

Many nutritional diseases are represented in the Congo; in addition to kwashiorkor, both pellagra and scurvy are found; goiter is common in the upper Uele region. Beriberi is said to be uncommon except in communities where unusual conditions exist and among the rice-eating groups. Rickets and osteomalacia are found, but not frequently. Ariboflavinosis is the most important of all the vitamin deficiency diseases.

Anemia is extremely frequent and is caused not only by ankylostomiasis and malaria, but also by the extreme lack of iron in the diet. The greatest number of cases of kwashiorkor seem to come from Kivu and Kasai Provinces. Jeliffe reports that there is an increasing abandonment of breast feeding in the urban and suburban area of certain cities of the Congo.

As reported above, considerable interest in nutrition and in the nutritional disorders of the native population has developed in recent years. The special laboratory of Feshi has done continued research on kwashiorkor. This research disclosed that the serum protein of the people of tropical Africa usually contained a low level of albumen but a high level of globulin, particularly the gamma fraction. A comparison of the development of serum proteins in African with American children shows marked differences. In the African infants it was found that the albumen level became stabilized at a point close to that found at the time of birth. This is ascribed to a deficiency of protein in the food, due both to a different composition of the maternal milk and to an insufficient availability of that milk. Contrary to what happens in the American controls, the blood of the African baby shows a continuous increase in gamma globulin from the second month on. This early increase may be due either to a dysfunction of the liver appearing early in life or to nutritional deficiencies or to both; perhaps also it could be ascribed to a genetic difference. A well known symptom of kwashiorkor is a change in the pigmentation of the hair so that it has a reddish color. A study by André and Holemans reported that 57 percent of the children of the Kwango showed this condition. When such children were weighed and their stools examined, it was found that they weighed less than children with normally pigmented hair and were likely to be infected with a higher rate of intestinal worms.

After powdered milk had been dispensed in the amount of 40 grams per day per child, the hemoglobin level increased, the weight improved, and the serum protein level rose. As stated above, cottonseed cakes have been used to increase the protein level of the diet of these children with a certain amount of success. It is recommended that this practice be increased in the future.

Nutritional differences are found if specific populations are studied. We have already mentioned the Bushong, who have a normal African state of nutrition. Among them, however, live the Twa, who, unlike the Bushong, have begun to abandon the hunting life they used to live in the forest and have been trying to adjust to a sedentary agricultural life. It was found that kwashiorkor was very common among the Twa and very rare among the Bushong. It is also interesting to record that studies made on the Pygmies living in the forest confirm the unusually large gamma globulin component of their serum and the high prevalence of kwashiorkor. Other blood components are normal and correspond to those found in Americans. The only striking difference between the blood contents of the Pygmies and that of Americans is the very low level of cholesterol for the Pygmies. In fact, the Pygmies have an even lower level of cholesterol than that of another low-cholesterol people, the Baniaris, a Bantu group living in the same area. The Baniaris have a different diet and way of life, which may explain the difference.

VI

CONCLUSIONS

In addition to all the problems inherent in the African environment and way of life, the Congolese have political problems of unusual magnitude, both domestic and international. There land tenure, poor quality of the soil, lack of fertilizers, lack of purchasing power, and scarcity of technicians in all fields combine with considerable tribal rivalries and unrest to jeopardize the production and distribution of food.

A situation is thus created that can be controlled only by international assistance. The high quality of this assistance is an asset. It can only be hoped that the various funds created through the United Nations and its agencies to deal with the many problems listed above will continue to be forthcoming for a substantial number of years. Otherwise, the chaotic situation that would result is too tragic even to consider.

BIBLIOGRAPHY: REPUBLIC OF THE CONGO (LEOPOLDVILLE)

1. Adriaens, E. L., Recherches sur l'Alimentation des Populations au Kwango. Bulletin Agricole du Congo Belge, 1951, Vol. 42, No. 2, pp. 227-270 and pp. 473-552, No. 3.

2. Africa Report, Vol. VIII, No. 9, Oct. 1963.

3. André, J. and Holemans, K., Significance of Red Hair in the Black Child in Kwango. Ann. Soc. Belge de Med. Trop., 1955, Oct. 31, Vol. 35, No. 5, pp. 467-477.

4. Araoz, J. de, Environmental Sanitation in Leopoldville Province, W. H. O. Document MHO/PA/2.61, January 11, 1961, (mimeographed).

5. Belgian Congo and Ruanda Urundi Information Office - Belgian Congo, Vol. II, Brussels, 1960.

6. Belgo-American Development Corporation, Exports of the Republic of the Congo in 1962, 511 Fifth Ave., New York 17, N. Y.

7. Biebuyck, D., Aspects du probleme foncier au Congo, Folia Scientifica Africae Centralis, Vol. 11, No. 3, Sept. 30, 1956, pp. 8-10.

8. Bohanan, P. & Dalton, G., Markets in Africa, Northwestern University Press, 1962.

9. Chinn, M., Sur l'Alimentation des Indigenes de la Province de Coquilhatville. Ann. Soc. Belge de Med. Trop., Vol. 25, 1945, pp. 57-149.

10. Close, J., Le taux des proteines seriques chez le nourrisson Africain, Annales de la Societé Belge de Medecine Tropicale, T. 25, No. 2, 1955.

11. Close, J. & Van de Walle, A., La composition du lait de femme au Congo Belge, Annales de la Societé Belge de Medecine Tropicale, Vol. 37, No. 2, 1957, pp. 191-202, 203-212, 213-224.

12. Congo Presse, 1962-1963.

13. De Maeyer, E. M., Nutrition in the Congo, Nutrition Reviews, Vol. 20, No. 8, Aug. 1962, pp. 225-227.

14. Encyclopedie du Congo Belge, Vol. I, Bieleveld Editions, Brussels, 1951, pp. 132-134 and pp. 190-197.

15. Folia Scientifica Africae Centralis, 1955-1959.

16. Food and Agricultural Organization of the United Nations, Adaptation of Export Marketing Organizations, ETAP Report No. 1528, Rome 1962.

17. Food and Agricultural Organization of the United Nations, Africa Survey, C 61/15, 1962.

18. Food and Agricultural Organization of the United Nations, Report to the Government of the Congo, Agricultural Mechanization, No. 1495, Rome 1962.

19. Food and Agricultural Organization of the United Nations, Production Year Book, Vol. 16, 1962.

20. King, Gordon, United Nations in the Congo, a Quest for Peace, Carnegie Endowment for International Peace, New York, 1962.

21. Gouvernement General du Congo Belge, L'Actualité Congolaise. Le Ravitaillement de la Cité, Indigene de Leopoldville, Ed. B., No. 104, Leopoldville 1958.

22. Hiernaux, J., Etat de Nutrition des Kuba (Kasai), Zaire, July 1954, No. 7.

23. Hoyt, M. P., Republic of the Congo, A Special Report on Africa, U. S. Department of Commerce Publication, March 1963, p. 27.

24. International Committee for Nutrition in National Defense, Food Composition Table for Use in Latin America, Washington, June 1961.

25. Jelliffe, D. B., Culture, Social Change and Infant Feeding, The American Journal of Clinical Nutrition, Vol. 10, Jan. 1962.

26. Johnston, B. F., The Staple Food Economies of Western Tropical Africa, Stanford University Press, 1958.

27. Kimble, G. T., Republic of the Congo in Focus (an American Geographical Society Publication), Vol. V, No. 1, July 1961.

28. Kimble, G. T., Tropical Africa, 2 vol., The XXth Century Fund, New York, 1960.

29. Lassance, M., Peeters, E., and Grailet, A.: A Note on the Existence of Endemic Avitaminosis C in the Region of Gety, Belgian Congo, Ann. Soc. Belge de Med. Trop., April 30, 1957, Vol. 37, No. 2, pp. 269 and 278.

30. Leurquin, Ph., L'organisation de la production en economie non-monetaire. Folia Scientifica Africae Centralis, Vol. IV, No. 1, March 31, 1958, pp. 5-7.

31. Malnutrition in African Mothers, Infants, and Young Children, Report on the Second Inter-African Conference on Nutrition, London, 1954.

32. Mann, G. V., et al., Cardiovascular Disease in African Pygmies: A Survey of the Health Status, Serum Lipids and Diet of Pygmies in Congo, Journal Chronic Diseases, Vol. 15, April 1962, pp. 341-371.

33. Maquet, J. J., Motivations culturelles des migrations vers les villes d'Afrique Centrale. Folia Scientifica Africae Centralis, Tome 11, No. 4, 1956, pp. 6-8.

34. Parent, M., Contribution a l'étude de l'état de nutrition des enfants au Katanga. Academie Royale des Sciences Coloniales, Tome VIII, fasc. 3, 1959.

35. Pieraerts, G., Recueil de travaux des Sciences Médicales au Congo Belge. Leopoldville, Vol. I, 1942, p. 109.

36. Steinberg, S. H., The Statesman's Yearbook, 1962-1963, St. Martin's Press, New York, 1963, pp. 888-892.

37. United Nations General Assembly, A/AC.113/1, Budgetary and Financial Practices of the United Nations, January 21, 1963.

38. United Nations Review, The Congo, Vol. 10, No. 2, February 1963.

39. United Nations Review, Civilian Assistance to the Congo, August-September 1963, pp. 27, 29 and 52.

40. United Nations, General Assembly, Sixteenth Session Official Record, Plenary Meeting, Friday, February 23, 1962.

41. United Nations, Report of United Nations Civilian Operation in the Congo. May 1, 1963 incl. introduction and additions.

42. United Nations, Statistical Papers of Population and Vital Statistics No. 1 and 2, April 1, 1963.

43. United States State Department Fact Sheet: Congo (Leopoldville), August 1963.

44. U. S. Department of Agriculture, Foreign Agriculture Service U. S. D. A. Pub. FAS-M-64, Notes on the Agriculture Economies of the Countries in Africa, Washington, Sept. 1959, pp. 2-7.

45. U. S. Department of Agriculture, Foreign Agriculture Service, Food Balances for Angola, Belgian Congo, Kenya and Nigeria, Washington, D. C., 1955.

46. U. S. Department of Commerce, Basic Data on the Economy of the Belgian Congo and Ruanda Urundi, World Trade Information Service, Part I, No. 58-60.

47. U. S. Department of Health, Education and Welfare - Public Health Service, Division of International Health, Republic of the Congo, Washington, D. C., 1960.

48. United States News and World Reports, July 22, 1963.

49. Van den Berghe, L., La valeur nutritive de la banane plantain. Folia Scientifica Africae Centralis, Tome IV, No. 4, Dec. 31, 1958.

50. Van Oye, E., L'anemie dans la Malnutrition et dans la Denutrition en Afrique Centrale, Inst. Royale Colon. Belge, Bulletin de Seances, 1953, Vol. 24, No. 2, pp. 632-668.

51. Xydias, M., Social Implications of Industrialization and Urbanization in Africa South of the Sahara in UNESCO, Tensions and Technology Series, Paris 1956.

REPUBLIC OF THE CONGO (LEOPOLDVILLE)

LIST OF TABLES

123

TABLE NO. 1

Provinces of the Congo (Leopoldville) 1963

Old Provinces	New Provinces
Leopoldville	Kongo Central
	Kwango
	Kwilu
	Lac Leopold II
Equateur	Cuvette Centrale
	Ubangi
	Moyen Congo
Orientale	Uele
	Kibali-Ituri
	Haut Congo
Kivu	Maniema
	Kivu Central
	Nord Kivu
Katanga	Nord Katanga
	Katanga Oriental
	Lualaba (Sud Congo)
Kasai	Sud Kasai
	Luluabourg (Kasai Central)
	Unite Kasaienne
	Sankuru
	Lomami

TABLE NO. 2

Main Tribal Groups by Provinces
Belgian Congo 1960

Leopoldville	Holo, Hum, Kondo, Kongo, Kwese, Lunda, Mongo, Pende, Sengeli, Suku, Sundi, Teke, Tschokwe, Yaka.
Equateur	(1) Bantu group—Doko, Mbuja, Mongo, Ngombe, (2) Sudanese group—Banda, Ngbaka, Ngbandi (3) Pygmies—Tschwa or Twa
Orientale	(1) Bantu group—Bali, Bira, Boa, Budu, Eso, Genya, Lokele, Mbole, Olombo, Poto (2) Sudanese group—Bale, Balese, Logo, Lombi, Makere, Mamvu, Maugbetu, Mba, Popoi, Zande (3) Pygmies—Mbuti, Efe, Aka
Kasai	Kanyok, Kete, Kuba, Lele, Luba, Lulua, Lunda, Mongo, Nkutu, Salampasu, Songye, Tetela, Tshokwe, Wongo
Katanga	Aushi, Boya, Lamba, Lunda, Tabwa, Tshokwe
Kivu	(1) Bantu group—Bangu-bangu, Boyo, Genya, Kusu, Lega, Shi (2) Sudanese—Mvuba (3) Hamite—Tutsi

Source: Belgian Congo - Information and Public Relations Office
Brussels 1960 pp. 9-11.

TABLE NO. 3

Population Data

(Belgian) Congo January 1, 1959

Population	Provinces						
Africans	Leopoldville	Equateur	Orientale	Kivu	Katanga	Kasai	Total
Adults - M.	736,341	504,679	786,782	550,373	430,829	555,933	3,564,937
Adults - F.	882,967	565,537	776,359	606,018	457,567	645,576	3,934,024
Children - M.	803,612	381,280	474,517	559,802	395,511	501,529	3,116,251
Children - F.	766,366	350,136	436,975	545,629	370,269	455,595	2,924,970
Total	3,189,286	1,801,632	2,474,633	2,261,822	1,654,176	2,158,633	13,540,182
Non-Africans							
Europeans & Americans	33,578	6,607	16,376	13,756	33,507	8,935	112,759
Asians	51	25	491	698	301	16	1,582
Others(1)	2,058	127	330	261	838	48	3,662
Total	35,687	6,759	17,197	14,715	34,646	8,999	118,003
Overall total	3,224,973	1,808,391	2,491,830	2,276,537	1,688,822	2,167,632	13,658,185

(1)Comprising non-pure Africans.

Source: Belgian Congo - Belgian Congo and Ruanda-Urundi Information and Public Relations Office Brussels 1960.

TABLE NO. 4

Detribalized Population
Belgian Congo 1959

		Leopold-ville	Equateur	Orien-tale	Kivu	Katanga	Kasai	Total
Adults	M	256,612	129,351	212,921	120,534	158,024	79,173	956,615
	F	194,664	95,769	155,593	93,575	132,554	68,435	740,590
Children	M	212,487	81,017	109,991	93,102	143,949	68,352	708,892
	F	204,846	77,732	100,647	90,289	135,558	64,238	673,310
Total		868,609	383,869	579,152	397,500	570,079	280,198	3,079,407
Percent of total pop.		27.24	21.31	23.40	17.57	34.46	12.98	22.74

Source: Belgian Congo - Information and P.R. Office for Belgian Congo and Ruanda-Urundi Brussels 1960.

TABLE NO. 5

Production of Agriculture
Congo 1949–62

Crop	Surface Planted in 000 Ha.			Yield in Tons per Ha.			Production in 000 Tons		
	1949 -53	1960 -61	1961 -62	1949 -53	1960 -61	1961 -62	1949 -53	1960 -61	1961 -62
Corn	337	358*	?	0.9	0.9	?	324	333*	?
Millet & Sorghum	91	83*	?	0.6	0.6	?	56	52*	?
Rice	151	153*	?	0.1	0.1	?	152	164*	?
Sugar	—	—	—	—	—	—	16	42	32
Potatoes	3	3*	?	5.9	3.4	?	18	12*	?
Sweet pot. & yams	57	56	?	6.2	5.6	?	353	316*	?
Manioc	655	633*	?	9.1	11.4	?	5935	7212*	?
Dry peas	92	135*	?	0.5	0.5	?	51	70*	?
Bananas (table)	8	18*	?	2.1	2.7	?	16	48	?
Palm oil	?	?	?	?	?	?	172	233.7	223.5
Groundnuts	250	280	230	0.6	0.6	0.5	155	175	130
Cotton seeds	333	?	121	0.2	?	0.3	92	91	40
Sesame seed	18	18*	?	0.3	0.3	?	6	6	6
Coffee	?	?	?	?	?	?	20.5	54	54
Cocoa	?	?	?	?	?	?	1.9	4.8	5.4
Tea	1	5*	?	?	?	?	0.2	3.4	3.4
Tobacco	?	3	3	?	0.8	0.8	?	2.5	2.5
Cotton (lint)	333	368*	121	0.1	0.1	0.1	46	46	20
Rubber	—	—	—	—	—	—	9.8	37.7	37.7

Source: FAO Production Yearbook, Vol. 16, 1962.
*1959–60
All these figures are given as unofficial and must be considered as "order of magnitude" rather than precise quantities.

TABLE NO. 6

Acreage and Production of Food Crops
Congo 1958

Crop	European acreage (in Ha.)	Native acreage (in Ha.)	European Products (in tons)	Native Products (in tons)
Manioc	1,462	635,833	13,682	8,320,548
Sweet Potatoes	221	48,884	1,744	355,606
Potatoes	132	2,095	393	14,342
Other Tubers	—	2,566	—	17,006
Corn	1,561	355,453	2,800	350,179
Rice Paddy	—	163,039	—	191,080
Wheat	—	3,639	—	2,969
Other Cereals	31	834,000	18	62,779
Plantain	300	223,700	1,419	1,955,621
Table Bananas	16,153	5,443	27,932	18,098
Other Fruit	1,000	2,685	1,311	24,388
Groundnuts	118	276,380	79	185,959
Peas & Beans	18	119,150	6	75,418
Market Gardening	939	4,236	5,060	20,237

Source: Belgian Congo, Published by Belgian Congo and Ruanda-Urundi Information Office Brussels 1960.

TABLE NO. 7

Surface Planted and Production of Cash Crops
Congo 1958

Crop	European Surfaces (in Ha.)	Native Surfaces (in Ha.)	European Production (in tons)	Native Production (in tons)
Palm oil			235,458	13,677
Palm nuts	119,766	59,245	102,905	55,631
Sesame	—	17,029	—	5,546
Cottonseed	146	339,546	91	157,072
Sisal	606	—	178	—
Urena & Punga	—	9,873	—	14,863
Coffee (robusta)	63,418	15,753	42,850	7,344
Coffee (arabica)	13,431	3,100	8,020	1,108
Rubber	48,000	10,000	37,352	3,941
Tobacco	447	968	?	?
Sugar Cane	4,822	898	248,370	10,417
Cocoa	15,425	103	5,276	20
Pyrethrum	2,953	41	307	65
Tea	3,546	27	2,781	10
Cinchona	3,146	—	1,770	—
Perfume Plants	650	207	qts. 64,563	qts. 4,477

Source: Belgian Congo, Published by Belgian Congo and Ruanda-Urundi Information Office Brussels 1960.

TABLE NO. 8

Composition and Distribution of Livestock
Congo 1958

Kind	Leopold-ville	Equateur	Eastern	Kivu	Katanga	Kasai	Total
European							
Cattle	107,579	28,799	64,137	17,880	176,957	73,790	467,781
Swine	12,560	6,951	5,810	3,102	15,433	2,034	45,890
Sheep	5,829	1,077	2,979	893	5,559	4,127	20,464
Goats	1,166	836	1,296	109	591	--	3,998
Horses	170	50	124	132	511	288	1,275
Donkeys	—	35	65	42	222	42	406
Mules	—	1	23	—	35	—	59
Native							
Cattle	15,921	3,048	309,727	196,524	8,126	3,634	536,980
Swine	125,967	4,566	21,115	60,598	15,123	80,350	307,619
Sheep	76,918	4,008	113,767	130,147	133,014	262,400	720,254
Goats	320,106	160,933	408,758	180,664	180,664	517,240	1,900,513

Source: Belgian Congo, Published by Belgian Congo and Ruanda-Urundi Information Office Brussels 1960.

Note: The above figures are official but are only relative, since natives do not usually disclose their wealth. No 1963 information is available.

TABLE NO. 9

Agricultural Exports
(in tons)
Congo (Leopoldville) 1959-1962

Item	1959	1960	1961	1962
Coffee	56,539	60,569	33,239	32,380
Cocoa	3,852	5,229	4,966	6,006
Palm Oil	183,610	167,800	153,523	151,949
Kernel Oil	60,674	52,379	49,881	41,896
Groundnut Oil	6,958	5,592	66	—
Cottonseed Oil	6,009	5,385	2,072	906
Oilcakes	98,149	77,714	61,221	53,029
Palm Kernels	39,836	20,399	12,703	18,861
Cotton	49,284	42,370	14,790	9,848
Corn	8,863	1,147	--	—
Manioc	49,865	26,484	5,731	2,393
Bananas	31,099	33,583	28,336	28,753
Tea	3,495	3,874	21	3,962

Source: Belgo-American Development Corp., 511 Fifth Ave., New York. Released June 1963.

TABLE NO. 10

Estimated Per Capita Caloric Intake in Kg. of
Food Consumed Per Year in the Belgian Congo
1953

Food	Calories Per Day	Percent of Total Calories	Kg. Per Year
Total Grain	330	13.9	33.3
Sugar	15	.6	1.4
Manioc	1,370	57.8	458.3
Sweet potatoes	60	2.5	21.7
Potatoes	5	.2	1.6
Dry Legumes	45	1.8	4.9
Other Vegetables	10	.4	20.2
Fresh Fruit	250	10.5	137.2
Meat	10	.4	2.7
Fish	10	.4	6.2
Vegetable Oils	250	10.5	10.4
Milk & Dairy Products	15	.6	7.2
Eggs	Traces	.4	14.0
Total	2,370	100	719.1

Source: U. S. Department of Agriculture - Foreign Agriculture Service -
Washington 1955.

TABLE NO. 11

Adequacy of Food Resources 1959-1974
Congo (Leopoldville)

Crop	Production 1958-59 in tons	Refuse in percent of crude crop	Balance available in tons	Calories per 100 gm, edible portion	Total Calories available in millions	Yields 1958-59 in T. per Ha.	Future Yields 1974 (estim.)	Gain in percent	Future Caloric Yields (in millions)
Manioc	8,320,548	32 percent	5,657,973	148	8,320,640	11.4	15	31 percent	
Sweet potatoes	335,606	25 percent	251,705	116	291,977	5.6	10	78 percent	
Corn	350,179	0	350,179	129	451,730	0.9	1.5	66 percent	
Rice	191,080	0	191,080	360	689,888	1.0	1.5	50 percent	
Plantain	1,950,621	35 percent	1,267,904	122	1,546,842	1.7	4	135 percent	
Groundnuts	185,959	30 percent	130,173	550	715,951	0.6	0.7*	16 percent	
Peas and Beans	75,418	60 percent	30,168	118	35,598	0.5	0.8**	60 percent	
					12,052,626			436 percent	52,577,336

*Yields in former French Equatorial Africa
**Yields in Rwanda

Source: Belgian Congo and Ruanda-Urundi Information Office - Belgian Congo, Vol. II, Brussels 1960.

International Committee for Nutrition in National Defense - Food Composition Table for Use in Latin America Washington June 1961.

Johnston, B. F. - The Staple Food Economies of Western Tropical Africa Stanford University Press, 1958.

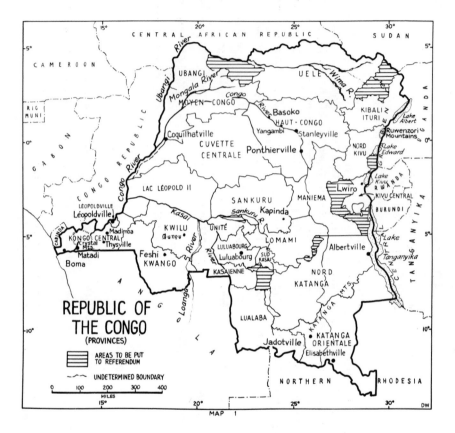

REPUBLIC OF
THE CONGO
(PROVINCES)

AREAS TO BE PUT
TO REFERENDUM

- - -   UNDETERMINED BOUNDARY

0   100   200   300   400
MILES

MAP   1

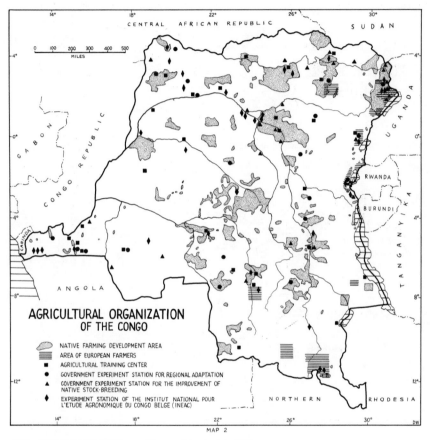

AGRICULTURAL ORGANIZATION
OF THE CONGO

NATIVE FARMING DEVELOPMENT AREA
AREA OF EUROPEAN FARMERS
AGRICULTURAL TRAINING CENTER
GOVERNMENT EXPERIMENT STATION FOR REGIONAL ADAPTATION
GOVERNMENT EXPERIMENT STATION FOR THE IMPROVEMENT OF
NATIVE STOCK-BREEDING
EXPERIMENT STATION OF THE INSTITUT NATIONAL POUR
L'ETUDE AGRONOMIQUE DU CONGO BELGE (INEAC)

MAP 2

Note: Part of the information on this map dates back to 1958.

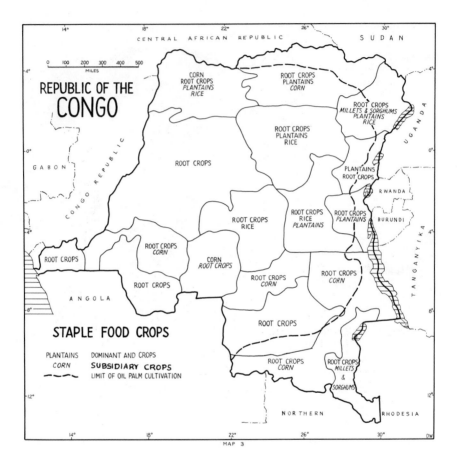

REPUBLIC OF THE
CONGO

STAPLE FOOD CROPS

PLANTAINS   DOMINANT AND CROPS
CORN   SUBSIDIARY CROPS
-------   LIMIT OF OIL PALM CULTIVATION

MAP 3

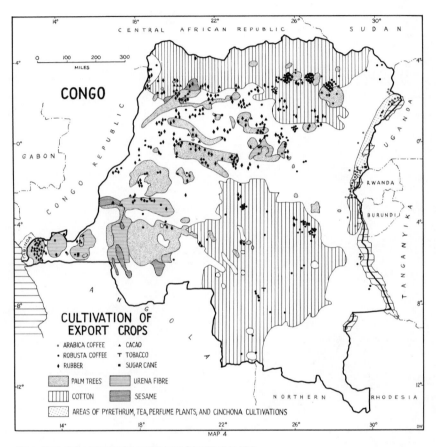

Note: Part of the information on this map dates back to 1958.

RWANDA AND BURUNDI

TABLE OF CONTENTS

RWANDA AND BURUNDI

Weights and Measures

1 Meter	= 39.370 inches = 3.281 feet
1 Kilometer	= 1,000 meters = 0.621 of a mile
1 Square Kilometer	= 0.386 square miles
1 Hectare	= 2.471 acres
1 Kilogram	= 2.204 lbs.
1 Quintal	= 100 kilograms = 220.4 lbs.
1 Ton	= 1,000 kilograms = 2204.6223 lbs.
1 Rwanda-Burundi Franc	= U. S. $0.02
1 U. S. $	= 50 Rwanda-Burundi Francs

RWANDA AND BURUNDI

BACKGROUND

After July 1, 1962, the Belgian Trust Territory of Ruanda-Urundi was splite into two independent countries: the Republic of Rwanda and the Kingdom of Burundi. Although the two countries are now politically separate, it is convenient to study them as a unit because most of the data and statistics concerning them still refer to the former combined territories. Special points for each country have been made when necessary.

The region is one of the poorest and yet most densely populated of Africa, where in a Swiss-like environment an agricultural population, lacking the usual gayety and cheerfulness of the African, competes for food with innumerable herds that produce neither milk nor meat in any significant amounts. Famines were frequent in the past, and an unstable political situation makes them a distinct possibility in the future.

A. GEOGRAPHY [8][15][16][9]

The two countries, Rwanda in the north and Burundi in the south, are located in the Southern Hemisphere. Rwanda's northernmost town, Kakitumba, lies just south of 1° South latitude, and Burundi's southernmost town, Nyanza Lac, is located at nearly 5° South latitude. The meridian of 30° East divides the two countries into two almost equal parts and runs through the capital area of Kigali in Rwanda.

To the west of the two countries lies the Republic of the Congo (Leopoldville), separated from Rwanda by Lake Kivu and from Burundi by the Ruzizi River and the northern part of Lake Tanganyika. At the northern tip of Lake Tanganyika lies Usumbura, the capital and main port of Burundi. To the north lies the Sovereign State of Uganda,* and to the east are the northern provinces of Tanganyika. The total area covers 54,172 square kilometers, of which 27,834 belong to Burundi and 26,338 to Rwanda. Since Stanley and Livingstone visited Usumbura in 1871, European influence has penetrated the country more and more. From 1899 to 1917 the combined areas were part of the German Colony of East Africa. After World War I they became a League of Nations mandate awarded to Belgium and remained under Belgian administration after World War II as a United Nations trust territory. In 1962 the two countries became independent after widespread and violent inter-tribal warfare, during which it is estimated that 5000 Africans died.

*Uganda, neither a republic nor a monarchy, is ruled by an elected "President" who happens to be the "Kabaka" (hereditary ruler) of Buganda.

The two countries are mountainous, with an average elevation of 2500 meters. There are extensive grassy plateaus, dotted with lakes, especially in the north and northeast of Rwanda, where the National Park of Kagera is located. The whole area, however, is one of the most eroded in Africa. On the plateaus the vegetation is savannah-like, with remnants of tropical forests in the west and scrubby trees in the east. The crestline separates the Nile Basin from the Congo Basin. The mountains slope sharply to Lake Kivu in the west, where two volcanoes are still active at nearly 3000 meters elevation. The eastern slope is gentle and drops to 1500 meters in the Kagera and Malgarasi Plains. The two rivers, Kagera and Ruvuvu, form the two southernmost sources of the Nile. Both rivers, at different places, also form the natural boundaries between the two countries and Tanganyika to the east, while in the south the Malgarasi and Lumpungu Rivers mark the boundary of Burundi. Where the Ruzizi River connects Lake Kivu and Lake Tanganyika, there is an area where climate and soil combine to create conditions favorable for agriculture; unfortunately, these conditions are also suitable for tsetse-fly breeding, which makes development difficult and costly.

The climate is mostly highland tropical, with pleasant, cool temperatures on the plateaus. In the lowlands near Lake Tanganyika and in the Ruzizi Valley the climate is warm and dry. Temperatures in the mountains range between 14° and 20°C during the day and may fall to the freezing point at night at the highest altitudes. In the valleys maximum temperatures may reach 33°C. Rainfall is irregular in location and amount. This irregularity is one of the many causes of the famines that have at times devastated the country. On the western slopes of the mountain range, in the central area, precipitation may exceed 1750 mm. annually; it averages 700 mm. to 800 mm. in the lowlands and even less in the northeast corner of Rwanda. There is a long, dry season from May to September, a rainy season from September to January, followed by a short, dry period extending to the middle of February, when a new rainy season begins and lasts until May. These long periods of drought have often brought about crop failures and starvation.

The soil is mostly of the red-yellow latosol type, with small patches of organic soils. The cover consists mostly of themeda-type grass, a fast productive cover that allows the subsistence of one beast of the Ankole type per hectare (2.47 acres). This combination of poor soil and erratic climate results in considerable difficulties, both in agriculture and in animal husbandry. In the highest regions, free of the tsetse fly, herds graze and compete for food with their owners. In the valleys the tsetse fly prevents the raising of cattle, and, for that reason, valleys are sparsely settled and remain an uncertain possibility of future development. In the poor soil the only crop that gives any guarantee of permanent success is the protein-poor manioc. Where soil is better, beans, sweet potatoes, and bananas are grown.

B. POPULATION AND POLITICS [8][9][12][13][15][16]

The total population of the two countries is estimated at about five million,* of which 84 percent are Bahutu, a Bantu group; 14 percent are Watusi, an Ethiopid group; and 1 percent are Batwa, a Pygmy group. About one percent of the population are European or Asian. Very few Africans, less than 100,000, were said to be detribalized in 1958. The two countries are the most densely populated in rural Africa: 92 inhabitants per square kilometer. The rate of increase, estimated at 3 percent by certain sources and at 2.8 percent by others, is high. The population, which is one of the most isolated and poorest in the world, could double in twenty-five years or less.

The Trusteeship Council had always agreed with the Belgian government that Rwanda and Burundi should be unified in a single state after independence; this, however, did not occur. Despite the resemblances between the populations, their language and their social, economic, and political way of life, there is a long history of rivalry and bitter feuds that has always pitted the people of the two fractions of the territory against each other. They have frequently been at war as a result of separate political organizations, land tenure systems, and ruling dynasties. At present, regardless of the probable economic advantages, these emotional considerations dominate the picture.

Before independence the territories derived considerable benefits from their association with the Congo; the social and health services Leopoldville had to offer were a progressive factor of importance; since the Belgian Congo became independent, these services have disintegrated, and the new countries are faced with the task of providing such services for themselves. This they have been unable to do, creating a vacuum that has a direct bearing on food and nutrition. With the assistance of the former Belgian services, some resettlement of populations had taken place in the late 50's from the fly-free but overpopulated highlands to the fly-liberated and sparsely-settled valleys; these operations have now ceased, and densely-crowded areas continue to exist around Astrida and all over the central plateaus. It is recommended by the United Nations experts who have visited the area that the two countries enter an economic union and also remain in contact with the Republic of the Congo and with the European Economic Community. Close ties with other African countries, such as Tanganyika and Uganda, are also desirable if the countries are to be lifted out of their present condition of poverty and precarious food supplies.

The African population of Rwanda includes Tutsi Hamites of Ethiopian stock, Hutus of Bantu Negro stock, and the Twa Pygmies.** The Twa represent barely 0.67 percent of the total, but they are undoubtedly the original population of the country. The date of the Hutu settlement in the area was not historically recorded. They represent 82.74 percent

*Rwanda 2,690,000.
*Burundi 2,500,000.
**Also spelled Tchwa by some authors.

of the Rwanda population. The Tutsi, representing 16.59 percent, came to Rwanda sometime before or during the fifteenth century as they drove their herds to the mountainous pastures. Tall (some are over 7 feet), active, and intelligent, they established their authority over the indigenous population and were soon in control of all administrative posts, thanks to a social system comparable to the Indian caste system, in which the Hutu produced the food and the Tutsi controlled the Hutus. Castes, however, were not highly separated; a worthy Twa or Hutu could become assimilated into a Tutsi, while a poor Tutsi could sink to the level of a Twa serf. Like all feudal systems, it had its good points—it established some sort of peace and gave the serf the protection of the lord. The Tutsi thus acted as benefactor as well as exploiter of the Hutu. The Tutsi cattle owners placed cattle and pastures at the disposal of the Hutu serfs for herding without relinquishing their ownership rights. The "Obutake," or cattle contract, was the basis of this social structure. The Hutu farmers wanted to possess cattle, the Tutsis wanted domestic servants and labor for their crops; so the Hutus mortgaged their services for the use of the cattle. The economic administration was based on "fiefs" defined essentially in terms of head of cattle, pastures, or real estate. Gradually the ownership of the land passed from the Hutus, who had settled it for centuries, to the Tutsi lord, himself a vassal of the supreme master, the King or Mwami. "The Mwami has eaten the land," went the saying. The Mwami also enjoyed divine prestige. He could make cows barren and the soil sterile if he chose to punish somebody.

Following a series of acts of violence, attacks by the Hutus against the Tutsi individuals and against Tutsi property, retaliation by the Tutsi warriors against the Hutus, and United Nations intervention, the Republic was eventually proclaimed on January 28, 1961. This historic tradition and the cultural traits described above must be kept in mind when studying agricultural policies and the ecology of malnutrition in contemporary Rwanda and Burundi.

In Burundi the composition of the population is similar, but the percentages are different. The Tutsis represent only 12.39 percent, the Hutus 86.48 percent, and the Twa 1.13 percent. The princes of royal blood used to form a separate group, the Ganwa, each enjoying a certain autonomy with their own private armies and courts, very much like the dukes in medieval Europe. The ruler, or Bami, also sometimes called Mwami as in Rwanda, was bent upon creating large domains for his relatives, whom he trusted to support him against Ganwa rivals and foreign enemies. This resulted in a lesser parceling of the land than in Rwanda. The cattle contract, which in Burundi is called Ubugabire, was less strict and binding than in Rwanda. Opinions are divided as to the degree of explosiveness of the Hutu-Tutsi situation in Burundi. Most experts agree, however, that it is less explosive than in Rwanda because of the personal and generalized prestige of the present Mwami. As of this writing, Burundi remains a monarchy.

In both countries the population is to a large extent illiterate. In 1960 the two countries had 3274 schools, of which 49 were run by the state and 325 by Catholic and Protestant missions. In these schools 7253 teachers, of which 547 were Europeans, taught 271,349 students. The enrollment covered approximately 35.5 percent of the estimated school-age population, while 0.9 percent of the adolescent group continued into secondary education. In 1958 there were four students in higher education, all involved in agricultural studies. The level of literacy is estimated at 25 percent and the shortage of qualified technical personnel is considerable.

The religion of these populations is still, in spite of the name they may give it when speaking to Westerners, deeply rooted in traditional beliefs; 50 percent of the people are said to be Christian. However, it is likely that among these 50 percent a large number combine their Christian faith with their native customs, fears, and traditions. Those customs, like those of most other Africans, consist essentially of animism and the worship and fear of spirits, and the ministration of specially-trained witchcraft doctors is essential.

C. AGRICULTURAL POLICIES [6][12][13][15]

Agricultural policies are now being worked out but have to take into consideration the complex situation discussed in the previous paragraphs. The United Nations Mission visiting the territories in 1960, prior to independence, found the problems connected with land tenure to be twofold: overpopulation and overstocking. The overstocking is made worse by the poor quality of the land. The land-tenure system is difficult to understand, but it is well established and forms the fabric of the social and political structure, both in Rwanda and in Burundi.

As a result of a succession of mortgages, food contributions, and allegiances, it is true that to a large extent "the Mwami has eaten the land." Large remnants of the former tribal system persist in Rwanda and form a body of traditions and contractual understandings called Ubukunde. Ubukunde persist mainly in the western chiefdoms of the Congo-Nile divide and in the Bugoye District.

Violence erupted in 1959 and in 1963-64 partly because the chiefs of tribes wished to reassert their rights while the tenants rebelled against them. In other areas, where cattle are abundant and pasture scarce, the Tutsi Chief owns the land while the Hutu control its use. This division of rights causes conflict between Hutu agriculture and Tutsi stock raising. Families established for generations on a piece of land claim it as their own in spite of the traditional Tutsi ownership. The Hutu tenants back their claim by the presence of a hut, a kraal, a banana plantation, and seasonal crops. These claims are favorably considered by the Administration in accordance with its policy of tying the farmer to the land and encouraging the growth of regular crops; but landlords with traditional claims on the land resist with all their power.

A complete revision of the various systems will have to take place
before the agricultural economy of the two countries can be reestab-
lished; but the dangers of any reform upsetting the present fabric are
great, and any disturbance could create famines.

The Food and Agricultural Organization's recommended policy is
to try to integrate agriculture and animal husbandry as well as food
crops and feed crops. This is difficult not only because of the psychological climate, which is far from prepared for such a drastic revolution, but also because many of the pasture lands could not be profitably
cultivated under present conditions, a conclusion long ago reached by
the Belgian INEAC* and confirmed in 1962 by FAO experts. The pastures are certainly overloaded, which results in the too early grazing
of the best nutrient grasses, such as Exotheca abyssinica, Themeda
triandrea, and Bracchiaria spp. This allows the less desirable species
to go to seed and increase; combined with the erosion resulting from
overgrazing, a situation is created that increases the acreage of poor
pasture land. One possible solution would be to disperse the herds onto
lands in the Malagarassi and Lumpungu Valleys, where 287,000 hectares
could be reclaimed if they could be cleared of tsetse flies. Whether
the returns would repay the investment, however, is still doubtful.

To improve the presently very low yields in meat and milk (average
milk production: 150 litres per active cow per year), the peasants are
advised to regulate grazing, procure dry-season fodder, keep herds off
the pastures at that time, and destroy old animals. These recommendations, however, go unheeded because to the Burundi peasant the food
benefits do not outweigh the spiritual and sentimental values attached to
the status of the cattle. The Belgian "Zone d'Action Rurale," known as
ZAR, has tried to influence the herdsman to change his attitude toward
his cattle; unfortunately, this program has considerably slackened its
activities since the territory has become independent.

The paysannat system is in existence in the two countries, as it is
in the Congo. Farmers are allotted a parcel of land and a hut. Their
work is closely supervised and directed. The results are said to have
been disappointing in densely populated areas where the system could
have done the most good but have been rather favorable in the Ruzizi
Valley, where, at the beginning of 1961, 9000 families were established
on some 60,000 hectares, leaving space for more. There rice is grown
in the wet areas and cotton in the dry. Unfortunately, while the agricultural side of the program has been encouraging, the animal husbandry
side has been disappointing. It was recommended that parcels of pasture be apportioned to a few animals tied to a stake so as to control
their grazing. The Burundi farmer found this practice insulting to the
cow, as well as demanding extra labor from the owner, and refused to
comply.

Agricultural policies remain defined as they were under the Belgian
Administration. They consist of: adoption of erosion prevention tech-

*Institut National pour l'Etude Agronomique du Congo.

niques; increased production and use of organic fertilizer; development of fodder crops; introduction of cash crops, such as tobacco, pyrethrum, and castor oil trees, in addition to the profitable but vulnerable coffee plantations already in existence; drainage of swamps in the valleys to get rid of the tsetse fly; irrigation expansion; development of tree agriculture, especially avocado; improvement of seeds for pulses; adoption of better agricultural tools, at present limited to the stick, the hoe, and the machete; creation of veterinary centers; adoption of measures to control grazing; building of stables; addition of social services to the paysannat villages, and creation of market places with consumer's goods to induce consciousness of a high living standard among the population.

II

FOOD RESOURCES

A. GENERAL [5][6][7]

The economy of the country is based almost entirely on agriculture; known mineral resources are scanty and industrial development negligible. The balance of trade is unfavorable, thus limiting food imports to a minimum. In spite of the large amount of animal husbandry already mentioned, the food resources of the country all come from agriculture. The distribution of arable land resulted in the creation of high-density clusters of population that have to subsist on a minimum of soil; 90 percent of the cultivated surface is in food crops such as manioc, rice, and corn, leaving only 10 percent for cash crops.

From a total land surface of 5,055,000 hectares (the total area of the two countries, including waters, is 5,417,000 hectares), 2,119,000 hectares are deemed arable, while 1,733,000 are considered permanent pastures. In addition, there are 222,000 hectares of forest and 1,343,000 hectares of nonusable land or built-up areas. The relatively small forest areas indicate that settlements have existed for some time, and also show how rapidly land can be deforested by the slash-and-burn method of agriculture. This land distribution leaves about one-half hectare for each individual, a small amount in view of the lack of technology and absence of fertilizer. Conversely, there are almost two hectares per head of cattle, providing little or no food. This unfair distribution, together with the irregular rainfall, explains in part the fearful famines that have occurred in the past, the most recent of which, in 1943 and 1944, is said to have caused the death of tens of thousands of people.

B. MEANS OF PRODUCTION

1. Agricultural Labor Force [12][13]

The farmers of the two countries, particularly those of Rwanda, have a choice among three systems: they can hire out as laborers to a landlord and live on the food they get as salary; they can work the fields of the family group to which they belong; or they can do a bit of both.

The salaries of the hired laborers were, as established by tradition, relatively high for Africa. In certain areas (Rukoma, north of the Nyanza territory) the worker was paid cash and also collected a basketful of food adequate to support a family of five, including three adolescents (ecyibo cy'umuhinzi). Yet only the poorest people became hired hands, on occasion, to increase their food resources. Most people preferred home farming to the risk of getting a job and then losing it. The labor force is organized in extended family units called inzu under the management of an elder who can, if he is so inclined, apportion the work consistently with each of the component family's resources and possibilities. Even now, when this traditional structure is slowly dissolving, a needy family has the right to call for help in times of trouble and can demand that relatives work the field or take care of the animals. During the height of the working season, the people band together to expedite work on each other's assigned land. This is the occasion for snacks and potations during and after work. Since the brewing of large quantities of sorghum beer or banana wine takes several days, it is usual to have a large gathering to drink away the product. In areas where the money economy has penetrated, these beverages are bought at the nearby tavern. In the money-economy areas cooperative work is on the decline and more salaried workers are found. It is estimated that in 1958 about 2.6 percent of the population were salaried workers; of this number, 21 percent were working in agriculture.

2. Farms [12][13][16]

There are two main types of farms in Rwanda and Burundi: the subsistence farm, by far the more numerous; and the paysannat farm, which is a mixture of guided subsistence farming and cash cropping. The subsistence land is part of that area that was divided in the past by the Mwami into fiefs for the benefit of his vassals. Some of these fiefs entailed political rights (ibikingi), while others were merely grazing concessions. After 1931 the holders of these fiefs lost their political authority over the residents but retained certain land-tenure rights. Even today a farmer settled on such a farm owes certain traditional services. The trend now, however, is to develop the family agricultural holding into quasi-ownership and to eliminate outdated feudal services. Centered around a hut, these family holdings seldom exceed two hectares. They are called isambu in Rwanda and itongo in Burundi. On these subsistence farms efforts are made to insure against starvation. Multiple crops are started in the same field, taking advantage of the microclimates available; one crop is planted under the banana tree, another in a swamp, another on open land. Crops are thus harvested in a staggered fashion intended to keep the larder as well provided as possible all the time. This arrangement also helps fight the vagaries of the weather. Beans and sweet potatoes are sown in the same area. If the weather is dry, the potatoes prosper while the beans wither; if the weather is rainy, the opposite occurs.

The paysannat farms, based on the idea of tying the farmer to the land while giving him a regular income in food and money, have been only moderately successful in Rwanda and Burundi. They have been established in recently surveyed and crop-tested areas to ease the congestion in the population-saturated regions of Central Rwanda. From the crowded district of Buyenzi people have been moved to the Mosso and to the Imbo areas of the Ruzizi Valley, while others have been moved from Bwana and Mukare to Bugesira. The land allotted to each family varies with its water supply; four hectares of dry land or 1.50 hectares of irrigated land are the basic common measure. The dry land is divided into eight lots of 0.4 hectares to be cultivated according to a compulsory rotating schedule of crops. In addition, 0.4 hectares are allotted for the hut and 0.4 hectares for trees. The recipients of irrigated lands are also allotted 0.3 to 0.5 hectares of dry land. The irrigated part of the land is divided in three lots of 0.5 hectare each. Rice and groundnuts are rotated, and some land is left fallow. Cotton—a cash crop—is often grown on this fallow land. Under these conditions rice yielded four tons per hectare (twice as much as in the former Belgian Congo), and cotton rose to 0.78 tons per hectare. Some of the fallow land was intended for grasses to be used as pasture, but most of these pastures were not used by the farmers because they prefer to assemble the cattle in large herds and drive them to graze on the old communal lands, thus losing the manure that would have enriched the fallow land and the fodder that would have grown on it.

As stated above, the policy is to increase the cash crops. About 30,000 to 35,000 hectares of coffee are cultivated throughout the two countries, interspersed with food crops.

3. Fertilizers

In a territory where cattle abounds to the point of endangering the economy rather than assisting it, one would expect animal manure to be abundant. This, however, is not the case; the traditional practice of taking the herds to graze on communal pastures located among the rocks of the mountains where the soil is poor results in the manure being wasted on unproductive land. The herds do not go back to stables, and fences are unknown. No chemical fertilizers are imported in any significant amount except for the benefit of a few Europeans whose farm lands represent less than 1 percent of the total.

4. Mechanical Equipment

There was no mechanical equipment in 1960 in either of the two countries.

C. PRODUCTION [7]

1. Basic Foods

Approximately six and one-half million tons of food crops, including manioc, plantain, and sweet potatoes, are estimated to be produced yearly in the two countries, supplying barely adequate food for the population.

Manioc was planted on 100,000 hectares in 1961-1962, an area that was reduced from 144,000 hectares in 1948-1953. This crop yielded 1,138,000 tons down from 1,601,000 tons in 1959-1960 (see Table No. 1).

Plantain was harvested in the amount of 1,892,671 tons (1956 figure).

Sweet potatoes yielded 971,000 tons in 1961-1962 from an area of 145,000 hectares; this was reduced from 177,000 in 1948-1953, when 1,193,000 tons were collected.

Other food crops include potatoes, 24,000 tons; corn, 98,000 tons; paddy, 3000 tons; sorghum, 148,000 tons; beans, 178,000 tons, a drop from 197,000 tons in 1948-1953 and from 250,000 in 1960-1961; peas, 58,000 tons, a drop from 77,000 tons in 1948-1953 and from 62,000 tons in 1960.

For most of these crops yields that had increased in the 1950 decade and in the two first years of the 1960's were found to have dropped suddenly for the third harvest of the decade.

The variety of beans and peas is considerable, and these pulses are in most areas a staple of the diet second only to manioc and plantain. One finds lima beans, mango beans, kunde beans (nkole), adzuki beans (recently introduced), cajan peas, and ordinary garden peas.

Cash crops are led by coffee (35,000 hectares), exported to Belgium and to the United States, followed by pyrethrum, tobacco, cotton, sisal, and cinchona in amounts listed below when known.

Item	Area Covered in Ha.	Quantity (1962) in 000 tons
Palm Oil	7,373	1,063
Coffee	35,256	23,200
Pyrethrum	1,141	762
Tobacco	2,051	1,231
Tea	?	0.1
Cotton	12,000	3,000

Groundnuts, most of which are eaten in the domestic market but some of which are exported, covered 5000 hectares.

These cash crops provide the countries with some foreign exchange but not with enough to give them significant purchasing power for additional food supplies.

2. Sources of Animal Proteins [7][6]

Meat. For countries as rich in cattle as Rwanda and Burundi the amount of animal protein available for the population is unusually small. The majority of the people eat meat very seldom, and some probably have never eaten any. The most favored group has meat once or twice every fortnight; yet cattle, sheep, and goats are abundant. There were in 1961 a reported 1,060,000 cattle in the two countries, 56,000 hogs, 620,000 sheep, and 1,830,000 goats. FAO experts feel that the cattle population represents the most important and complex problem facing the two countries. According to these sources, this enormous capital does not produce more than 13 litres of milk and approximately 3 kilos of meat per capita per year. Other sources report a slaughter of 25,000 cattle, 8000 swine, and 81,000 sheep a year; using the average carcass weight given, this should amount to a total of 22,860,000 kilos of meat per year or approximately 4.5 kilograms per consumer per year. In both cases the amount of meat available is exceedingly small and the supply is probably concentrated in a small proportion of the population. Only old cows and very young calves are sold for slaughter, which explains in part the low yield in meat. The Burundi cow produces 300 litres of milk annually, of which 150 litres are drunk by its calf.

The cattle belong to the Zebu or pseudo-Zebu species. Burundi cattlemen consider the long horns a sign of beauty and have only very recently consented to accept the introduction of short-horned or hornless species better suited for meat and milk production. As already indicated, cattle are a symbol of wealth and prestige; castration is not accepted, and meat production is not the goal of animal husbandry. The solution offered to the problem of meat production is to transfer a substantial number of animals to sparsely settled areas, such as the Mosso alluvial plain, where 53,000 hectares of pastures could be created if the area could be freed of tsetse flies and if the people would agree to move.

Fisheries.[5] Under the Ten Year Plan (1952-1962) of the Belgian government, fish culture had been intensified and lake stocking had been started. Demonstration units and fish farms had been established that had increased the production of fish in the two territories four times between 1948 and 1960 (1948—2300 tons of catch, 1960—9200). Institut pour la Recherche Scientifique en Afrique Centrale has begun to study the biology of tropical lakes, about which very little is known. The higher temperature of their waters promote, it is believed, the accelerated growth and development of the fish and other living things. When mass hatchings, migrations, and reproduction periods are better known, more scientific fishing with improved nutritional yields may be expected. On the basis of the above figures, 0.400 grams of fish would be available per capita per year, but a substantial amount of fish is caught and not reported by the people living in the neighborhood of the lake; the rest of the people have a contempt and even a disgust for fish.

D. FOOD SUPPLY[16][12][2]

The establishment of food reserves in Rwanda and Burundi is a burning problem; never solved in the past, it is critical for the future. Two major factors contribute to the famine in Rwanda and Burundi: the uncertainty of the rains and the high rate of population growth. To cope with the climatic conditions, the Belgian Administration had introduced new food crops less susceptible to drought, like potatoes. Traditional crops had been improved wherever possible; yield in sweet potatoes had increased from 6.7 to 7.7 tons per hectare; rice yields had grown from 1.4 to 3.7 tons per hectare; marshy lands had been cultivated; erosion had been fought, and stocks had been built to the extent that by 1956 there were 81 kilos of manioc meal available in reserve for each inhabitant. Unfortunately, this had dwindled to 10 kilos per inhabitant in 1961, and the present figure (1963) is not available.

To help offset the effect of famine, adequate transportation over passable routes are important. The basic road system has a remarkable density, considering the mountainous nature of the land and the cost of road building. There are 8600 kilometers of roads, of which two-thirds are classified as local roads or tracks. Unfortunately, these roads are at present in very poor condition, and many of them are reported to be impassable. The port of Usumbura in Burundi has been improved and can serve as a distribution center for food. Steamers (plying Lake Tanganyika) carry export products from Usumbura to both Tanganyika and Albertville, in the Congo. There are no railroads in Rwanda and Burundi. There is a good airport at Usumbura, and smaller airport facilities are located at Kigali, Astrida, and Shangugu. Air transportation is risky because of atmospheric conditions such as fog and clouds overhanging mountain peaks.

In 1952 the Belgian government started foreign aid with a $20 million appropriation, part of which was earmarked for agriculture and part for relocation and dispersion of the crowded population. Development of cash crops, surveys, the fight against erosion, irrigation of small areas, well digging in drought-threatened areas, terrace work and planting, improvement of cattle, and development of markets and outlets have also been undertaken and supported by this grant. In June 1957 the International Bank for Reconstruction and Development (IBRD) made a loan of $4.8 million at 5.8 percent interest to improve the port of Usumbura and to repair the roads. The Development Fund of the European Economic Community has allotted $10 million for economic and social improvements, inclusive of the development of the Bugesira Maryaga area. American aid to Rwanda and Burundi totaled $6.1 million as of June 1962.

E. FOOD INDUSTRIES[16]

There are practically no food industries in Rwanda and Burundi. Two beer factories, operated mostly for the benefit of the European community, produce an average of 83,515 barrels of beer a year. The local crop of tea is processed in a new plant; soft drinks are produced in the amount of 6000 barrels; 4000 tons of milk are processed; 1245 tons of meat are packaged, and 769 tons of fresh-water fish are processed; and 1000 tons of flour are milled every year. All the above are mainly for European consumption.

F. IMPORT-EXPORT [16]

The two countries export some raw material and import manufactured goods; in terms of food their export consists of cash crops such as coffee, tea, some spices, and cottonseed cakes and oil, for a total of 131,020 metric tons in 1960, valued at $45 million. Imports of wheat, flour, and tobacco from the United States, milk and dairy products from Denmark, and meat from the Union of South Africa, for a total value of $49,757,000, almost without exception reach the European community and a few évolué Africans. These imports do not in any way influence the diets of the masses.

III

DIET TYPES

A. GENERAL [5][6][2][1]

Before discussing the diets of the African population of Rwanda and Burundi, a quick glance at the standard of living is required. The population is poor, as is the land, and the standards of living are low. According to an estimate published in August 1963 and based on 1961 market prices, the total gross national product of Burundi was $135 million, giving a per capita income of $60 annually. Rwanda is still poorer, with a gross national product of $110 million and a per capita income of $40, one of the very lowest in Africa. Since 1954 the ordinary budget of the government has shown increasing deficits that in 1961 reached an estimated $8 million. This was due to increased spending for education,* civil servants' salaries, and social services without a balancing increase in revenue. The masses living on a subsistence economy escape taxation, which is levied only on foreigners and private enterprise. As a result dependence on Belgian direct financial assistance has grown in recent years, even after independence.

---

*A Department of Agriculture has been established at the recently created University of Astrida.

B. NUTRITIONAL LEVELS [(2)(5)(13)(12)]

The African farmer of Rwanda and Burundi does not buy his food. He takes it out of the ground as the need arises, picking the tubers, one by one, uprooting the beans, plant after plant, cutting the corn, ear by ear, the sorghum, stalk by stalk, and collecting the plantain, small bunch after small bunch. Other necessities of life come from barter and occasionally from gifts, but more Africans have occasions to make such gifts than to receive them because they go to people who may exert or who are believed to exert more power than oneself, or to persons in a position or believed to be in a position to cast a charm or an evil eye.

There are numerous taboos, including avoidance of eating vegetables and drinking milk at the same time; this in order to avoid hurting the cow that produced the milk. Cows and totem animals continue to remain sacred, and, of course, ghosts and spirits abound and influence diets and nutrition in many ways.

Our knowledge of the food situation in the two countries is based on extensive studies made after 1955 under the supervision of IRSAC. Samples of the population studied, totalling 0.25 percent of the people, had been carefully selected to represent a good cross-section of the people. Research was carried out in May and June and in November and December, at opposite poles of the agricultural seasons: end of the dry season and end of the rainy season. These studies revealed that most people in Rwanda and Burundi eat two meals a day, but some eat only one meal, always in the evening, and some eat three meals. A bare majority of children (in Burundi), however, eat three meals as shown in the short table below:

Rwanda	1 meal	2 meals	3 meals
Men	19.58 percent	72.14 percent	8.28 percent
Women	9.22 percent	75.43 percent	15.35 percent
Children	1.03 percent	37.52 percent	61.45 percent
Burundi			
Men	7.26 percent	74.22 percent	18.52 percent
Women	5.05 percent	71.58 percent	23.37 percent
Children	2.72 percent	46.82 percent	50.46 percent

The above information does not include the snacks that one-meal people often eat in the fields; these snacks consist usually of an ear of corn or one or two yams. Children, of course, eat whatever additional nondescript items of food they can manage to lay their hands on. The level of nutrition of the school-age child is probably worse than in other African countries; it is this g r o u p that represents the percentages mentioned in the one-meal and two-meal columns of the table above. The government offered to serve a midday meal at schools at a low price; this was unanimously rejected, probably for fear that food taboos would be broken. In Rwanda meals are seldom composed of more than one food item, while in Burundi two foods are usually included in the menu. The foods in both countries are mostly of vegetable origin; in Burundi

> 69 percent of meals include beans
> 32 percent of meals include sweet potatoes
> 27 percent of meals include manioc
> 18 percent of meals include bananas

In Rwanda the proportions, according to J. Close, are slightly different:

> 50 percent of the meals include beans
> 56 percent of the meals include sweet potatoes
> 6 percent of the meals include manioc
> 13 percent of the meals include bananas

Greens take on some importance in case of famine or in very poor families; otherwise they are eaten occasionally and as a complement to the basic foods. These greens are usually the leaves of many different plants, cultivated or wild, and include leaves of the bean plants (Umushogoro-Umukubi), marrow (Umusuma), and manioc (Amarara).

In addition to these foods, the diet of certain groups include other items, occasionally or seasonally. Mushrooms and fungi (Ibizimu) are eaten around Bwome in Ruzizi territory (the Hutus rather than the Tutsi are interested in them). Tomatoes are grown and eaten around Usumbura. Rice may be eaten anywhere by those who can afford to buy it. Peanuts are not commonly planted or appreciated. Certain tribes will occasionally cultivate and eat white sorghum (Urubere) in the Mosso area and anjola peas (Inteugwa) also in Mosso and Buyogama. Eighty to 85 percent of all meals include spices such as ground chillies. In addition, 30 percent of all meals in Burundi and 40 percent in Rwanda include onions. All meals are salted (see chapter on the Congo (Leopoldville) for the preparation of salty fluids).

In spite of the abundance of cattle, meat consumption is at a minimum. Some people claim never to have eaten meat in their entire lives, others, "not since last year." Many have no money for this luxury. If available, meat is reserved for the male head of the family. Women (especially among the Tutsi population) do not eat meat. The reasons for this taboo are unknown and might include anything from a religious taboo to a lack of taste for it. A respect for the bull and ox may also influence this situation, as is suggested by the fact that when meat is eaten it is always cow.

Fish is traded and consumed along certain rivers near Lake Tanganyika and where governmental fish ponds have been established. It is unknown in most parts of the interior. There is in places a disgust for fish, as is shown when dried fish distributed free to workers is thrown away untouched.

Fats come from palm oil, butter, and peanut oil, but only the two first items are found in Burundi. Few people have any fat ration in their regular daily meal. Palm oil is not produced at high altitudes and would have to bought. Butter is not regularly made from the available milk and, if produced, is used as a cosmetic rather than as a nutrient. Close found that 55 percent of the population had not eaten fats for weeks or months.

In Burundi butter is eaten twice as often as palm oil, except in low altitude regions where the latter is produced; in Rwanda the reverse is true. Peanut oil is consumed only in Kibungu territory.

Milk is drunk fresh or curdled. While only a small fraction of the people drink it regularly, cow's milk is generally popular. As might be expected, 90 percent of the Tutsi cattle owners in Burundi and 85 percent in Rwanda are regular consumers. Only 23 percent of the Hutu in Burundi and 34 percent in Rwanda drink milk. This consumption varies, of course, with the seasons and the supply. In November 65 percent of the people of Burundi and 54.8 percent of the people of Rwanda do not drink milk regularly. When it is available, first children, then women, then men consume it. Only cow's milk is popular; goat's and ewe's milk is never tasted except when prescribed by the "doctor"; it has the bad reputation of giving colic to children.

Fermented beverages are well liked, and a substantial portion of the banana and sorghum crop is used for the production of beer. In both countries the consumption of the beverage is universally popular; only old women and sick people abstain; 35 percent of the children drink it even before being weaned.

Certain insects, especially termites (Iswa), which are available during certain seasons, are popular as food.

In both countries menus include, when possible, a basic food rich in vegetable proteins and another rich in carbohydrates. This balanced diet, however, is not always available, and boiled sweet potatoes or beans are often served alone or with some green leaves and spices. Boiling the food in water is the most common way of cooking it, but sweet potatoes and beans are sometimes cooked between stones in hot ashes.

The basic food is first cooked in water to which the chopped green leaves are added. When the meal is ready, the chillies or salt are either added to the broth or distributed to each person eating. Flour when available, is cooked to a paste in boiling water. Meat and fish are also boiled, and the fats are added when the food is almost done. Occasionally a meal may be fried in oil. Leftovers are used the next day and supplemented with fresh food. When possible, termites are dried for two or three days, then boiled.

The amount of water used for cooking is calculated to evaporate about the time the food is cooked; if some water is left after the vegetables are cooked, it is thrown away. Peanuts, when available, are crushed with onions, chillies, and salt and then fried in butter or fat.

During the rainy season or immediately thereafter, in April, the food situation improves, and almost everybody has at least two meals. Most of the main staple foods remain the same except that manioc loses its predominance, and corn tends to replace sweet potatoes in Burundi. Meat, fish, fats, and milk keep their insignificant place in the diet.

IV

ADEQUACY OF FOOD RESOURCES

IN NORMAL TIMES [2][3][4][5][12][16]

It is clear from the above that the food resources of the countries are inadequate and that irregularity of the rains, combined with population growth and cultural habits, create the climate for malnutrition and even famine. The two countries have not lacked advice. Wise recommendations have been made in abundance, but the future is bleak. The people are not ready to listen to advice and to abide by recommendations; in addition, a financial crisis is in the making.

The first problem is to solve the question of land tenure, which is the basis of life of every citizen in the two countries. The old system has been severely shaken by recent developments, custom has become unsettled, faith in the judgment of arbitrators has been lost, and the proper development of agriculture and stock breeding cannot take place without the existence of a land-tenure code, fair to and accepted by all.

Once land tenure is decided, the technical problems will remain. These have been solved in part by the paysannat program; but this system has a compulsory character that only a strong and at the same time benevolent authority can impose. The mushrooming of various political parties representing different local interests, each fighting to get on top, is not usually conducive to the kind of paternal dictatorship that makes paysannats prosper. In addition, paysannats need good land, and that is scarce in Rwanda and Burundi; where it exists, it is already crowded. Further, the integration of husbandry and agriculture requires the eradication of tsetse flies from the valleys to be settled. Naturally, the less populated valleys are also those where the tsetse flies abound since their breeding sites in the bush are undisturbed.

The proper development of animal husbandry requires the destruction of inferior animals, a grazing policy, and adequate veterinary and breeding techniques. The citizens of Rwanda and Burundi are not yet ready to accept the first two conditions, and the technicians needed for the third are not available. The Belgian ZAR program was really educational. It was designed to start pilot projects in a variety of activities, such as erosion control, stable building, swamp reclamation, introduction of commercial and industrial crops, and planning of irrigation and fertilization.

An unprejudiced but firmly supported central direction is needed for such a program, too.

The needs of technical education are not met. Just before independence courses had been established, degrees had been offered, and scholarships had been instituted. The budget for education had risen to 25 percent of the total budget in 1960; but primary, secondary, and technical education competed for the available funds, and progress toward better nutrition through education was slowed.

All these measures are contingent upon sound financing. Unfortunately, as stated above, since 1954 revenue has failed to balance expenditure. Deficits have increased yearly and were met by Belgian subsidies. There is little hope of correcting this situation by increasing taxes in a country in which the economy is based on subsistence and in which the taxable income is derived from foreigners who are likely to go home if taxation becomes confiscatory. Exports, which center around coffee, are limited by world demands; new ventures capable of bringing money in, such as the extractive industries, require technicians that can only be foreign for a long time to come. Thus, the adequacy of food resources in the future is, to a very large degree, contingent upon the availability of foreign aid.

IN TIMES OF STRESS

In primitive economies nutrition is less affected by times of stress than is the case in more sophisticated countries that depend on technology. Even primitive economies, however, can be devastated by tribal warfare and by uncontrollable events such as drought or floods. When such catastrophes become so severe that crops are destroyed, workers are killed, and communications are disrupted, famine is unavoidable.

A foreign army operating in the two countries would not only have to support itself entirely, but would also have to support, as best it could, the indigenous population. Guerrilla warfare, if it broke out, would undoubtedly spell complete ruin, as the guerrillas would support themselves entirely at the expense of an already famished population.

V

NUTRITIONAL DISEASE PATTERNS[4][5][10][11][14]

It is not surprising, in view of the above, that the pattern of nutritional diseases proves to be as complex in this cattle-rich country as it is in other tropical African areas. A number of studies have given us a picture of the anthropological and pathological features of the two lands.

Anthropologically, Hiernaux finds that the various ethnic groups of Rwanda and Burundi show "highly significant differences" in spite of reciprocal inbreeding. People calling themselves by the same tribal designations are different in Rwanda and in Burundi. The Tutsi show traits that are neither Negro nor European. The Hutus reflect three components, one Ethiopid and two Negroid, one of which shows affinities with the Pygmy stock. The Twa appear similar to the Bambutu Pygmies in spite of traceable signs of Bantu influence.

Pathologically, these populations also differ in their state of nutrition. The muscular system of the Tutsi is poorly developed. Physiological parameters are also different in each group and this difference seems to be the effect of nurture rather than of nature. The Bakinga people, a Hutu subgroup living in the mountains where they enjoy more regular rainfall and hence more regular and substantial diets, have higher mean indices of anthropometry than the people living in the plains. Of general interest was another finding: a sample of Hutus selected to work in private European companies, where they enjoyed high salaries and a well-above-average diet, were still, in all indices, significantly below the Bakinga, who had enjoyed the better fare in childhood. The conclusion is that the development of the bones and muscles depends on an adequate diet in childhood and that this cannot be compensated for by a good diet in the adult age. In view of the deplorable condition of child nutrition in all African countries, this statement is highly significant.

Another authority (Close) found that serum protein levels in children were lower than normal in albumins and in beta globulins. Between 18 and 22 months of age the curve of total proteins differs from the general course of the curve. This difference may be the result of the sudden changeover from a protein to a rich carbohydrate diet after weaning. The curve also shows a continuous increase of the gamma globulin fraction from the second month on, not observed in American children. This may be due to a hepatic dysfunction, or to nutritional deficiencies, or to a genetic difference. Other studies (by DeMaeyer and Close) seem to indicate that nitrogen is poorly absorbed and that under experimental conditions a positive nitrogen balance appears as soon as the intake is in excess of approximately seven grams a day. There are also indications of defective absorption and probably insufficient hydrolysis of lipids. DeMaeyer, Chardome, and Peel found a normochrome anemia present in three groups of genetically homogenous people living at 1600 meters, 1800 meters, and 2200 meters, respectively, a particularly significant feature in view of the usual increase of red cells found in populations living at a high altitude. This they believe to be caused by the lack of animal protein in the diet, even among people living on the lake shore. Studies (by Roels, Debeir, and Trout) found vitamin A deficiencies to be patent in the population of central areas around Astrida, as evidenced by an average ratio of Bitot spots in the s a m p l e s examined, of 9.3 per 1000. By sex and age, the findings were as follows:

Men	13.3 per 1000
Boys	15.4 per 1000
Women	2.6 per 1000
Girls	3.6 per 1000

No explanation is offered for the significant differences between the two sexes. The staple food of this population consists of sweet potatoes but of a variety that contains no carotene.

Endemic goiter is also common in Rwanda and Burundi, but the prevalence varies considerably from place to place. Areas of minimal prevalence show rates of 1.83 percent (Nyakatara); areas of maximal prevalence show rates of 28.37 percent (Kitabi). Goiters are more frequent in the female than in the male and are mostly of parenchymatous type. The authors believe that there may be a correlation between the chemical composition of the rocks and the rainfall since the action of the rain, washing the surface of the rocks, governs the amount of iodine available in the free waters of the environment.

VI

CONCLUSIONS

The brief conclusions that can be drawn from this report do not vary considerably from those that can be derived from the reports on other African countries, except that the prospects for Rwanda and Burundi are probably still more gloomy. Adverse factors, such as overpopulation, poor soil, erratic rainfall, mediocre communications, strong traditional prejudices, and lack of political maturity are not compensated for as they are in some places by potential resources or strong economic and political alliances. More than other African countries, Rwanda and Burundi must depend on foreign assistance, which does not seem to be readily forthcoming in significant amounts from any source.

BIBLIOGRAPHY: RWANDA AND BURUNDI

1. Africa Report, 1960-1964.

2. Close, J., Enquete Alimentaire au Ruanda-Urundi, Academie Royale des Sciences Coloniales. Memoire in-8. Nouvelle Serie. Tome 11 fasc. 4 Brussels, 1955.

3. DeMaeyer, E. M., Chardome, M. and Peel, E.: Enquéte parasitologique et variations de la proteinemie en fonction de l'altitude chez les indigènes de la région de Katana-Lwiro. Annales de la Societé de Médecine Tropicale, 1955, June 30 vol. 35, No. 3, pp. 293-313.

4. DeMaeyer, E. M. and Vanderborght, H. L., Enquéte sur le Goitre endémique au Ruanda. Annales de la Societé Belge de Médecine Tropicale Tome XXXIII, No. 6, 1953, pp. 579-592.

5. Folia Scientifica Africae Centralis. Years 1955-1959.

6. Food and Agricultural Organization of the United Nations, Amelioration de la Production des Terres pastorales Rapport aux Gouvernements du Rwanda et du Burundi, No. 1575, Rome 1963.

7. Food and Agricultural Organization of the United Nations, Production Yearbook No. 16, 1962.

8. Gildea, R. Y. and Taylor A., Rwanda and Burundi, Focus, Vol. XIII, No. 6, February 1963.

9. Halberstam, D., Rwanda and Burundi become independent African States, The New York Times, July 1, 1962.

10. Hiernaux, J., Les Caractères physiques des populations du Ruanda et de l'Urundi, Institut Royal des Sciences Naturelles de Belgique. Mémoires 2eme serie fasc. 52. Brussels, 1954.

11. Hiernaux, J., Nutrition et Developpement physique, L'Anthropologie, Tome 56, No. 5-6, Paris 1952.

12. Leurquin, Ph., L'Etude du Revenu indigene en Milieu coutumier, Folia Scientifica Africae Centralis, Tome 2, Vol. 1, March 31, 1956.

13. Maquet, J. J., The premise of inequality in Rwanda, International African Institute, Oxford University Press, London 1961.

14. Roels, O. A., Debeir, O. and Trout, M., Déficience en Vitamine A au Ruanda-Urundi, Folia Scientifica Africae Centralis, 1957, Vol. 3, fasc. 2, p. 46.

15. Steinberg, S. H., The Statesman's Yearbook 1963-1964, St. Martin's Press, New York.

16. United Nations, Report on Ruanda-Urundi. Trusteeship Council 26th Session, April 14 to June 30, 1960. Supplement No. 3, Document T/1551.

TABLE NO. 1

Production

Rwanda & Burundi 1948–1962

Crop	Area (000 Ha.)			Yield (tons per Ha.)			Production (000 tons)		
	1948 -53	1960 -61	1961 -62	1948 -53	1960 -61	1961 -62	1948 -53	1960 -61	1961 -62
Wheat	17	5	?	0.7	0.6	?	12	3	3
Corn	117	126	137	0.9	1.1	0.7	108	149	98
Sorghum	129	162	164	1.1	1.2	0.9	144	197	148
Millet	49	31	?	0.5	0.7	?	27	23	?
Paddy	?	1	0.8	1.4	3.3	3.7	1	3	3
Potatoes	13	17	4	8.6	5.9	6.5	112	101	24
Sweet potatoes	177	141	145	6.7	7.7	6.7	1,193	1,090	971
Manioc	144	122	100	8.2	12.3	11.4	1,174	1,601	1,138
Dry beans	308	348	353	0.6	0.7	0.5	197	250	178
Dry peas	122	87	94	0.6	0.7	0.6	77	62	58
Palm kernels	?	?	?	?	?	?	0.3	0.2	?
Palm oil	?	?	7	?	?	?	1.3	1.0	1.0
Groundnuts	10	10	5	0.5	0.5	1	5	5	5
Cottonseed	7	10	12	0.35	0.3	0.2	3	6	6
Coffee	?	?	35	?	?	?	11.4	20	23
Tea	?	?	?	?	?	?	?	0.1	?
Tobacco	?	2	2	?	0.6	0.6	0.8	1.2	1.3
Cotton	7	10	12	0.19	0.3	0.2	1	3	3

Source: FAO Production Yearbook 1962, Vol. 16 (figures for 1959–60 have been omitted).

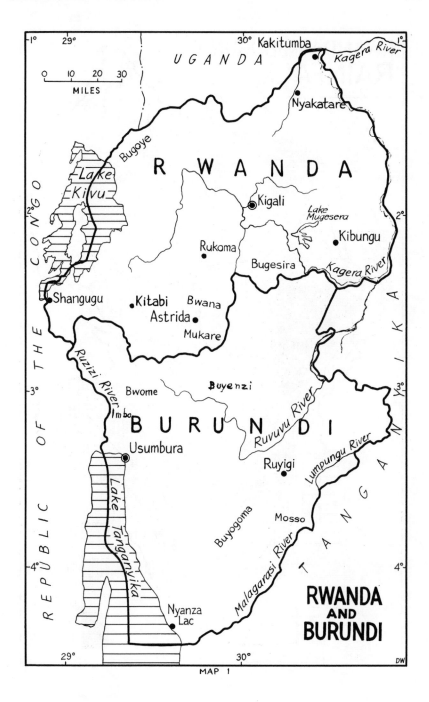

MAP 1

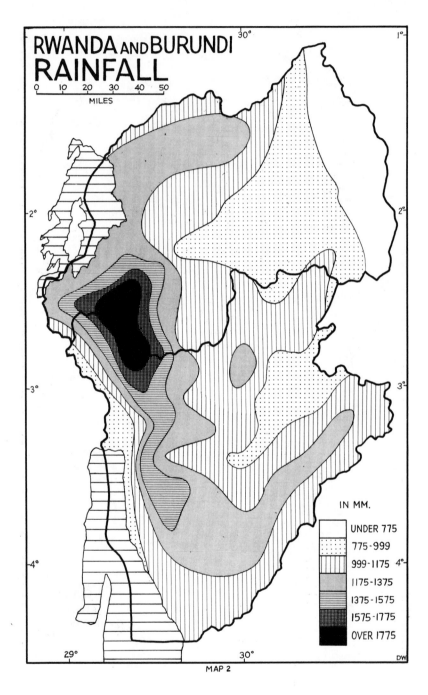

RWANDA AND BURUNDI
RAINFALL

0   10   20   30   40   50
MILES

IN MM.

UNDER 775
775 - 999
999 - 1175
1175 - 1375
1375 - 1575
1575 - 1775
OVER 1775

MAP 2

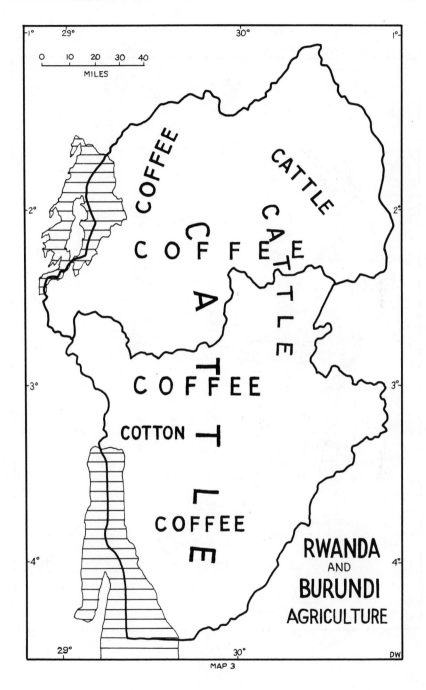

MAP 3

MAP 4

THE STATES OF THE FORMER FRENCH EQUATORIAL AFRICA

TABLE OF CONTENTS

THE FORMER FEDERATION

INDIVIDUAL TERRITORIES

GABON REPUBLIC

Table of Contents (Continued)

Table of Contents (Continued)

Table of Contents (Continued)

GABON, CONGO (BRAZZAVILLE),
CENTRAL AFRICAN REPUBLIC AND CHAD

Weights and Measures

1 Meter	= 39.370 inches	= 3.281 feet
1 Kilometer	= 1,000 meters	= 0.621 of a mile
1 Square Kilometer	= 0.386 square mile	
1 Hectare (Ha)	= 2.471 acres	
1 Kilogram	= 2.204 lbs.	
1 Quintal	= 100 kilograms	= 220.4 lbs.
1 Ton	= 1,000 kilograms	= 2204.6223 lbs.

GABON

1 CFA Franc	= $0.004
1 U. S. $	= 247 CFA Francs

CONGO (BRAZZAVILLE)

1 CFA Franc	= $0.004
1 U. S. $	= 247 CFA Francs

CENTRAL AFRICAN REPUBLIC

1 CFA Franc	= $0.004
1 U. S. $	= 247 CFA Francs

CHAD

1 CFA Franc	= $0.004
1 U. S. $	= 247 CFA Francs

THE STATES OF
THE FORMER FRENCH
EQUATORIAL AFRICA
THE FORMER FEDERATION

I

BACKGROUND

Four new states were created from the former territories of French Equatorial Africa. These new states are: the Republic of Gabon, formerly Gabon Territory; the Republic of the Congo (Brazzaville), formerly Middle Congo; the Central African Republic, formerly Ubangui Shari; and the Republic of Chad, formerly the Territory of Chad.

These four states have a common historical background, common geographical borders, and complementary interests. Those interests are represented by an Economic, Technical, and Customs Union, which, it is hoped, will preserve the benefits of their past association. In the Union, however, Gabon has retained certain special privileges in her relationship with France not enjoyed by the three other states.

At the same time there exists between these states the differences that can be expected from lands that stretch between 5° latitude south of the equator to 23° north, from the Atlantic Ocean to the Sudan, from the rain-drenched tropical forest to the dry, sandy wastes of the desert. Hence, major differences in resources, diets, and culture are striking, particularly when the two extremes of Gabon in the south and Chad in the north are compared.

To avoid repetition and to portray simultaneously the similarities and the differences, this report deals first with the common traits of the former Federation as a whole, then with the different characteristics of each territory successively.

A. GEOGRAPHY

The area of the former Federation is equivalent to one-third of the United States. Its longest distance from north to south is 3186 kilometers; its narrowest width is 224 kilometers, and its widest is 1491 km.

Three main geographic regions can be identified.

A northern region is represented by the Logone and Shari River basins, which drain into Lake Chad from the South and the Bahr El Gazel river basin, which drains into the lake from the North; this encompasses a vast peneplain centered around the depression of the Lake, where the climate varies from a two-season tropical type in the

173

South, (yearly precipitation 900 to 1200 mm.) to a desert climate in the north (yearly precipitation under 200 mm.).

A central region largely corresponds to the Ubangi-Congo rivers basin, to which most of the Congo and Central African Republics belong; it has two rainy and two dry seasons; precipitation is abundant in the South (up to 1800 mm. a year), less abundant in the North (800 mm.).

A coastal lowland region forms the major part of the Gabon and a small part of the Congo Republic; the climate is typically equatorial, warm and humid with two rainy and two dry seasons, one short and one long each.

In between these three regions two mountain ranges divide the water drainage as follows: the Bongo Massif is the culminating point of the range separating Chad from Ubangi-Congo; the Mayombe and Chaillu Mountains separate Ubangi-Congo from the Coastal Lowlands where local rivers, broken by rapids such as the Niari, the Nyanga, and the Ogoue, cut through the dense equatorial forest.

B. POPULATION [19][7]

Many African tribes have travelled through these regions, and many have formed settlements; among these tribes are the Negrillo, Bantu, Bateke, Poupangui, Bakalai, Fang (from the north and northeast), Mpongoue, Orounigou, Nkomi, Bakili, Bayaka, and Mba (from the southeast). In addition, Hamitic people (Arabs and Berbers) penetrated from the north, introducing the Moslem faith; first the Portuguese and then the French penetrated from the seacoast in the south, introducing some elements of Christianity and some of Western culture's good and bad characteristics.

No accurate population census has been made in the Federation. It was estimated at 5.5 million in 1963, of which 26,000 were Europeans; the average density was 12.95 per square kilometer with the highest rate in Chad and the lowest in Gabon. The rate of growth of this population is low for a tropical underdeveloped country. It does not exceed 1.5 percent a year in some groups but may reach 1.8 percent or even 2 percent, according to some sources, for the area as a whole. While the overall birth rate is relatively high, infant mortality is high, too. As a result, there is no population pressure except in towns and no immediate threat of it. On the contrary, in many areas, such as among the Likoula, Bakota, and Bateke the birth rate is as low as 7 to 15 per 1000. The average number of children per woman, computed after menopause, is 3.3. As many as 50 percent of the women never become pregnant. Respective ratios of females to males vary inversely in urban and rural areas where average figures are:

Urban -   713 women to 1000 men
Rural -   1148 women to 1000 men

As the young men are in the towns seeking work and the older men remain in the rural areas, the slow population increase is understandable. Further, polygamy, still practiced in the rural areas, results in a monopoly of the women by the older, wealthier men, while the men of reproductive age cannot afford the bride price. Various measures, such as the "bride price fund" and lower taxes on married men, were taken to remedy this situation. They were not very successful, however, since they ran counter to customs, v e s t e d interests, and local prejudices. Disease and malnutrition also keep the birth rate down.

The ethnic composition is extremely complex. Ninety percent of the people are Negro Africans and include the following main ethnic groups, proceding from south to north: the Pahouin- Fang nomadic group, which is the most dynamic in Gabon (this group will be discussed again in the section covering that country); the Bantu-speaking agricultural tribes of the south; the Oubanguian fishermen; the Shari-Ouaddaian; the Nilo-Chadian group, a sedentary Negro population of the Tibesti area.

The remaining 10 percent are white nomadic groups of Hamitic and Semitic origin, such as the Touareg, the Teda, and other moslemized, stock-raising Peuls, all living north of the fourteenth parallel.

C. AGRICULTURAL POLICIES [11][19]

All policies devised during the past fifty years to promote wealth and welfare in these forsaken lands have had to deal with the following basic problems: too few men, too little money, too many square kilometers to cover in order to harness the resources.

These difficult conditions have always produced a vicious circle: without capital no economic development was possible and without expansion no capital investment could be invited.

Especially after World War II, serious efforts were made by the French government to lift the area from the mire of these circumstances; from 1947 to 1962 three successive Plans were introduced to prime the pump of prosperity.* One of the first problems that had to be solved was that of land tenure; this aspect of African life offers a striking illustration of a cultural clash. Because no records of ownership were available in either written or oral tradition, the French Administration felt authorized to grant large acreages of "vacant and ownerless land" to commercial and industrial corporations under certain performance conditions; after the corporations failed to comply with the specifications under which these grants of land had been made, many of these acreages eventually returned to the trusteeship of the French government. The native leaders, however, claim that there is not an inch of African soil that is not traditionally assigned to a nation, a tribe, or a family.

In the confusion that existed in the native and traditional sector, it was difficult to discover what tribal and family rights were the foundation of real estate ownership. As explained in other chapters of this report, the West Africans practice agriculture in ill defined zones; within these zones people slash, burn, and move as they see fit. All

---

*These Plans have different durations in each territory or state.

efforts to induce Africans to Westernize their concept of land tenure
met with little success in rural areas. Therefore, two types of land
ownership became recognized: the customary right, responsible to
tribal laws; and the registration right, according to the Western
cadastral system. After May 18, 1955, a new law was passed that confirmed the customary rights to land ownership and streamlined the
administrative machinery needed to transform this customary right
into individual properties.

These measures were part of the so-called paysannat programs
started in 1952. They were intended to educate farmers to feel ownership for the land they cultivated and to settle their families more or
less permanently. To make a success of such an ambitious plan involved careful preparations. The soil's suitability for certain food
crops attractive to the farmers had to be studied. Commercial outlets
for surpluses had to be considered. Research and technical stations
had to be established to support this nascent agriculture. Last but not
least, community life had to be organized to allow education, public
health, and markets. Paysannats started in the Congo and soon were
established everywhere with different measures of success. Some involved only 200 families, others as many as 10,000 people. While most
groups devoted their work to food crops, others (as in the Voleu N'Tem
area of Gabon) cultivated cash crops such as cocoa. Under this system
thousands of new hectares were brought under cultivation, with the result that some improvement of diets, monetary resources, and well
being (in the Western sense of the word) were developed.

Under the new autonomous governments the future of the paysannats
remain in doubt, as the financial and scientific investment they involve
may be beyond the reach of the new governments.

Another government-sponsored group of organization played a big
role in framing agricultural policies. They were the Societés Indigenes
de Prevoyance (S. I. P.) organized in 1937. These foundations, with
chapters in almost every community, were intended to help the improvident African farmers and herdsmen to think about and protect their
future. The Rural Government Agent was ex officio Chapter Chairman
while another official, usually an economist, centralized all operations
at territorial levels; the Government General at Brazzaville exercised
final control. This effort met with considerable success despite sporadic local opposition. In 1946 there were 128 S. I. P. chapters with a total
membership of 2,218,526, more than half of whom were from Chad.
Adverse arguments centered around the compulsory nature of the
financial contribution of five to fifteen C. F. A. francs a year and around
the arbitrary utilization of these funds by the local administrator. In
spite of these jibes and criticisms the S. I. P. chapters were not sup-
pressed when the territories became independent states, a fact which
seems to underscore their usefulness in helping farmers work toward
a better future.

II

FOOD RESOURCES [8][9][13][19]

The total land surface of former French Equatorial Africa was computed in 1950 at 251 million hectares. The amount of arable land was evaluated at 30 million hectares, prairies and pastures of a permanent nature at 52 million hectares, forests at 135,420,000 hectares, and built-up areas or otherwise unusable lands at 33,580,000 hectares. These lands and the waters in their midst provided food resources from:

1. Herds and animal husbandry.
2. Subsistence farming, hunting, and gathering.
3. Cash-crop farming.
4. Fishing.

1. Herds and animal husbandry

As Kimble puts it, the African tropics are tough on the pastoralists. A number of factors combine to make a pastoral way of life difficult: animal diseases; lack of veterinarians; scarcity of pastures; poor quality of grasses; spoilage of dairy products under tropical conditions; vagaries of the rains; lack of technical knowledge resulting in overgrazing and ecologic disruption. All these and more are stacked against the development of a healthy cattle industry.

A number of measures have been taken by the various responsible governments to offset these handicaps; but all encountered the resistance and inertia of the conservative herdsmen. An attempt was made to reduce the size of the herds and to improve their quality; cattle, however, are valued as a symbol of wealth rather than as a source of food, so a reduction in the number of animals meant a loss of prestige. This reform was not popular. An attempt was made to introduce grazing control. This reform, however, interfered with centuries of nomadic habits and received a mixed welcome. The attempt to encourage the raising of food crops was relatively more acceptable, and this reform succeeded in tying some groups to the land for a time every year.

Only Chad, of all four countries, derives some diet benefit from its cattle population.

2. Subsistence-crop farming, hunting, and gathering [13][12]

Farming for subsistence crops on a tribal or family basis is not conducive to development and abundance; it is a day-by-day and hand-to-mouth kind of living. Its future, under the present conditions in Africa, remains in doubt and will be discussed later. It must be recognized, however, that in the environment of Africa subsistence farming has its merits; it requires very little labor and is a system well suited to people whose strength and vitality is sapped by worm infestation and diseases; the slash-and-burn method provides the farmer with fertilizers that are otherwise hard to obtain, especially because the tsetse fly prevents them from obtaining it from animal manure. Weeds, which the African farmers seldom bother to remove, provide a protection against soil erosion in a country of torrential rains. Moreover, in certain places the farmers recognize that it is a good practice to plant seedlings and new trees before moving on from a patch of land that they have worked for three or four years. This practice allows the forest to take over and protect the soil.

The greatest merit of this form of agriculture is that it respects the natural life cycle of the land and does not mortgage the future.

The nearby forest and its resources—in roots, leaves, animals, and insects—has contributed its share to the casualness of the African toward his subsistence crops. When the crop is poor or when the small surplus stored in the soil or in the granaries is down to nothing, the farmer turns to hunting or picking and gathering to sustain himself until the next crop matures. The African spends much time hunting with bow and arrow. He usually carries two types of arrows, one with a piercing end for big game and another with a blunt end for small birds. Occasionally a big animal, such as an elephant, is killed. This is an invitation for whole villages to swarm over its carcass and literally swim in blood and meat.

What is produced in the Federation on these subsistence farms is mainly, as already stated, manioc and plantain with cocoyams, rice, and corn as runners-up. One can understand the preference. Manioc grows well in forest clearings if there are conditions of abundant rainfall, mild temperatures and sunshine; it is a hardy plant that resists long periods of drought and does fairly well on the poor leached soils of the tropics. The addition of potash fertilizer, if it were economically feasible, would give remarkable results, as has been proven by experimentation. Manioc needs only one or two weedings a season and can even be stored in the ground. Its two drawbacks are that it needs preparation before being eaten because it contains a chemical that by hydrolysis is changed into hydrocyanic acid and that its proteins are of poor quality. In 1961, 3,177,000 tons were probably harvested throughout the former Federation from a reported cultivated area of approximately 366,300 hectares (see Table No. 1).

Plantain's requirements are similar to those of manioc. Yields for both manioc and plantain vary enormously. Manioc, cultivated on poor, overfarmed land, yields no more than two to three tons per hectare, as opposed to yields of 75 tons on experimental farms (Achimota College Farm, Ghana). Yields for plantain may average up to 20 tons per hectare under very favorable conditions; but its energy value is only a fraction of that of cereals and is below that of manioc and yams. The labor requirements per ton, however, of those two major crops are far less than those of any other tropical crop. The following table (after G. Geortay) gives the comparison:

Crop	Hours of Labor Per Ton
Manioc	30 to 31
Plantain	18 to 20
Rice	153 to 162
Indian Corn (following manioc)	103 to 107
Indian Corn (as initial crop)	78 to 122

Putting it on a cost basis, manioc and plantain, in spite of their low energy value, cost less per 1000 calories than yams, rice, millet, sorghum, cocoyam (taro), Indian corn, or sweet potatoes. Unfortunately, although they offer a high caloric yield, they are poor sources of protein and other nutrients. Cocoyams, of which there are two varieties (the old kind, Colocasia esculentum, and the new kind, Xanthosoma sagittifolium), thrive in very moist, damp soil and can be grown under cocoa trees. The yield seems to be less than four tons per hectare.

Rice requires water, sunshine, and an alkaline soil. The area occupied by rice in 1960 was 25,000 hectares. This acreage produced some 25,000 tons or 1 metric ton per hectare, a yield equivalent to that obtained in the former Belgian Congo.

In the same year 24,000 tons of corn were produced on 84,000 hectares.

3. Cash-crop farming [8][9]

The cash-crop sector was inaugurated in Equatorial Africa by the collection of noncultivated items such as timber, ivory, seeds, and so on. Following the Second World War the Federation government encouraged the development of cultivated cash crops such as coffee, groundnuts, cocoa, cotton, and rubber. From a start of 4400 tons of coffee in 1952, an output of 9200 tons was reached in 1962 (see Table No. 1). During the same period cocoa grew from 2300 to 3300 tons. It was hoped that this added income would allow the purchase of better and healthier diets, but it was soon found that the African's newly developed interest in money resulted in a craving for small luxuries such as tobacco, trinkets, clothes, bicycles, and watches, rather than for food. It had to be pointed out that some food crops, such as rice, could also bring cash returns if sold on the local markets; some interest developed among cash croppers in growing selected food crops simultaneously with cash crops. But rice has not displaced manioc as a staple of diet, and occasionally its cultivation has to be curtailed to avoid gluts in areas where transportation is lacking.

4. Markets [19][20]

The transition from a subsistence agriculture to a market agriculture is slow and difficult everywhere; but it is especially so in the former Federation of French Equatorial Africa. The isolation—of the communities or of family groups—hampers the exchange of goods and services. The land tenure system discourages individual initiative, because the labor of a man and his family will little improve their standard of living: by tribal tradition, the largest families are allotted the best land. If a man has a small family, any improvement he makes on his allotment will result in his losing it to a larger family, and if he has a large family, he will receive one of the best lots anyway. Food production is limited also by the nature of the land. Few crops, some-times only one, succeed in poor soil, leading to a monotonous diet. When a surplus is produced, the proceeds are used for the purchase of a specific tool, or for meeting a specific need, or for gratifying a specific fancy. The additional resources always have a definite target; they will never be invested in a productive way. The introduction of a totally different philosophy, in which needs can be unlimited and rep-resent a desirable target to be reached by investment, prudence, and expansion, implies a profound shakeup of the African outlook on life.

Yet more and more subsistence farmers bring their surplus to town for sale. In licensed market places prices are government con-trolled. Goods offered for sale in the markets include manioc leaves, which are very popular in rural areas;* smoked fish; the local bread, chickwangue, made of fermented manioc paste; and such items as fufu, gari, Indian corn, peanuts, sweet potatoes, cocoyams, yams, palm oil, and regional rice.

5. Fishing

There are over 150 species of edible sea fish available in the waters of Gabon and the Congo, but the native population has shown little ambition for fishing. A French and Norwegian company has at times operated a whaling fleet off the shores of Gabon, but there is no indication that their catch has played a significant and persistent role in the diet of the population. One thousand tons of fresh fish are re-ported shipped by rail (on the Congo-Ocean)**to Brazzaville markets every year. Although some processing facilities for smoking and drying the catch are found at Pointe Noire, further refrigeration facilities are needed to enlarge the scope of fishing activities. The only significant supply of fish protein comes from lakes and rivers. They provide over 100,000 tons a year of fish, 75,000 of which come from Lake Chad. The tribes that live near the major rivers of the Federation—such as Logone, Shari, Ubangi, Congo, Ogoue—are expert fishermen and supply markets in the vicinity of their villages.

There are a few tilapia-breeding stations that developed from the activities of the Brazzaville (Djoumounia) Station. They supplied breed-ers for the many family ponds (25,000 in 1958)*** dispersed throughout the Federation.

---

*This might explain why nutritional deficiencies that would otherwise be ex-pected do not occur.
**Name of the railroad linking Brazzaville and Pointe Noire on the Atlantic Ocean.
***1962 information indicates the existence of 25,000 such ponds in the C. A. R. alone.

6. Transportation [19]

Transportation problems have for centuries hampered the development of the area. Contrary to the expectations of earlier geogra-
phers, there is no wide-spread network of navigable rivers in the
Federation. Only one long stretch of navigable waterway is available
between Bangui,* capital of the Central African Republic, and Brazzaville. It therefore became imperative to supplement the navigation of
the lower Congo River, which was impassable because of rapids, by a
railroad. The railroad was started in 1922 and completed in 1934. The
heart of Africa was then linked to the sea. Other rivers are open only
between rapids, and impenetrable forests limit the possibility of expanding the highway systems. The tsetse fly has exacted a tremendous
tribute from animals and men engaged in portage, the primitive way for
man and goods to be transported inside Equatorial Africa.

The improvement of the transportation network is a concern of
all four states because of resulting complementary benefits. Chad, for
example, might supply the other three states with meat and rice, while
they in turn might offer cereals, tubers, fruit, and vegetables in exchange. The cost of research and experimentation could be met by exports of timber and mineral from the three southern states.

All-season roads link Chad to Bangui and bring cities of the
Gabon coast in contact with the railway-loading depots of the Congo-
Ocean Railroad. Bangui is also linked to Douala in the Cameroun. This
network of roads covers approximately 60,000 km., twice its 1946
length. Planning, construction, and maintenance are still under a
French-led federal authority, but maintenance of certain local roads
is being turned over to local governments.

Inland waterways—the Ogoue, Shari, Logone, Congo, and Ubangi
Rivers—provide more than 5000 miles of navigable channels. Large
river dredges are in operation during the dry seasons of the year.

Air transportation has developed rapidly in all territories of the
Federation. It is adequate and is used extensively even for the transportation of fresh and frozen foods to and from Chad. It is conceivable
that it will in the future develop sufficiently to solve the transportation
problem.

Many factors—geographic, psychological, economic, and cultural—have contributed so far to keep Central Africa in a state of con-
cealed, if not obvious, malnutrition.

---

*During the dry season the terminal point is 100 km. south of Bangui, and a nar-
row gauge railroad is used.

III

DIET TYPES

A. GENERAL REMARKS [12][13][1][2][3][4][13a]

Three main food patterns can be recognized in Equatorial Africa's four territories: the diets of the rural people; the diets of the detribalized urban populations; the diets of the pastoralists.

To avoid repetition, we will discuss here the foods and diets common to the four territories, adding special remarks about each state when applicable. Before going into more nutritional detail, it may be useful to describe the standard of living of the people of Equatorial Africa.

Average per capita incomes are low. Kimble gives a figure of U. S. $125 annually for the whole of the Federation; yet the per capita income listed for each state is under $100. This discrepancy is due to the inclusion in the computation of the special budget of the former Government General. The income from exports of nonagricultural as well as of agricultural products benefits only a few but inflates the individual figures. In fact, the actual purchasing power of the Equatorial African through cash or barter is somewhere around $40 a year.*

Undernourishment and hunger are accepted as inevitable by the population. When periods of plenty occur, no one would dream of storing food for lean months. The people, when given a choice between a moderate but continuous supply of food and alternate periods of plenty and hunger, have always shown their preference for the latter system. This pattern has also been characteristic of the behavior of the wage earners. As a rule, during the week following pay day the diet is unbalanced but filling, while toward the second half of the month it is neither balanced nor filling.

The period before harvest—April, May, June, and sometimes July— is a difficult period in most of tropical Africa. Although the stricture is more acute in the savannah areas, it can be observed in the forest zones as well. As a continued result of improvidence, failure of the rain, poor harvest, and destruction of grain or tubers to make fermented beverages, this preharvest hunger is a common dietary characteristic of tropical African populations. It is known also as the hungry season, or as the soudure (meaning welding) in the French-speaking areas.

During these periods daily caloric consumption may drop to 1400 or even to 850 calories in certain villages. Hungry-season foods include forest products, leaves and berries, roots (which may contain toxic elements), any animal that can be killed, and insects and termites. According to Pales, 100 grams of termites produce 347 calories and include: water, 44.52 percent; fat, 28.55 percent; total nitrogen, 3.70

*1962 information lowers this income to $18 in the C. A. R.

percent; and total proteins, 23.22 percent. No vitamin A has been found in the fat. The governments have repeatedly tried to force the people to store harvested food for the lean months, but these measures are always unpopular. When African politicians became influential in the 50's, most administrations had to cancel the food contributions that the people had been forced to make to the reserve funds. In cereal areas efforts are made to induce subsistence farmers to plant some manioc as a ground-stored, built-in reserve. In other areas low-grade cereals (fonio) are eaten as a last resort.

B. THE DIETS OF THE RURAL PEOPLE

From the Nile to the Zambezi and from one side of Africa to the other, sticky, highly seasoned porridge is the staple food that African stomachs crave for. Unfortunately, craving does not always mean fulfillment. Over most of the area the food supply is irregular and particularly low in the months preceding harvest. At best, diets are unbalanced. Even when food is available, chronic malnutrition may result from a lifelong impairment of tissues (especially in the liver) that prevents proper absorption and storage of valuable nutrients. In most territories of Equatorial Africa, with the exception of Chad and the adjoining portions of the Central African Republic, the basic foods are manioc and plantain.

Out of manioc a meal called gari is made, which has the same caloric value as wheat flour but, unfortunately, a much lower protein content. It can withstand a two-to-three-month storage period before deteriorating. Gari is prepared in the following way. The roots, after being cleaned and peeled, are pressed under stones or logs and allowed to drain for three or four days; this rids them of the hydrocyanic acid potential. Then the roots are passed through a sieve, and dried.

Manioc roots are reputedly low in thiamine and riboflavin and lose most of their vitamin C in processing, especially if the soluble vitamins are allowed to dissolve in soaking water (see Table No. 2). Manioc can also be made into a starch; the roots are soaked in water for four days, then beaten into a pulp, and finally drained under pressure. This can be the base of a porridge eaten with a spicy sauce, made with palm oil, green manioc leaves resembling spinach, peppers, and chili. Occasionally meat or fish are added, especially in the Central Republic. The same treatment applies to plantain, which may be sliced, dried, and pounded into a meal. All these roots, as well as fruits, can be cut into small slices and fried in palm oil to make fritters. the fermented manioc paste may be wrapped in plantain or other leaves then steamed and dipped in sauce. This preparation is sometimes called "bread" in the southern and western parts of the Federation. The native name is chickwangue.

Fufu is another technique for preparing the same roots.* Fufu uses boiled roots, pounded or grated into a sort of dough. The dough is molded into balls or cut in strips and fried in palm oil or baked. Taros (cocoyams) are boiled after peeling, and seasoned with salt and chilis pounded together. Rice is often made into a meal to which water is added to form a paste that ferments and rises. Sometimes rice is boiled or steamed as in Asia.

Large amounts of cereal are used for making beer. This diversion of grain for an alcoholic beverage may contribute to malnutrition and certainly contributes to alcoholism. Certain nutritionists, however, feel that an actual benefit can be derived from the brewing process because it adds vitamins C and B and some bacterial proteins to the original cereal. Especially in the north of the Federation, manufacture of millet beer is an important industry. The brew is stored in casks and barrels of 300-litre capacity, in earthenware jars, or in hollowed tree trunks. The recipe is as follows: Moist grains of millet after germination are placed in huge kettles and boiled. During the boiling period the mixture is stirred with a wooden stick. When ebulition is completed, the liquid is filtrated and placed into large vats for fermentation. After a few days fermentation increases and the alcoholic content rises. Palm wine is made every day in areas where the palm trees grow (Raphia sudanica). Fermentation of the sap occurs immediately and after a few days the alcoholic content becomes high. Although no recent precise studies are available for the former French Equatorial Africa, it is believed that such food as described in this section, represent 90 percent of the daily diet.**

C. THE DIETS OF THE DETRIBALIZED URBAN POPULATION

The problem of the detribalized urban population is not limited to the former French Equatorial Africa. It affects the whole of Africa south of the Sahara and is described in greater detail in the chapter on the former Belgian Congo. The problem arose as laborers fled to the cities from the dullness and meager resources of the rural areas. Recruitment of labor by administrative offices also added to the problem. The men flocked to the towns while the women and older folks stayed in the villages. Three major factors influence the diets of these people and are responsible for their malnutrition: different foods, cost of the new foods, and irregularities in food availability.

The changing diet has two aspects. The laborer from the savannah moving to a town in the forest zone has to switch from a cereal diet to a manioc and plantain diet. Conversely, the man from the south moving to a northern city is confronted with a cereal diet. Reluctantly at first

---

*Western man also has various recipes to change wheat flour into bread.
**Fats are provided by palm oil in the south and by groundnut oil in the north. Bascoulergue insists on the important role of the groundnut in the diet of school children and finds it a valuable protective food, especially in the rural areas, where it contributes to a large extent toward balancing the diet.

the new city-dweller will turn to imported foods such as canned sardines and potatoes that are available in the stores; he soon finds his salary inadequate to support this new diet, and he will eat only sparingly. Moreover, as a villager he never had to buy food, and when transplanted to a town, he is reluctant to take the cost of his daily diet out of his salary. His morale is also affected by his longing to get news from home: Do the folks at home need money? Are they going into debt? Are they extravagant with hospitality to relatives?* All these problems add up to a moral misery that may induce the transplanted villager to turn to alcohol. This he will find plentiful and cheap in the various liquor stores of the town, and gradually most of his salary will be diverted from nutrients to beer or liquor.**

Even the food supplies in the stores may be subject to the ability and willingness of the surrounding farming population to supply the towns with native foods. When the laborer wisely wants to stick to the food he is accustomed to and save his money for the return to his village, he may find that the supplies of his food are not as abundant as he had hoped for nor as regularly available on the city's markets as he would wish. For all these reasons, collectively or acting in succession, a serious degree of malnutrition occurs in most of the towns and will increase as long as the trend to the city does; year after year, towns fill with a famished population that is missed in the rural areas where it could conceivably have produced the food it needs.

D. THE DIETS OF THE PASTORALISTS

The diet of pastoralists, most if not all of whom live in Chad, is usually satisfactory and represents at times an island of adequate nutrition in a sea of malnutrition. Milk and cheese are available, and although pastoralists do not usually slaughter cattle for food, animals that die a natural death are eaten. Thus, the diet of the herdsmen contain good quality proteins as well as cereals. Nonetheless, adverse factors, including disease and drought, remain a constant threat to the herds, while cereals for the men and roots for the women may be in short supply.

E. SPECIAL DIETS [5][7]

The worst off, as everywhere in Africa, are the women and children, victims of taboos and male priorities. This situation is not necessarily an indication of contempt toward women. As a provider of food and as a cook, the woman is a valued symbol of life itself, and in some African

---

*Studies made in the C.A.R. indicate that gifts represent 13.1 percent of the total budget of the African, second only to clothing (26.2 percent).
**If he brings his family with him, his finances melt more rapidly. As resources dwindle, so does the diet; greens, palm or groundnut oil, dried fish and bananas are gradually omitted and the fare reduced to manioc.

languages her name means grain. The child she bears is compared to a fish swimming in water; when she is pregnant, her husband tries to find fish for her. Her spiritual association with food, however, also explains the male indifference about feeding her; since she is so much identified with food, it is believed that she can take care of herself, and there is no need to worry. In the rural areas, even among some of the few who can be rated as Westernized évolués, women and children eat the crumbs from the table, or rather from the family calabash, after the father and all other males of productive age have satisfied their appetites. This leaves the children very badly off. Nonetheless, even under such conditions, children are better off in rural areas than in urban centers wehre there are not even food scraps to glean from the barren environment of city streets. A number of school-lunch programs have been developed under government auspices with the help of international agencies but never on a scale that would make a significant difference. UNICEF started in 1955 to distribute powdered milk to school children in the Middle Congo and in Gabon but found it difficult to persuade the mothers to prepare it properly and to persuade the children to drink it.

Women survive during pregnancy in spite of a wide range of taboos. They cannot eat an animal that is shy lest that trait be transferred to the child. Nor can they, for the same reason, eat anything that is considered repulsive. Caterpillars, snails and termites, otherwise a valuable source of animal protein, are forbidden; eating such foods might result in a difficult childbirth. Eggs are said to cause sterility. Milk and dairy products are rightly reputed to make the baby fat and, hence, to increase the chances of a difficult labor. Other groups believe that drinking milk may cause abortion. Fish is the only protein source permitted, but it is not always available. All these taboos vary with the various ethnic and cultural origins.

IV

ADEQUACY OF FOOD RESOURCES

IN NORMAL TIMES [13][19]

With the exception of a few privileged groups and of the tribal groups that live by hunting and fishing, few Africans in the former Federation have a diet adequate in both energy-producing and protective elements; but, given manpower and capital, this situation could be improved. What is most needed is a transportation system so that the meat from the north can be exchanged for the fruits, vegetables, and roots of the south. Today neither manpower nor capital are available.

Under prevailing conditions the types of food grown are restricted by geographic factors. Even if more varieties could be produced, the general poverty would prevent their wide purchase. In addition to these geographic and economic problems, there are psychological and cultural factors that are against storing food for hungry days.

Under French rule between 1947 and 1962 successive plans to improve the situation were initiated. They cost the French taxpayers over $30 million, the American taxpayers $2 million, and the territories themselves about $12 million. These programs have brought some economic improvement in the rural areas, but the sums involved are obviously too small to cover needs and too large compared to the actual benefits they brought about. It can be hoped that in the future investment of French and other private capital will help develop islands of growth where, as an indirect result of prosperity, nutritional equilibrium may be reached. Around such privileged islands, however, it can be expected that the food resources will remain inadequate for a long time to come. Slash-and-burn methods are still well suited to many African situations; disasters have followed and will continue to follow the quick adoption of agricultural methods that take into account none of the experience acquired by centuries of living in the African habitat.

Improvement of nutrition is a long-term problem: forests must be converted into fields; people must be persuaded to settle down and cultivate these fields; fertilizers must be available and people taught how to use them; and finally, improved technology must be introduced and mastered.

IN TIMES OF STRESS

In an area where survival is an everyday problem, any added stress may be lethal. Modern wars are not easily conceivable in Africa where there are but a few cities to be destroyed, and few communications lines and industrial centers. Tribal warfare has existed for centuries. The peace that was enforced by British, French, or Belgian authorities was but an interlude; tribal warfare could resume at any time as a normal way of life in former French Equatorial Africa. This has happened in the former Belgian Congo and could happen elsewhere. Pockets of starvation would be created; destruction of man- and woman-power would result in long interruption of food production. Any modern army operating in the area would have to supply its own food because no surplus could be expected. What would be left of the population would be in danger of returning to cannibalism.

V

NUTRITIONAL DISEASES [3][2]

Various deficiency diseases occur in the four states of the Economic, Technical, and Customs Union. Few Africans fail to show some sign

of-malnutrition at some time. Beriberi is often seen in Gabon and Brazzaville hospitals, especially in the spring and before the harvests; lip
sores, angular stomatitis, and cheilosis expressing ariboflavinosis are
common. Rickets and slow growth are found in children, especially in
the towns. Bascoulergue and others have examined 1313 children in
16 rural areas (136 aged 0-1 year, 448 aged 2-5, and 729 aged 6-12).
No case of kwashiorkor was found although the general physical condition of these children was poor and their nutritional status below par.
Serum protein was normal, but serum albumin was low and gamma
globulin high. The authors state, however, that this is general among
the peoples in Central Africa, whatever their diet, and usually appears
in infants between the ages of one and two. Some observers believe that
this condition is due to genetic factors; others believe it is due to diet
or infections.

Certain differences are found in the urban areas; 2332 children from
the same age groups were studied in Brazzaville, and nine cases of
kwashiorkor were identified. In view of the known facts of urban diets,
this is understandable.

Anemia is common and occurs in connection with a high rate of
ancylostome infestation. This anemia is often associated with depigmentation of the hair but is seldom accompanied by low protein levels
in the serum. Treatment of hookworm infections other than through diet
and transfusions is not recommended before general health has been
restored, as antihelmintic drugs, especially when based on tetrachlorides, are not tolerated well by deficient livers; mixed cases, where
symptoms are traceable to multiple vitamin and mineral (Fe) deficiencies, do occur frequently. Tropical ulcers, expressing a wide
spectrum of protein and other deficiencies, are very common, especially among women and children. (See section on the Central African Republic for more data from samples studied in that state.)

In addition to known deficiency diseases, there are mysterious ailments allegedly caused by unidentified poisons such as those found in
certain roots and tubers or in the flesh of certain animals, such as
the forest rat.

INDIVIDUAL TERRITORIES

GABON

I

BACKGROUND

A. GEOGRAPHY [14][18]

The westernmost state of the Economic, Technical and Customs Union of Equatorial Africa is the smallest (267,000 sq. km.), the most sparsely populated (421,000 inhabitants), and potentially the richest of all. Allowing for the small Spanish Guinea Enclave in the northweat, it lies between 3°58' South and 2° North. It extends approximately 576 kilometers inland from the Atlantic Coast.

The lowlands consist of a large band of coastal sedimentary terrain cut by the estuaries of the short Cocobeach and Gabon Rivers in the north; the large (80 km. wide) Ogoue Delta in the center; and the small Nyanga River in the south. All the coast is forested with little or no agriculture. Farther inland a mountain range, the Mayombe, rises to 800 meters in the south; next there is a depression covered with a mixture of dense forest and tall-grassed savannah. The Chaillu Mountains in the south (500 to 600 meters high with one peak rising to 1800 meters) and the Cristal Mountains in the north form the second and third group of mountain ranges that reach from the Atlantic Coast to the hinterland. Still farther east, beyond the Cristal Range, there is one of the richest and most fertile plateaus of the country, the Voleu N'tem. This area produces profitable cocoa and coffee crops. (It also produces the foremost politicians.) The climate is constantly hot and humid. Both heat and humidity increase in the northwest, where the rainfall reaches 4000 mm. a year at Cocobeach and 2500 mm. at Port Gentil, in contrast to an average of 1500 to 1600 mm. a year in the northeast and 1400 to 1500 mm. along the southern part of the coast. Monthly temperatures average 25° to 30°C in the west and 23° to 28°C in the northeastern part of the country.

These physical features of the environment have led to an economy based on the exploitation of forest resources more than on the development of food crops. Gabon is the world's largest exporter of okumé,* a softwood tree used for plywood; its cash economy has been for half a century almost completely dependent on this resource. Considerable malnutrition prevails in the lumber camps, where most of the population is concentrated. Agricultural regions are few: the Tchibanga Region,

---

*Estimated at 668,000 tons in 1962.

189

where rice is cultivated; the Voleu N'Tem Plateau; the Ogoue-Ivindo Valley, where cocoa and coffee are grown; and the Lower Ogoue area, where palm-oil products are extracted. In all other regions agriculture is represented by small patches of subsistence crops.

B. POPULATION [19][14][17]

The population is small and sparsely settled. It is estimated at a little over 421,000 people and comprises more than 40 different ethnic groups that enjoy different degrees of influence and prosperity. The overall density does not exceed 1.6 inhabitants per square kilometer. Concentrations of population occurs in towns such as Libreville (22,000), Port Gentil (16,000), Lambaréné (16,000) home of Dr. Albert Schweitzer, and in the mining and forest centers. As elsewhere, the population tends to leave the rural areas for the cities. The rate of growth is estimated at between 1 and 2 percent a year.

The dominant ethnic and cultural group is the Fang Nation, of which 127,000 live in Gabon. Traditionally, they are warriors and traders rather than farmers. However, it has been possible to get them interested in cash crops, and some of them are now engaged in cocoa farming in the Voleu N'Tem and Ogoue-Ivindo regions; the rest are scattered in the forest areas. The Fang live in cases (houses) of rectangular form, sometimes with a veranda and a two-sloped roof, all built of wood.

Other groups include the Eshira, Omiene, Bakota, and Babingo. Some, like the last, are akin to the Pygmies of the deep forest. They live from hunting and gathering. Their name means "hunter." They are considered untouchable by the more évolué population. They fish with their hands in waterholes with considerable skill; women and children go into the forest and return loaded with berries, leaves, roots, worms, insects, small wild animals, or wild honey. They have a way of digging deep into the ground to find wild yams, using a special stick several feet long. Sometimes they kill elephants by trapping them and releasing a heavy wooden block attached to tree branches above the trap; the animal is stunned long enough to be killed with a spear, after which the whole tribe feasts on the blood and flesh.

The Fang have produced the men who are leading the new country now. They are sometimes also called the "Big Negroes" in opposition to the small Babingoes. Some of them have been Europeanized and converted to Christianity. It is for them that the word évolué (evolved) has been coined. In addition, there are 3700 Europeans, two-thirds of whom are engaged in nonagricultural pursuits.

C. AGRICULTURAL POLICIES [8][9]

The agricultural policies of the new government are first concerned with the most essential aspect of Gabon's economy, namely forestry.

The problem is to delimit a state forest domain and find personnel to staff and exploit it. The past proved that private enterprise in the forest leads to inefficiency and malnutrition. To make the forest pay, mechanization and high technical skills are needed. These entail such enormous capital investments that geophysical, social, and economic conditions in Gabon leave no choice but state ownership of the forests. To sustain the output of okumé trees and to keep some private enterprise working side by side with the state, the forest has been divided into two zones: a zone of two million hectares, easily accessible, to be reserved for Gabon nationals; and a second zone in the hinterland region requiring heavy investment for exploitation, which is open to only to foreign enterprise.

The Gabonese have always shown a rather astonishing indifference to food crops. Growing food is the occupation of women, not of men. Before independence, the French tried a number of devices to get the population interested in growing more food. One method was to re-group villages along lines of communication; the farmers were told to grow more manioc and more vegetables, such as beans, potatoes, peppers, and onions. This they did in a token fashion and as long as there was supervision.

The food situation did not become critical, however, until the middle of World War II, when the trend to the towns began in earnest. In spite of the new markets afforded by the growing towns, and available roads, the production of food crops lagged dramatically behind the cash crops like coffee and cocoa. Even in the rice-growing area of Tchibanga, the people eat manioc and sell their rice. The paysannat was intended to supply an answer to this problem, and to a large extend it did. The paysannats were established first in the regions of Voleu N'Tem, Ogoue-Ivindo, and N'Gounie-Nyanga. The government attracted people to these settlements by promising profits from cash crops. Food crops were to come later, after the farming families were tied to the land by their profits. Where no cash crops existed to show the way, results were slow in materializing; and the problem of feeding the towns by surrounding them with farms has not yet been solved satisfactorily.

II

FOOD RESOURCES[8][9][12]

A. GENERAL

In a country dominated by forests, with few farmers and poor land, the food resources are bound to be meager; food is produced by women working near their huts, using the slash-and-burn method. In Gabon the limited amount of really good agricultural soil, the dominant in-

terest in the cash crop okumé, and the lack of animal husbandry have
resulted in a disequilibrium of food resources. Either the food is imported, and thus is available only to those who have money, or it is
scarce in quantity and monotonous in nature. Gabon is essentially a
manioc and plantain country. Cocoyams are planted in patches, but the
total crop is less than 2 percent of the manioc and plantain crop. Indian
corn and rice are occasionally added to the fare. Yams and sweet potatoes are also found, but in smaller quantities than cocoyams. These
crops, except for rice, require less work per calory supplied than most
other foods do. The tsetse fly in the bush has prevented the establishment of meat resources on any significant scale. Deep-sea fishing is
practiced along the coast; river, and lake, fishing are practiced in the
hinterland.

B. MEANS OF PRODUCTION [20]

    1. Agricultural labor force
        There is no agricultural labor force in the strict sense of the
word. No more than 500 Africans and 15 Europeans were wage earners
in agricultural enterprises in 1956; yet, every woman and child in the
country is an agriculturist after a fashion, and some families in the
paysannats are rising to the level of professional farmers.

    2. Farms [19]
        There are three types of farms in Gabon: subsistence farms,
paysannat farms, and experimental farms.
        The subsistence farm of the mid-African area has often been
described. It is not really a farm in the Western sense, in which the
tools for bringing maximal production of a well-defined piece of land
are stored, maintained, and used according to a well established rou-
tine. The subsistence farm of Gabon is the temporary rallying point
of a family that gets its subsistence from the ground around its hut as
long as the yields are sufficient. The bush is burned, usually in two
sessions, the branches first, then the stumps. Ashes are used as fertilizer, holes are dug in the ground with a stick, and the seed is planted
by hand. This is done during the two periods when the rains relent—
July and August (oyone) and January and February (esep). As in Ghana
and in neighboring countries, the land is not cleared and looks unkempt.
It is often difficult to say where the farm begins and the bush ends. In
many cases farming the land is not the sole occupation of the family.
The men may hire themselves to nearby foreign-run enterprises, if
there are any, or do a little trading of forest products on the side,
leaving the job of supplying the family with manioc and plantain to the
women. Harvest time is stretched over several months. After one harvest of plantain and two of manioc, the land is usually returned to the
bush. Peanuts are sometimes planted between crops in patches that
neighbors have vacated. Occasionally, small gardens of vegetables are

planted around the hut and fertilized with domestic garbage of all kinds. The most common vegetables are eggplants, beans, and a kind of pea called voandzou.

The paysannat farm developed from the concept that in order to enlist the people's cooperation, it was essential to create rural living conditions that would successfully compete with urban conditions. The development of paysannats required considerable preparation and the lure of cash crops to persuade the indolent Gabonese to grow the food they needed. Since, by tradition, males were sure to get whatever food was available, there was little incentive for the tribal leaders to encourage more production.

The three groups of paysannat farms of Gabon are located at Voleu N'Tem, Ogoue-Ivindo, and N'Gounie-Nyanga. They were started in 1950, each with a different purpose. While the first is geared to the production of cocoa and other cash crops and has to be provided with most of its food, the two latter were primarily intended to produce better food crops. Even in the latter, however, it became necessary to introduce some cash crops and to create roads, health centers, and eventually schools to tie the farmer down to the location and his work. Depending upon the soil, these farms cover approximately one and a half hectares per adult worker, plus a small plot for growing coffee, and another one to raise a pig. These farms became the property of the family that farmed them. The food crops grown are peanuts, manioc, plantain, Indian corn, and a variety of green crops for plowing under. On these farms the buildings have a more permanent character, tools are more sophisticated, and better seeds and some fertilizer are made available by the government. It is expected that these paysannat farms will do much to teach the African to become a farmer, to help him develop a sense of ownership in personal property, and, eventually, by increasing both food and cash crops, to improve his standard of living and diversify the economy. Most of these settlers are former laborers recruited in the towns; they have known the hardships of urban living and have learned to appreciate the security offered by the new scheme. They know little about agriculture but are willing to follow the advice of the government agents who guide them in their work.

Scientific farms are generally supported by the government. Private companies, which stand to gain most from research and improvement, have supported them very little. Gabon has a research and experimental station near Lambaréné for oil palm and fat products; this is one of the three large oil-producing centers that may change the economic future of agriculture in Gabon. Another scientific farm at Tchibanga produces dry rice and does research to improve this cereal; while the productivity and yields are successful, poor communications make it difficult to distribute the harvest where it is most needed.

Other specialized farms or plantations include the Oyem enterprise, devoted principally to rubber. It is worth noting that all these scientific farms or research stations are essentially, if not exclusively, concerned with cash crops.

3. Fertilizers [19]

Only the farms that produce cash crops, and among them mainly the large concerns and scientific farms, can afford to import chemical fertilizers in significant amounts. The lack of animal husbandry results in an almost total absence of manure on the acreage devoted to subsistence farming. As the price of chemicals is prohibitive, the restoration of soil fertility in this sector rests entirely with the age-old system of burning the bush. The ashes have been shown to contain potash, phosphate, calcium, and some other minerals. This may turn a slightly acid soil into a slightly alkaline one for a short time. The fertilizer situation may improve in the future, because phosphate deposits are said to exist along the coast of Gabon. It is also believed that some low-grade potash is to be found in the area of Lake Azingo.

4. Mechanized Equipment

There is no significant amount of mechanized equipment for the production of food crops in Gabon. However, following the efforts of the French government-sponsored Research Institute for Oil, mechanized equipment was used to plow the land and process the harvest of palm oil. Another company succeeded in establishing the mechanized cultivation of peanuts. About one hundred tractors are also used in some of the paysannat settlements.

C. PRODUCTION [8][9]

No reliable information is available on the amount of subsistence crops produced in Gabon each year. It is estimated that the producer consumes 50 percent of his crop and sells the balance on the local market. According to a United Nations study made in 1954 and covering several African countries, subsistence production accounted for 65 to 75 percent of the total crop area of tropical Africa. In the states of Equatorial Africa the percentage for 1956 was estimated at 88 percent, higher than in most other states of West Africa. Crops are harvested in minute quantities and for immediate consumption.

1. Cereals and Tubers

As elsewhere in the area, manioc is the most important tuber found in Gabon. The amount of land planted to manioc in 1960-1961 was estimated at 37,000 hectares with a production of 152,000 tons (see Table No. 1), giving a yield of 4.1 tons per hectare, one of the lowest yields for any country of tropical Africa. The Congo produces yields of 8 tons per hectare.

Corn is sown on 2000 hectares, yielding 1000 recorded metric tons, equalling the rate of the Republic of the Congo (Brazzaville) (0.5 tons per hectare).

2. Other Crops

Unrecorded amounts of plantain, cocoyams, and rice are also raised. In the Uplands dry rice is planted; yields are estimated at 0.5 tons per hectare.

3. Sources of Animal Proteins [19]

Animal proteins are limited in quantity and quality. A few animals, such as pigs and chickens, may be seen around the native huts, but they receive no care from their owners. The urban areas import some meat from Cameroun or from Chad. Wild game is not abundant in Gabon, and since firearms are strictly rationed and controlled, hunting is not encouraged. Several efforts were made to establish a demonstration center for animal husbandry at Owendo. These efforts did not at first meet with success. At present there is an agreement in force whereby village chiefs may receive two or three pairs of animals for breeding but must pledge the return of the equivalent in four years. The same system was followed at Tchibanga, where byproducts of the rice station facilitate the feeding of these animals. All these resources, however, are inadequate, and large quantities of meat will still have to be imported for many years to come.

No dairy products are available in significant quantities other than those imported by the towns.

Fishing is an important activity in Gabon. It is practiced mainly by one tribe at Fernan Vaz, where the industry is well developed. Sporadic and part-time fishing is conducted all along the coast. There is a salting and smoking plant at Ozouri, near Port Gentil. Inland fishing is actively pursued; the recorded production reaches 8000 to 10,000 tons of fish per year. Grade A fish is available for those who can afford it; other fish, graded B, C, D, and E, according to species (including the lower-priced shark), are also available at most local markets on certain days. As elsewhere in the territories, there are tilapia-breeding stations. About 110 ponds are operated throughout the country, but around Libreville the inhabitants have indicated that they would gladly eat the fish if the government would do the fishing for them.

D. FOOD SUPPLIES

Available food supplies in Gabon are very limited. This situation exists, as in other parts of Africa, because the population consumes the harvest without much consideration for the future, and because without proper storage facilities most foods cannot be kept for more than two or three months. Manioc, however, will keep in the soil, and provident farmers sometimes let it stay there for a year before harvesting it. Plantain cannot be stored for long. Rice grain does not absorb moisture as do other cereals and so has some storage advantages. Cocoyams do not store well. Government food supplies are limited to items of international trade. In Nigeria a project of pit storage for Indian corn is afoot and in the former French West African territories a program of compulsory grain reserves was instituted; no such fareseeing schemes have been initiated in Gabon. There seems to have been no concern for the kind of actual famine that at times plague other African areas. There was undernourishment and malnutrition, to be sure, but real

famine was avoided in the past because of the small population and because of the nearness of the forest, where everyone could eventually
find leaves and berries to pick.

Transportation in Gabon is poor and, in spite of recent efforts, is
hampered by the vastness of the territory and the sparseness of the
population. Roads are difficult to build and, once built, are almost impossible to maintain. But a number of short roads of local interest link
Libreville and Lambaréné to the Congo-Ocean Railroad. Another road
links Franceville and Lastoursville to Mayoumba on the coast. The total
mileage amounts to approximately 4000 km.

Waterways have long been the best means of transportation inside
the state and will continue to be for some time to come. About 1000 km.
of rivers are navigable but not in all seasons. As a result, little or no
significant exchange of crops between regions can be counted on in the
near future.

Air transportation, however, is good, and there are more than 100
landing fields in Gabon.

E. FOOD INDUSTRIES [19]

No food industries worthy of the name are located in Gabon. Machines are lacking except for four oil presses and those machines
needed to condition cocoa and coffee for export purposes. There are
four coffee-processing plants and two rice mills. A Franco-Norwegian
company once established a factory to process whale oil at Cape Lopez.
It was discontinued, but a new limited license was granted in 1959.

F. IMPORT-EXPORT

Agricultural production for export is limited to cocoa, coffee, and
palm oil. Imports consist chiefly of flour, amounting to about 2000 tons
annually since 1953. Rice, fish, and alcoholic beverages are also imported but go chiefly to the towns and do not significantly influence the
local food subsistence economy of the rural areas.

III

DIET TYPES

There is little to add to the study of diet types described above
(p. 184). Gabon is largely in the plantain-manioc area, and its goods are
typical. Certain population groups can avail themselves of the fish
smoked in the Libreville area or caught in the rivers. The caloric value
of these diets is not known but is roughly estimated at no less than 2200
calories in the average day. Nutritional levels are particularly critical
in the forest camps and in the town slums. Lumber enterprises grow
their own manioc, but the overconsumption of this relatively poor

staple, inadequately supplemented by canned goods, rice, and manioc leaves, results in an unbalanced diet that causes several cases of malnutrition every year.

To help solve some of the problems of the slum population in the cities, the SIP (Societé Indigene de Prevoyance) started establishing mess halls or local restaurants where inexpensive meals can be bought. Such eating places, however, do not influence significantly the general level of nutrition of the population.

THE REPUBLIC OF THE CONGO (BRAZZAVILLE)

I

BACKGROUND

A. GEOGRAPHY [15][18(17)]

The Republic of the Congo (Brazzaville) lies astride the equator in a general northeast-southwest direction, extending from the 5th° of latitude south of the equator to the 4th° of northern latitude. It is bounded on the northwest by the Gabon Republic, on the north by the Republic of the Cameroun and the Central African Republic, on the east by the Republic of the Congo (Leopoldville), and on the southwest by the Atlantic Ocean. It has an area of about 361,000 sq. km. Four geographical regions can be recognized:

> The Southern Maritime Region
> The Southern Mountain Region
> The Central Savannah
> The Stanley Pool Region

The Southern Maritime Region. This region is a low, treeless coastal plain extending inland for about 70 km. Ocean currents have built up many sand pits that shelter lagoons or lakes. The region is very sparsely settled and contributes little to the agricultural economy.

The Southern Mountain Region. This region parallels the coast and is known as the Mayombe Escarpment. It correlates with the Mayombe Region in Gabon. It consists of a succession of sharp ridges with altitudes varying from 550 meters to 800 meters. It is not high enough to block off the climatic influence of the antarctic current. It is cut by the deep gorges of the Kouilou River and is almost entirely covered by rain forest.

The Central Savannah. Farther inland the Niari Valley stretches eastward in the form of a savannah-covered lowland. This is one of the most fertile areas of the territory, where the most successful experimental farms are located. The northern slope rises toward the wooded central massif of Gabon, and the southern slope toward the treeless plateau of the Cataracts.

The Stanley Pool Region. South of the Niari Valley the Stanley Pool Region consists of hills, for the most part untimbered, which give way to grassy plateaus toward the north. These dry and monotonous plateaus are separated from each other by the deep valleys of the northern tributaries of the Congo River. The savannah that lies farther north is cut by wooded ravines along the watercourses.

Part of the Congo Basin lies in this republic. Here the rivers form a jumble of branches, linked with one another, and northeast of the Sangha River they flow through a dense forest that is almost always inundated.

Two distinct climatic zones are generally recognized: the southwest plateaus, with an annual rainfall of less than 1500 mm., a dry season extending from three to four months in duration and average monthly temperatures that vary between 23° and 27°C.; and the tropical rain forest region of the north and northeast, which experiences rain that totals between 1500 mm. and 3000 mm. annually and where no month is really dry (during January, the driest month, the precipitation amounts to 67 mm.).

B. POPULATION

The Republic of the Congo has a population of approximately 845,000 people with an average density of about 2.2 people per sq. km. The people are scattered very unevenly throughout the country, depending on the suitability of the land for agriculture and on tribal history. Two regions are appreciably more populated than the others. One is the Brazzaville area, where the density reaches 7 people per sq. km. and the other is the Niari Valley, where it reaches 6 people per sq. km. The forest zones of the north and the Bateke Plateaus, however, are practically uninhabited, with less than 1 person per sq. km. The population has been increasing steadily as a result of the advances in education and of the creation of dispensaries and mobile health and vaccination units. As in other parts of Africa, there is a migration from rural areas to the towns. For the past thirty years people have gone to the capital, Brazzaville (pop. 135,000), to Pointe-Noire (pop. 55,000), and to Dolisie (pop. 18,000). There is, of course, an excess of labor and considerable unemployment in the towns.

Congolese ethnology is characterized by two essential features. The northern boundary of the country almost coincides with the southern limit of the Bantu and Sudanese people. Another line cutting through the middle of the country divides the people belonging to a matrilinear society west of Brazzaville from those belonging to a patrilinear society north of the capital. The population is subdivided into four major ethnic groups: the Kongo, the Bateke, the M'Bochi and the Sangha. The four groups are in turn divided into many tribes.

The Kongo, the largest of these groups, comprise about fifteen tribes, including the Balali and the Bakongo; they occupy the entire area south of Brazzaville. The 350,000 persons of this group account for 45 percent of the population of the Republic and occupy 15 percent of its area. In past centuries they formed the Kingdom of Kongo and Loango. They are good farmers and good tradesmen.

The Bateke (150,000) are found north of Brazzaville and are descended from the former subjects of King Makoko. They live in houses with arched roofs without top crests. They are the most traditionalist of the ethnic groups and are chiefly hunters and fishermen, except for the Bakoukouya, whose agricultural techniques are among the most advanced in black Africa.

The Sangha group comprise of about fifteen tribes and inhabit the inundated forest zone in the north. The Pygmies also live in this region.

The M'Bochi group (95,000) is divided into ten tribes that live where the savannah and the forest meet. The tribes that dwell along the major rivers of the Congo Basin are for the most part fishermen. They are less exposed to malnutrition because fish is available to supply them with adequate animal proteins.

The M'Bochi-Kouyou-Makou group, which occupies a more central region, has furnished many emigrants to the urban centers. Its members form 10 percent of the population of Brazzaville and the majority of the skilled workers and government employees. They are more "exculturized" than any of the others.

C. AGRICULTURAL POLICIES [17][19]

The main policy of the government is to diversify the agricultural economy of the state, whose major export (58 percent) is still represented by forest products coming from its 21 million hectares of forest. As a result of the growth of urban centers, French aid was more concerned with assistance to social work in the towns than it was with agriculture in the rural areas. Only 12.3 percent of the funds available under the first Plan went to the paysannat and other agricultural endeavors. In the second Plan 32.4 percent was appropriated for the rural economy.

II

FOOD RESOURCES

A. GENERAL [19]

The food problems of the Republic of the Congo resemble those already discussed.

The Congo is an agricultural country with a relatively large urban population that the rural areas cannot feed. The farming population is relatively small; the farmers are reluctant to grow the foods that city people demand or to grow enough of their own foods to have a surplus for market. The soil resources are poor and yield only poor harvests. There are an impressive variety of crops but none in a significant amount. The Republic of the Congo produces manioc, rice, plantain, citrus fruit, sugar cane, coffee, cocoa, peanuts, oil palms, and so on. The total amount of arable land is not known with precision. There is a potential acreage that will depend on the ability to clear more land. The Niari Valley is said to have 400,000 hectares of excellent humus-covered land. It is also reported that truck farming is being developed around the urban centers to provide fresh food for the city dwellers.

B. MEANS OF PRODUCTION

1. Agricultural labor force [19]
As in Gabon, the agricultural labor force is small and consists mainly of the subsistence farmers and their families. Of a population of approximately 800,000 people, nearly 200,000 live in the towns, and only 40,000 are considered to be employed in agriculture; 10,000 of the latter are found in the Niari Valley area. The surplus rural population grows food only as a part-time activity.

2. Farms [19][17]
As in Gabon, three types of farms can be identified: the subsistence farm, the paysannat farm, and the scientific farm.

The subsistence farms are similar throughout the manioc-plantain-yam belt and need no special description here.

The paysannat farms are also organized on a basis similar to that already described for Gabon. The first paysannats were established in 1952 at Divenie and at Loudima and Madigou in the Niari Valley. They were promoted by large French companies for their African employees, who benefited from mechanical clearings made by the company's equipment. The companies also took care of the distribution and marketing of the products. At Komono and Mankassou food crops were planted together with oil palms, coffee, and peanuts. True to the principle of mixing cash crops with nutrition crops, an effort was made, as in Gabon, to win back to the farm the unemployed slum-dwelling mobs of the town. Under the leadership of President Fulbert Youlou* there were plans for extending the paysannat system into vast holdings, in which both the promoting European companies and the African paysannats would be shareholders.

There are a number of scientific farms in the Congo. The Niari Valley Experiment has several research stations. The Boutouali Project employs 10,000 Africans and has shown that given adequate skill and capital, modern farming is possible in the Congo. In this project new crops are introduced, and improved methods of cultivation are adjusted to local conditions. The Committee for the Development of the Niari Valley was established in 1952 to coordinate the various programs that had already been established there by public and private agencies. The valley's fertile soil and favorable climate make it a suitable region for the introduction of new crops. Experimental farming

---

*Now out of office (1963), replaced by Mr. Massembat-Debat.

is being carried on by the Loudima Agronomic Research Center and the experimental stations of the Research Institutes for Oil. The Niari Industrial and Agricultural Corporation operates four plantations employing 10,000 Africans. As its name implies, the Corporation places great emphasis on local processing of its agricultural products. It operates a sugar refinery and an oil mill that produces ongokea, a quick-drying oil much in demand for use in varnishes and foundry bolts.* There is a Central African Institute for Research in Brazzaville, which includes agricultural and entomological stations; an Experimental Peanut Cultivation Center at Loudima; other scientific farms at Botouali and Inoni; and several others concerned with fibre study and palm oil, notably at Boudouhou.

3. Fertilizers
Little information is available on the amount of fertilizer produced and/or imported. The remarks made in the chapter on Gabon would apply here. The European scientific farms and plantations undoubtedly have to import some fertilizer as long as the deposits mentioned in the Gabon chapter are not fully developed. Subsistence farming does not use fertilizers other than the ashes of its burnings. Some animal manure may be available in spots to some paysannat farms, due to the existence of small centers of animal husbandry (see below).

4. Mechanical Equipment
All the European enterprises use mechanical equipment and have used it for the benefit of the Africans in starting a number of paysannat communities. As of 1959, 140 tractors, 51 crawlers, and 89 wheeled tractors were used in agriculture, as well as 7 small garden tractors.

C. PRODUCTION [8][9]

The economy of the Congo is still primarily agricultural. Eighty percent of the arable land is owned and farmed by the Congolese, and 75 percent of the production is grown for home consumption. In 1959 only 20 percent of the agricultural products were exported.

1. Main Crops
The main food crops are manioc, plantain, yams, sweet potatoes, rice, and sugar cane. Manioc occupies 100,000 hectares (1960). This acreage yielded 800,000 metric tons or 8 tons per hectare (see Table No. 1). No individual figures are given for the production of plantain and yams. In 1960 there were 5000 hectares of paddy, yielding slightly less than 4000 tons or approximately 0.7 tons per hectare, a very low yield by all standards (the Congo, Leopoldville, 7 tons; Algeria, 4.6 tons). Among the African producers of rice, the Mossendjo area is the largest. Other places where rice is produced are the Stanley Pool Re-

---

*Source 19.

gion, the Ewo area of Likouala-Mossaka, Alima Lefini, and the Sangha. No official figures are available for sugar-cane production.

2. Other Crops

Corn was planted on 2000 hectares in 1960-1961, producing 1000 tons or a yield of approximately 0.5 tons per hectare, a small one by all standards. Other crops include palm oil, which was produced at the rate of 5200 tons in 1960-1961 from the pressing of 6500 tons of kernels in 1960 and 5000 tons in 1961. Groundnuts also represent a good nutritional as well as commercial crop. The 1961 output reached 4400 tons of shelled nuts and 5800 tons of unshelled nuts, sold locally. In 1959, 1200 tons of shelled and 1100 tons of unshelled nuts were exported. In addition to the above, both nutritional and commercial crops include coffee from the Sangha, Stanley Pool, and Niari Regions and cocoa from the Souanke and Ouesso Regions. Seven hundred tons of coffee and 800 tons of cocoa were produced in 1961.

Tobacco is grown primarily in Djambala and in the Bateke Plateau. Sugar cane is found in the Niari Valley on the Congo-Ocean Railroad but has known difficult beginnings.

Fruit cultivation includes bananas for export. They are found mainly in the region of the Mayombe and near Pointe-Noire, where the output reached 4000 tons in 1961. This culture was started in 1955, and it is believed that within a few years crops of 15,000 tons might be expected. Citrus fruits and pineapple are grown in the vicinity of Brazzaville as commercial crops; they are not consumed locally.

3. Sources of Animal Proteins [8][9][19]

Despite the climate and the tsetse-fly problem, the Mindouli Research Station has developed from N'Dama stock in the Congo, Leopoldville and from Guinea stock a strain of cattle that can adjust to local conditions and resist sleeping sickness infection (nagana). These herds are found in the Niari Region. Small herds are under the care of individual African farmers; large herds are on scientifically managed European ranches. From 7000 head in 1957 the herds have grown to 18,000 in 1960. During the same period the number of hogs grew from 15,000 to 37,000; the number of sheep grew from 31,000 to 58,000; and the number of goats reached 68,000. These resources influence the nutrition of the masses very little since meat is too expensive except for the better situated classes of the towns. The amount of meat and other products derived from these herds is not known. Meat is transported to Brazzaville by air from Chad; it is kept in cold storage at the Brazzaville Airport and reshipped to the main towns of Dolisie and Pointe-Noire by rail. As the herds increased, breeding animals were distributed by the same method used in Gabon (see previous chapter). In 1958, according to Thompson and Adloff, there were 1500 cattle in African hands. The Mindouli Station, with their herd of 2000 cattle, meets the demands of the herdsmen for breeding animals, while the Mouyoundzi Station, on its 5000 hectares, has a herd of over 10,000 head. It must be remembered that the African authorities are much less enthusiastic about animal husbandry than the French were; they are suspicious of enterprises requiring considerable technical skill and large concessions of grazing ground. The future of animal husbandry in the Congo under the new government remains in doubt.

Fisheries. Most of the fishing is for local consumption. Fish is the basic source of animal protein in the local diets. For the most part, fish are caught in the lakes; but, in addition, over 2700 tons of seafood are caught every year. In the Mossaka Region the fresh-water catch approximates 4000 tons a year. In addition, there are thousands of family and village fishponds where fish breeding is practiced. The tilapia fish stock was provided by the Djoumounia Pisciculture Station at Brazzaville. There are plans to industrialize the fish industry and process the catch into canned fish cakes and fish oil.

D. FOOD SUPPLY [17]

As in Gabon, there is no significant food storage in the Congo, either centrally or regionally. The European and évolué communities store some of the export and import crops; the rural farmers leave some of their crop in the ground to harvest for daily use as long as it lasts; but long-term preservation of food is such a problem that no food reserves of any significance exist in warehouses or granaries.

The following regions produce most of the following foods: Manioc is raised in the Komono area between the Djoue and Kouilou Rivers, in the zone northeast of Brazzaville, and in the extreme north just south of the border with the Central African Republic. Plantain is grown in the extreme southwest, in the lower Kouilou Basin just south of the railroad, and in the north between Ubangui and Sangha—often intermingled with manioc. Palm groves are found in the south near the lower Kouilou and the Gabon border, in the Jacob area near the Congo (Leopoldville) border, north of Sibiti, in the Likouala-Mossaka Valley, and in the north between Sangha and Ubangi (see maps). Rice is grown in the Mossendjo Plain, bananas in the Mayombe, and citrus fruit near Brazzaville. The Niari Valley produces all of the types of foods found in the state.

The Congo has the best transportation system in the whole former Federation. The Congo-Ocean Railroad runs through the tropical rain forest and down the Mayombe Escarpment, crossing 92 bridges and passing through 12 tunnels. The port of Brazzaville is an important center for trade with the neighboring states (Central African Republic, Republic of Chad, and the former Belgian Congo). The annual traffic at Brazzaville has increased to 210,000 tons a year. From Brazzaville goods are transshipped by boats that ply the Congo-Ubangi River system up to Bangui; this route could be extended even beyond Bangui as far as Fort Lamy, the capital of Chad, by the construction of another railroad line, which would help to increase the present volume of trade between Chad and the Congo.

There are approximately 9000 kilometers of permanent roads. Another 1200 kilometers can be used by automobiles during certain seasons to supplement other means of land transportation and are for the most part connected with the Congo-Ocean Railroad. A few can be used for heavy-duty traffic.

As in Gabon, road maintenance in the Republic of the Congo is costly. Heavy rains constantly flood the roads and would wash them away entirely in a few years if road repairs were not made incessantly. The opening of new roads calls for heavy equipment, since, in addition to the usual work of grading, a way must be cleared through the dense Congolese forest. For these reasons, one can wonder what will be the future of the existing roads after the French foreign aid has either subsided or completely disappeared.

Because of the great distances and the difficulties of land travel, airplanes have rapidly become the sole means of long-and medium-distance passenger transportation. Airplanes are also used increasingly for carrying freight, especially perishable goods and meat, which, as already stated, go directly from Chad to Brazzaville. As a result of this extended network of communications (unlike the situation in Gabon), the various districts of the Republic can be supplied from other districts in case of emergency. But any disruption of these communications would result in starvation among the unemployed and isolated town populations.

E. FOOD INDUSTRIES

There are a number of food industries in the Congo whose output is not reported. They process local produce and consist of such small enterprises as a few rice mills; a manioc-flour mill; thirty palm, palmetto, and peanut-oil mills; two fish-processing plants; and a modern brewery. There is also a sugar refinery that produces 14,000 tons of sugar a year, almost enough for domestic use.

F. IMPORT-EXPORT

As in Gabon, the imports of the Republic of the Congo are limited chiefly to wheat flour and meat, which reach only part of the urban population. With the exception of peanuts and bananas, exports of agricultural goods are made up chiefly of cash crops such as cocoa, coffee, and oil.

III

DIET TYPES [1][2][3][4][19][9][9a][4a]

There is little of significance to add to previous chapters on diet types. Bergeret* reports adequate supplies of animal foods and fresh vegetables and fruit at the markets of the Bamileke groups even during the dry season. The people living along the rivers, including part of the Bateke and M'Bochi groups, have a better diet than others, either because they have retained the tradition of hunting and may occasionally find game in the forest, or because, as fishermen, they use their catch to feed their families. Meat consumption has increased in the past years, reaching about 20 kilos per capita per year** in the urban areas. However, manioc and porridge provide the usual daily fare. Laborers will accept rice in the rural areas only as a supplement to their ration, not as a basic food. In the towns rice is priced high and is often beyond the means of the African consumer. Because of this, rice cultivation is discouraged by the government, and an effort is being made to stabilize production at 3000 to 4000 tons a year, about the maximum that the population can absorb.

(*Bergeret, B.) Les Marchés Bamileke de Saison Sèche. Med. Trop. Marseille 1956 Sept.-Oct. Vol. 16, No. 5, pp. 698-708.
**This figure, from source 19 and also found in French sources, seems very high; does not agree with FAO figures.

CENTRAL AFRICAN REPUBLIC

I

BACKGROUND

The Central African Republic, formerly the territory of Ubangi-Shari, became a member s t a t e of the French Community on December 1, 1958. In January 1959 it formed an Economic, Technical, and Customs Union with the other three territories.

A. GEOGRAPHY [6]

The Central African Republic is an inland country, more than 900 kilometers away from the sea. It has an area of 610,800 square kilometers, slightly less than that of Texas. It is bounded by the former Belgian Congo, the Republic of the Sudan, the Republic of Chad, the Republic of Cameroun, and the Republic of the Congo (Brazzaville). Close to the equator, most of its territory lies between 3° and 11° of northern latitude (see map). This is a transition zone; the north is dry and subhumid, the south moist and humid. The country consists of a vast rolling plateau with an average altitude of 600 to 700 meters. Most of the rivers drain toward the Congo Basin; but because of rapids and thick vegetation, navigation is often difficult.

The climatic differences have for a long time governed the diets of the people. Traditionally, manioc was the staple diet of the south, while cereals of the millet and sorghum types were the main diets of the north. This situation has changed somewhat in recent years and will be discussed later.

B. POPULATION [7][10]

The total population of the country is 1,229,000 inhabitants, slightly less than that of the state of Colorado. The average density is 13 inhabitants per square kilometer, but in the east and northeast there are areas with less than one inhabitant per three square kilometers. With the exception of a few regions along the rivers or on the Chad frontier, there are no densely populated areas. The principal urban centers are the capital, Bangui, with a population of 100,000; Bouar, with 20,700; and Bambari with 19,700. There are a dozen towns with over 5000 inhabitants that look more like large villages. More than 80 percent of the people live in the rural areas. The Ubangi house is a round mud hut; but northward, in the cereal areas, straw becomes available and a brick type of building material, made of straw mixed with earth, is sometimes used.

Infantile mortality is high, averaging on the order of 190 per 1000 live births; this is higher than in the Congo, Leopoldville (148 per 1000 live births) or Ivory Coast (138 per 1000 live births), or Ghana (90 per 1000 live births).

There are four main ethnic groups among the Central African population: the Mandjia-Baya, the Banda, the M'Baka, and the Zande. Each has a language of its own, but there is a sort of lingua-franca called the sangho, which is spoken in all parts of the country. French, which is the Central African official language also is used extensively. In addition to the African population, the Republic has about 6000 European residents, mostly French.

C. AGRICULTURAL POLICIES[19][6][10]

The Central Republic's problems are somewhat different from those of Gabon and the Congo, Brazzaville. While it can be said that Gabon has too many economic resources for its population and the Congo too much population for its resources, Central African Republic has both population and resources; its problem is where to start and how best to apply its labor to the development of its resources in the context of the prevalent geographical conditions.

While the population is larger than that of the two other territories discussed so far, it is just as sparsely settled and just as unskilled. Although the transportation system, especially the highways, is fairly good by Equatorial African standards, it is still inadequate and costly because of the heavy bulk and the relatively low value of the exportable products that use it.

The first two Plans, which ended with the year 1957, emphasized the basic equipment of the country. At the same time, the trend to the towns, especially Bangui, was depleting the countryside and creating both scarcity of agricultural resources in rural areas and unemployment in the towns.

Nine paysannats were created between 1952 and 1956. As in other territories, these farms were at the outset mostly devoted to raising cash crops. Food crops have been introduced gradually. The administration's policy with respect to rice is to limit its production to a level dictated by consumer demand, an amount currently not in excess of 700 tons a year. The cereal is not popular among manioc eaters, and any surplus is too difficult to market from the Lobaye, Bambari, and Bossembele regions where it is cultivated.

The third Plan (1958-1962) appropriated about U.S. $7 million to the development of the country, of which U.S. $2 million was earmarked for agriculture. Agricultural development emphasized cash crops, as evidenced by the activities of the agricultural stations, only one of which, at Grimari, experiments with food crops. Various educational programs have been initiated (by governmental authorities and by missionaries) to teach the villagers how to plant such fruit-bearing trees as mango, orange, lemon, and so on; but it has proved difficult to educate the people to protect their seedlings, to keep an interest in their plantations, and to water their new trees during the dry season.

II

FOOD RESOURCES

A. GENERAL

Arable land in the Republic has not yet been adequately computed, because of the vagueness of the boundaries of tribal holdings. As in Gabon and the Congo, agriculture is primitive; the women of the group dig some manioc holes around the house and casually nurse a few plantain trees. Forest-dwelling tribes pick and gather, as well as hunt and fish, activities that have little connection with the Western concept of agriculture. Only in the Ouham area does one find people whose original culture was based on anything like farming in the Western sense of the word. In certain places where land resources have been computed and where agricultural processes have been studied, crop rotation is carried out as follows: in the north cotton (a cash crop) is sown the first year; in the second year millet or sorghum are planted, along with manioc, groundnuts, gourds, or pumpkins. The same crops are often repeated the third year.

In the forest zones corn is almost always combined with manioc, and when it is possible, groundnuts are added.

B. MEANS OF PRODUCTION[20][19][8a]

1. Agricultural labor force

A recent investigation throws some light on the agricultural labor force of the Central African Republic. The rural population is estimated at 949,300 inhabitants, representing 80 percent of the whole population. Of these, 541,400 (57 percent) are considered active agriculturists. An average of four persons depend for their food on each agricultural unit or farmstead. Two of these people are active, and the other two are dependents; each active agriculturist works an average of 0.76 hectares. Approximately 300 Europeans are considered professional agriculturists.

2. Farms[19][6]

As in the other states, the Central African Republic has three types of farms: the subsistence farm, the paysannat, and the scientific farm. The subsistence farm is comparable to those already described.

The paysannat farm, with its labor force of 35,000, specializes in coffee (at Bilolo, Baya, Gaigne and in the Azande area), in palm oil, and in cash crops to stabilize food supply around Bangui.

Scientific farms stress cotton at Bambari, Bassangoa, and Gambo and food crops at Grimari. Pig-raising stations exist at Bambari and Bouar, poultry farms around Bangui. Scientific fish farms are located at Bangui, Bambari, Berberati, and Alindao.

3. Fertilizers and Mechanical Equipment

No information is available on the use of fertilizers to develop food crops or on the extent of mechanization outside the European sector of agriculture.

C. PRODUCTION [8] [9] [19] [8a]

1. Main Food Crops

Because of its position in a transition zone, the Republic grows manioc as the major crop and millet and sorghum as secondary crops. Manioc is all-important in the south, and the millets are in the north. The change in emphasis occurs approximately along the sixth parallel north, following a progressive gain of manioc over sorghum and millet. The preference for manioc is the result of the advantageous properties of this tuber and of the competition between cotton and millet for labor at the same time of the year; no such competition occurs between cotton and manioc.

Sorghum is now cultivated for manufacturing beer; but brews made from manioc and plantain are more and more appreciated. The following short table* shows the areas devoted to various crops and the production of each crop according to 1962 computations.

Crops	As Single Crop	Associated With Other Crops	Production
Manioc	109,900 Ha.	117,200 Ha.	752,119 tons
Groundnuts	8,500 Ha.	82,100 Ha.	29,600 tons
Corn	5,380 Ha.	66,800 Ha.	11,986 tons
Millet	2,600 Ha.	81,700 Ha.	19,198 tons
Gourds	4,600 Ha.	81,800 Ha.	N. A.
Bananas	4,300 Ha.	13,300 Ha.	170,000 tons
Sesame	14,000 Ha.	13,800 Ha.	6,822 tons
Yams	4,000 Ha.	14,600 Ha.	32,200 tons
Palm Oil from kernels (uncultivated)	—	18,000 Ha.	800 tons

*Source = FAO Report 1450 - Slight differences exist with FAO Production Yearbook - 1962.

2. Other Crops

Other food crops include rice, which is discouraged by the Administration (see above) but is still raised in the Lobaye area. It is reported that when the Administration introduced better seeds in 1948, the recipients ate the seeds rather than plant them. Cash crops include cotton, coffee, peanuts, and sisal. Cotton is still the major export crop and covers 167,000 hectares producing 20,000 tons of seed and 10,000 tons of lint. Coffee is grown on 30,000 hectares producing 6000 to 8000 tons every year.

Groundnuts utilize 90,000 hectares* producing over 29,000 tons a year, of which about 50 percent are exported and 50 percent sold on the local markets.

Palm kernels (800 tons), sesame seed (6800 tons), and tobacco (250 tons) are also included in the cash crops for export. Last but not least, bananas cover 17,000 hectares producing an export crop of 170,000 tons in 1961.

Other sources of fat include the karite or shea tree, of which there are about 400,000 in the country. About 400 tons of butter, used more for cosmetics than for diet, are produced each year from the seeds of the shea tree.

3. Sources of Animal Proteins [19][6]

Cattle. Animal husbandry is practiced in the Central African Republic north of the tsetse-fly area, mostly by the Bororos and the Peuls. These cattlemen occupy territories in some areas of the east and in the Ouham-Pende area. Cattle are not necessarily raised for meat but are an indication of wealth and traditionally provide the means for paying the bride price. The herds of the Central African Republic are estimated at 500,000 to 600,000 head, distributed as follows: in the Bouar area, 250,000 to 300,000 head; in the Bambari-Alindao area, between 100,000 and 150,000 head; in the district of Birao, between 100,000 and 150,000 head. In addition, there are about 80,000 sheep and an unknown number of goats and pigs.

Measures similar to those of other states were taken in the Central Republic to improve animal husbandry. Since the early 1950's scientific stations have distributed breeding animals to selected farmers. Several new grazing grounds have been created in recent years, some in the M'Bomou Valley and some even in the south, challenging the tsetse fly with the trypanosoma-resistant N'Dama cattle.

Forest tribes and southern people obtain some of their animal proteins from hunting and fishing. In 1960 hunting produced 1100 elephants and 10,000 wild buffaloe plus numerous antelope, rodents, and birds. Wildfires are sometimes started in the jungle to frighten animals into traps and nets where they are slaughtered. Feasts then take place, with all members of the families gorging themselves with meat. Part of the supply, however, is sometimes smoked and dried by the women and stored for the rainy season, when hunting is not possible.

*Estimate, combining single crop and associations with other crops.

Wild game, once abundant, has been so depleted that hunting has had to be controlled. This control was imposed at a time when the government was also encouraging cotton planting; the measure was effective in inducing idle hunters to work on the plantations, thus resulting in a shortage of meat that some people hold responsible for the influx of people into the towns.

In spite of this progress the Central African Republic still has to import more than 5000 tons of meat every year to satisfy the needs of its urban population. In addition, there are 330,000 sheep and goats slaughtered every year, yielding approximately 500 tons of meat. The elephants and the buffaloe yield 2200 tons and 1500 tons of meat, respectively. The use of meat in diets is limited to the cattle-raising areas because of transportation and refrigeration difficulties.

Some 31,500 tons of milk are produced annually. The only milk plant is found at Bocaranga; it processes 1500 litres of milk a day during the rainy season for the butter and cheese outlet at Bouar.

Fisheries. Fishing is the main occupation of all the tribes living along the banks of the rivers, especially the Ubangi; most of the catch is smuggled across the river to the former Belgian side, where it fetches better prices; this practice causes an unusually low level of fish consumption in the Republic. Pisciculture includes 500,000 ponds of at least 30 square meters in size for tilapia breeding; but, due to lack of funds for training and maintenance, only 25,000 are in operation. Each pond produces an average of ten kilos of fish a year for a total of 250 tons of tilapia.

D. FOOD SUPPLY

The food reserve of the Central African Republic is small. In the north the granaries and cereal reserves that existed under the colonial administration have been discontinued. At present the only food reserves are the meager supplies some farmers keep in the ground and whatever wholesale dealers keep in their warehouses. Manioc and plantain can be purchased almost everywhere. Sorghum is available in isolated areas north of the seventh parallel. Rice can be obtained in Grimari, Lobaye, Bambari, and Bossembele, and peanuts in the savannahs. Cattle are raised in the Ouham area where the Bororo live, in M'Bomou Valley, and in the area east of Bangassou. Pigs are raised mainly around Bouar, where the European element of the population creates a brisk demand for pork.

Transportation. Transportation in the Republic is good. There are 17,000 kilometers of roads, of which 5700 are of the all-weather type. Bangui is linked to Bossangoa, Berberati and Nola. Bangui is linked to Douala in Cameroun and to Fort Archambault and Fort Lamy in Chad. These roads carry, among other things, a traffic in salt, flour and sugar.

Waterways extend over 590 kilometers. Bangui is almost linked to Brazzaville by water, although in the dry season cargoes must be unloaded 100 kilometers south of the town. Other waterways, such as the tributaries of the Ubangi, are not always navigable.

The Republic has three major airports at Bangui, Berberati and Bouar. The airlines, like the roads, are used for food transportation.

E. FOOD INDUSTRIES

There are practically no food industries in the Republic as most of the food is processed at home.

F. IMPORT-EXPORT [6][20]

Most of the food consumed is produced locally. However, the urban population has to import the four major staple foods of European diets that are not adequately supplied by the countryside. These are flour, sugar, meat, and alcoholic beverages. In 1959 total food imports, exclusive of meat on the hoof, amounted to 4800 tons, were valued at U. S. $470,000 and represented 2.7 percent of all imports.

III

DIET TYPES [12][8a]

Even more so than in the other two Republics, the food economy of the people in the Central African Republic is based on home-grown food and barter. The purchasing power of a native African has been computed at U. S. $18 per capita per year for the Republic as a whole. In certain areas it rises to $28 or $29 and in others it drops to $4 or $5.

The most important items of a typical budget can be divided as follows: clothing 26.2 percent, gifts 13.1 percent, food 10.8 percent, bride price 9.4 percent, and drinks 9.1 percent.

This throws an interesting light on the attitudes and habits of the average African, who spends a large part of his budget on gifts to other people.

Meals are eaten twice daily, but between-meal snacks are common. Breakfast is eaten at dawn and supper at dusk. Manioc and an oily sauce, as elsewhere in tropical Africa, are the principal elements of the meal.

It has been estimated that an average of 2050 calories per capita per day was needed in the Republic, taking into account the population profile, the climate, and the activities involved. This should include 55 grams of proteins per capita per day. The known resources described in previous sections, exclusive of gathering (greens), hunting, and other unrecorded sources of food, just about meet average needs. Some groups undoubtedly have better diets, while some are on the brink of starvation. Protein resources as a whole are far lower than the needs; protein calories represent only 7 percent of the total calories, and animal protein represents a still smaller proportion. Table No. 3 gives a summary of the food resources for the year 1960.

Tables No. 4 and 5 show a low fat and protein intake with a barely adequate caloric level. The poor quality of the basic food consumed is responsible for the low amount of protein intake.

Animal protein intake, needless to say, is generally very low except among certain minority groups. Calcium intakes are low in all diets, although no obvious signs of rickets have been detected in sample studies. Iron intake seems to be adequate. Thiamine and riboflavin intakes are below the recommended level but niacin and ascorbic acid seem adequately represented in the diet. The consumption of vitamin A is low everywhere except in these areas where palm oil abounds.

Regional Diets. Tables No. 4 and 5 show typical diets summarized by regions. In the Bouar region, the economy is based on cotton; the income is around $12 per capita per year. In this area, there is practically no game, but fishing is plentiful in the rainy season, and one person can catch up to 300 or 400 grams of fish in a morning. Fats are supplied by sesame seeds, which are harvested in February and March and stored in the hut in wicker baskets. Each family has a stock of 25 to 30 kilograms, which should last them from March until September. After that fats are provided by the groundnuts that every family cultivates for eating. See Table No. 4 for the amount of each food and Table No. 5 for their nutrient and caloric equivalent.

1. Berberati

The economy of Berberati is based on the finding of diamonds, of which there are few, but the people still look for them because a find represents food and plenty for a certain length of time. Income is unknown but must be relatively higher than in the other areas, judging by their way of life. There is little agriculture and most families buy their food, including manioc. Beef is purchased when diamonds have been found. Other protein sources include crocodile and fish, both available in the Mamberere River. Groundnuts, which are bought, supply the fats (see Tables No. 4 and 5).

2. Bambari

Bambari is one of the richest areas of the Republic. The economy is based on cotton (cash crop) and groundnuts. Most families have incomes in the $20-to-$30 a year bracket. Animal protein, in the form of beef, is consumed on a regular, year-round basis and not, as elsewhere, on festive occasions only. The farmers keep some poultry and some goats. Fat-yielding seeds, such as groundnuts and gourds, are available seasonally, the former from September to February, the latter from March to September. Agriculture is active; at sowing time workers often sleep in the fields to be ready at dawn. The fields are not more than a mile from the villages and work is harmoniously divided between men and women.

3. Nola

In Nola a different type of diet predominates. The villages of the area are built in forest clearings created by fire. Farming is mixed; coffee (cash), manioc, corn, and groundnuts (food) are grown under forest cover. Animal proteins from game are available on a year-round basis. Wild palm trees (oil) are the principal source for fats, and shea tree seeds are the secondary source.

4. Bocaranga

The area centering on Bocaranga is occupied by two different groups, the Bororo cattlemen and the Yanghere agriculturists. The former have a good diet based on animal protein from the herds—meat and milk available on a year-round basis. Income from the sale of milk is reserved for the women of the tribe and is used to purchase manioc and greens from the agriculturists. This exchange, however, often breaks down at the end of the dry season, when the farmers themselves are short of tubers. On the whole, the two-way trade between the two groups is beneficial to both. As is true in other areas, more manioc is cultivated than millet.

5. Bangassou

The Bangassou area is agricultural; consequently its diet reflects a deficiency of animal protein, being limited to occasional game. The chief foods are manioc in its various forms, gombo, and plantain. Fats come from palm oil. The end of the dry season is frequently characterized by severe food shortages.

6. The Babinga People

In the Babinga area the forest shelters several Negrillo groups estimated at 6000 or 7000. These groups make their living chiefly by hunting and gathering. Some trade ties exist between them and the neighboring Bantus, who give them manioc in exchange for game or other forest products. These people migrate from place to place in the forest, seeking the areas where the rains are least intense. Their diet is rich in animal protein provided by antelope, monkeys, elephants, and other animals of the wet tropics. Fats come from bartered groundnuts and gourds.

IV

ADEQUACY OF FOOD RESOURCES

The food resources of the Central African Republic are precarious, as shown by Tables 4 and 5; no improvement is foreseen. Meat protein

is very low at best and under expected conditions may become lower.
It is believed that game resources will be greatly reduced in the next
thirty years as hunting methods are modernized. Even if the domestic
herds were to double their yield in the same period, the daily ration of
the average man in the bush would remain unchanged as a result of the
expected population increases. In terms of calories, the prospects are
also dim since it is feared that production increases will be more than
absorbed by the population growth. It is expected that in a few years
the number of nonproductive members of rural families will rise from
51 percent to over 80 percent.

V

NUTRITIONAL DISEASES

Nutritional deficiencies are common, as shown by the samplings
made in the six areas discussed above and reported in percentage form
in Table No. 6. Where protein intake is low, kwashiorkor is prevalent;
signs of protein deficiencies are found in 73.41 percent of the population in the Bangassou area and 12.8 percent in the Bambari area. Goiter
is very common in many areas, but, surprisingly, the Babinga Negrillos
seem to be free of it in general—a situation particularly striking in the
M'Baiki region where other ethnic groups show signs of goiter in some
25 percent of the population. Other deficiencies are evidenced by mono-
symptomatic forms of kwashiorkor, glossitis, xerosis, Bitot spots,
angular stomatitis, and so on. Hemoglobin rates are low. One-third of
the population is below 80 percent of normal in this respect; this anemia is also due to the heavy load of intestinal parasites and to the
prevalence of the sickle cell trait and other possibly hereditary
features.

THE REPUBLIC OF CHAD

I

BACKGROUND

A. GEOGRAPHY[16][21]

The Republic of Chad has an area of 1,000,284 square kilometers or approximately the combined areas of Washington, Oregon, California, Nevada, and Idaho. The Republic is situated between the 8th° and 23rd° of northern latitude and between the 14th° and 24th° of eastern longitude. In the heart of Africa, some 1600 to 3200 kilometers from the coast, it is bounded on the south by the Central African Republic, on the east by the Republic of the Sudan, on the north by the Kingdom of Libya, and on the west by the Republic of Cameroun, Nigeria, and Niger. Chad's landlocked position near the equator, its great size, and its relative inaccessibility have determined in the past and will determine for a long time in the future its fundamental cultural and economic characteristics.

The Republic consists of a vast peneplain, deeply incised by the valleys of the Shari, Logone, and Bahr El Gazal rivers, with a low sedimentary basin around Lake Chad. The land slopes gradually upward from an altitude of around 300 meters to almost 2000 meters in the Ouaddai Mountains and more than 3000 meters in the volcanic Tibesti Mountains in the north. The sandstone Ennedi Plateau in the northeast lies between these two groups of mountains. In the south-central region the Guerra Mountains reach 2000 meters. In the extreme south a low ridge separating the Shari and Congo Basins serves as the boundary between Chad and the Central African Republic.

Lake Chad, a shallow triangular depression, is the meeting point of the boundaries of Chad, Nigeria, and Cameroun. Into this lake flows the 1200 kilometer-long Shari River. The Logone River joins the Shari at Fort Lamy and forms a common delta with it. Depending on the fluctuations of the Shari, the area of the lake varies from less than 11,360 square kilometers to almost 25,900 square kilometers. East of the lake the rivers such as the Batha and the Bahr El Gazal are dry during many months of the year. The small number of rivers, coupled with the poor distribution of the rains, makes water one of the foremost problems of Chad agriculture. As the map shows, it lies entirely in the arid and semiarid zones of Africa from the edge of the equatorial forest on the south to the Sahara on the north; its geographic zones include a wooded savannah, a bush-covered steppe, and a desert region. In the wooded savannah, of which the Fort Archambault region is the center, the climate is semihumid and tropical, with a rainy season of six or seven

months in the summer and autumn and an annual rainfall of from **85**
mm. to 110 mm. In the intermediate zone around Bongor and Fort
Lamy, for example, there is a dry, tropical climate with four or five
months of rain in the summer and an annual precipitation of 60 mm.
to 90 mm. In the desert region to the north the climate is very arid
with less than 24 mm. of average rainfall a year; as a result, there is
little or no vegetation.

B. POPULATION[16]

The population of Chad is estimated at 2,800,000 people or slightly
more than the state of Washington. This gives it a density of approximately 13 people per square kilometer. As might be expected, the
density varies considerably with area, being densest in places where
climatic conditions allow agricultural activities. In the Shari-Logone
Basin in the southwest, most of the inhabitants are engaged in growing
cotton, and the population density averages 40 inhabitants per square
kilometer. Northeast of the Shari, up to the fifteenth parallel, are
farmers and stock raisers and a few nomads; the average density here
is approximately 17 people per square kilometer. North of the fifteenth
parallel, where some 50,000 nomads roam over an area of more than
600,000 square kilometers, there is only one person to every 15 or 20
square kilometers. An interesting demographic aspect of the area is
the greater abundance of females over males in the African population.
At the last estimate there were 1,353,000 males and 1,440,000 females.
The European population comprises approximately 4800 people, of
which 2200 are males.

The country is overwhelmingly rural, with only three important
urban centers where 3.5 percent of the population live. The main towns
are Fort Lamy, the capital, with 95,000 inhabitants (a mere village and
military post until 1920); Moundou, with 25,000 inhabitants, a new town
that did not exist before World War II; and Fort Archambault, with
18,000 inhabitants, a trading post and transit station.

Two broad groups may be distinguished: a Moslem population in
the north, most of whom belong to the Caucasian race, and a predomi-
nantly Negro, non-Moslem population in the south.

The Moslem population is divided into the following ethnic groups:
the Arabs, who occasionally live in fixed settlements but who are mostly
nomadic and raise Bagarra cattle or Abbala horses; the Fellata or
Peul, who are nomads and raise cattle, sheep, and goats; the Hausa
(also found in Nigeria and northern Ghana) who are tradesmen and
farmers; the Ouaddaians who are chiefly farmers; the Kanebou who
are stock raisers and farmers; and the Toubou, who live in the Borkou,
Ennedi, and Tibesti regions, known as B.E.T., and who are nomads.
The Moslem population of the north speak an Arab dialect all their own.

The non-Moslem population comprises four main groups: the Sara,
the largest single group in Chad, which is subdivided into numerous

tribes living in the Shari and Logone valleys, who engage in agriculture and fishing; the Hakka, who inhabit the same region as the Sara and earn their livelihood exclusively from farming; the Massa, who live in the Logone Valley, the Mayo Kebbi, and Bongor regions; and the Moundang, who cultivate farms in the Mayo Kebbi.

The linguistic variety is great among native tribes. French has become the common language of the more educated people and the official language of the government; each of the Negro populations of the south has its own local dialect. These dialects belong to one of three main linguistic groups: Shari-Ouaddaian, Nigero-Chadian, and the Sharian. As well as different languages, these peoples have different customs and cultures; they also nurture reciprocal hatreds and prejudices.

For a long time difficulties have existed between them, especially between those who prefer a nomadic life and those who are attached to the soil. Conflicts arose over land-use problems and especially over watering points; bloody quarrels are not unusual, and frequently in Colonial days governors had to put down bloody feuds between groups of agriculturists claiming on the one side that the water had been stolen and on the other side that migrating herds had destroyed valuable crops.

Such problems are more acute because of the century-old hatred between the peoples of Arab stock and Moslem faith and the peoples of Negro stock and animist faith. Over the centuries the former enslaved the latter. In recent years, however, the Negroes have become emancipated and have gradually improved their lot to the point where they now constitute the elite while the Arabs have remained the same throughout the centuries. As a result, the Arabs resent the advancement of the Negroes and the Negroes cannot forgive the fact that their ancestors were the slaves of these present-day, backward, nomadic tribes. Even today some powerful Arab chieftains still rule oases in the north to which they return at harvest season to collect the dates, to trade, and to oversee the work of their servants, tenants and—some say—slaves.

C. AGRICULTURAL POLICIES [19][16]

The agricultural policies of a country like Chad cannot be guided by outside experience, since Chad has a geographical and ethnic situation all its own. The climate precludes the cultivation of rice and tropical export crops, and the diversity of the population precludes, at least for the time being, a unified productive (in the Western sense) type of life. All economic developments will have to be paid for by the earnings of cotton—a low-value commodity—and meat exports. All plans and policies in the past 18 years have centered around this cotton-and-meat export program, with little done by the population itself to improve its lot. Whatever improvement there has been has occurred as a fringe benefit of the development of cotton and animal husbandry and was made possible by F r e n c h economic aid and, for a short period, by American aid.

The concern with cotton exports has resulted in developing transportation. The concern for animal husbandry has resulted in creating new sources of water. Under the first Plan 3,705 million C.F.A. francs (at that time 175 C.F.A. francs were worth U.S. $1) were apportioned as follows: 672 million to improve rural economy, 425 million to improve animal husbandry, and 2,510 million to improve transportation. This raised severe criticisms because it neglected the desert and semidesert areas of the so-called B.E.T. Area and the Ouaddai who were quite badly off nutritionally (see Regional Food Supply).

Finally, the third Plan reaped the fruits of the goundwork that had been laid out during the first two Plans. Cotton export earnings were high enough almost to balance the foreign trade budget; and meat exports also increased as a result of the development of new pastures.

The third Plan also provided for increased general consumption and paid especial attention to the neglected areas of B.E.T. and Ouaddai.

In an attempt to diversify agriculture, rice cultivation was introduced after World War II in the Logone Valley, where floods create waterlogged areas at regular intervals. Nutritional as well as export benefits are expected. It is planned to convert cotton acreages into rice, especially in the area known as "Casier A," a 57,000 hectare zone populated by Massa farmers who have begun to adopt rice as their staple food. The success of this plan depends on the ability of the government to persuade more Massa tribes to eat rice and to move the crops for export without unduly raising the costs. Wheat has also been introduced in the second Plan for the same purposes.

In addition to developing the country's resources, the agricultural policies of the government are concerned with pacifying various feuding groups; their quarrels have deep historical origins, often found in the conflict between Islam and the customary laws.

Agricultural policies also included the creation of the SIP, whose activities, although greater in Chad, were less resented than in other territories. More than a million farmers contributed to and received services from the SIP. Farm-credit facilities have been extended to farmers, cultivated areas have been increased substantially by large-scale development programs, and an effort has been made to persuade farmers to use the modern techniques taught at the pilot centers and scientific farms.

Paysannats were also developed, especially in uncultivated areas. Financed by the SIP, a first paysannat was created in 1955 in the Shari-Baguirmi area near Fort Lamy to teach farmers to use draft animals, collect manure, use fertilizers and produce garden vegetables. Ten or twelve more were created in ensuing years. They remain small in scale, but all are considered very promising for further growth.

II

FOOD RESOURCES

A. GENERAL [16][19][12]

The food resources of Chad vary with the climate. In the B.E.T. areas in the north, under the hot and dry Saharian climate, agriculture is practiced in a few oases where water is obtained for irrigation from wells and in the Kanem area where water is obtained from the oueds.* Here, the main product is dates, of which 20,000 tons were produced in 1957. They are important to the local people who can barter them for grain. In the Sahel-Sahara region south of the Ouaddai Mountains and along the Batha River, millets and finger millets (Eleusine colocana) are the dominant crops; nursery plantings occur in August and October; transplanting into the fields occurs from October to December. Farther south manioc, rice, wheat, and corn are found where moisture conditions are favorable, particularly in the vicinity of Lake Chad, where plant growth is assisted by fertilizer in the form of manure from the herds. In 1957 these food crops covered 1,700,000 hectares. In view of the importance of meat and fish to the economy of the country and of the migration of herds in the dry season from north to south, the water resources are equivalent to food resources. Extensive hydraulic works have been developed in recent years; 50 wells have been sunk north of Ati in the Batha Valley. Seventeen productive artesian wells have been drilled in the Shari-Baguirmi region east of Fort Lamy along the trail coming from the Batha region. An abundant supply of ground water was discovered in Kanem. Prospecting for water is carried out in the northern part of Ouaddai.

B. MEANS OF PRODUCTION

1. Agricultural Labor Force
Agriculture and nomadic or seminomadic herding occupy more than 90 percent of the population. Some 290,000 people are engaged in stock raising, especially in the semiarid regions of Shari-Baguirmi, Kanem, the Batha Valley and the Ouaddai. Only 64,000 are classed as wage earners, some of whom are undoubtedly employed in the cotton industry. The rest of the labor force, by whom food crops could be planted, is formed by the subsistence farmers themselves, as in the rest of Equatorial Africa. No figures are given for the workers of the Arab chieftains who take care of the palm groves between date harvests, while the owners are away from their properties.

---

*Oueds are half-dry rivers, tributaries of Lake Chad.

2. Farms

Like the rest of the Federation, Chad is characterized by three kinds of farms: the subsistence farm, the paysannat, and the scientific farm. In addition, the nomadic and seminomadic herdsmen and the people of the oases form a different type of agricultural activity. The Chadian paysannat settlements are small; none exceeds 1000 members. This is possibly due to the fact that these farms had to be created around newly dug wells whose water resources were limited and in some cases unknown.

There are farms for scientific rice production at Lai and Boumo on the Logone River. Another scientific farm is located at Tikem in the peanut development area. A cattle-improvement station operates at Farsha, near Fort Lamy, together with a meat packing and freezing plant that will be discussed later. Other pilot projects, scientific farms, and land-development programs are found at Youhe, Dade, and Torok.

3. Fertilizers and Mechanical Equipment

Fertilizers are used principally on the large estates that produce cash crops such as cotton. Some fertilizers are being introduced into traditional subsistence agriculture, especially where a combination of animal husbandry and farming exists. Unfortunately, animal husbandry and farming usually belong to two different population groups with different traditions and cultures. It is only recently that it has been possible to combine the two on a small scale in specific areas, particularly under the paysannat settlement scheme. The fact that there is some animal husbandry in Chad has facilitated the introduction of animal manure as a method for fertilizing.

C. PRODUCTION [19][6][8][9]

1. Main Crops

Chad is essentially a cereal country, but in recent years manioc (see below) was introduced from the south. But the millets and sorghums still cover 1,500,000 hectares in the savannahs and the inundated zones, up to a line (according to Thompson and Adloff) running about 100 kilometers north of Rig-Rig. Four varieties of millets and sorghums are grown, allowing harvests at different times of the year; they yield an annual crop of over 860,000 tons or an average yield of 5.5 quintals per hectare. Sorghum and millet are sown between August and September. The main problem is to protect the seeds from predatory birds. Farmers shake the seeds with powdered charcoal before sowing and take turns in the fields to chase the birds away.

Wet rice covers 17,000 to 20,000 hectares, depending upon water levels. As the floods ebb at the end of November, the seeds are sown in the rich mud that becomes exposed.

Corn covers 8900 hectares in the southern part of the Republic, producing 10,000 tons a year; it is said that this constitutes the main cereal of the people living in the immediate vicinity of Lake Chad. Wheat is also found, often in the same areas as corn. One paysannat is said to have been established in the region for the purpose of growing wheat, thus capitalizing on the current trend of certain populations to prefer wheat flour to millet flour in imitation of the Europeans. It is also said that 4000 hectares of arable land will be made available very soon after the completion of a dam at Bol on the Logone. This would improve the food situation among the Arabs who have a fondness for wheat.

Twenty thousand tons of dates are grown along the oueds. Wheat, millet, and corn are grown between the palm trees. Manioc and millet are imported from the south. Sweet potatoes and yams cover 9300 hectares and produce 43,000 tons of roots. Groundnuts are said to be a promising crop, especially if transportation can be improved. Surface cultivated in groundnuts is said to cover 160,000 hectares (1957), producing 137,000 tons of unshelled peanuts, more than one-third of which comes from the Shari-Baguirmi area and the Bokoro district. Other groundnuts are found in the Batha and Mayo Kebbi regions. It is hoped that extension of this culture to the Ouaddai underprivileged area might spread some beneficial cash returns among that population.

Manioc is planted almost everywhere in the southern regions; the area for which reports are available is 9300 hectares, producing a 25,000-ton crop, but much more of this root crop is grown and not reported.

2. Other Crops

Cotton is the mainstay of the Republic's economy. It was planted on 273,000 hectares in 1961, producing a crop of 34,000 tons. In addition to the cereals and tubers listed, vegetables such as squash and beans are also produced on a subsistence basis. The country produces its own spices, and, with the exception of sugar, tea and kola, Chad is self-sufficient in foodstuffs of vegetable origin. We shall see now that it could also be self-sufficient in animal protein.

3. Sources of Animal Protein [19][16][21]

Cattle. Since the end of World War II a great effort has been made to modernize this sector of the economy. Still, diseases take a large toll of the animals; when a herd reaches large numbers, epizootics set in and destroy many. In spite of these and other hardships, there are 150,000 horses, 300,000 donkeys and 330,000 dromedaries in the state. Chad has a herd of four million cattle and thus ranks fifth in Africa, after Ethiopia with 22 million, South Africa with 12 million, Tanganyika with 8 million, and the Sudan with 7 million. Of these, between 700,000 and a million may be cows in the reproductive age. Chadians never tell the number of animals they own any more than most people would reveal the amount of their bank balance. Whatever their number, it is probable that a ratio of one and one-third cattle per inhabitant prevails. These provide 100,000 carcasses of cattle every year and a million carcasses of sheep slaughtered or dead of natural causes. Granted a carcass weight of 118 kilos for cattle and 10 kilos for sheep, this would mean over 8 kilos of meat per capita per year.

Cattle ranching is under continuous development. Large migrations of animals, followed by flocks of men, women, and children, start during the dry months to find water and pastures in the south. These migrations arouse hostility from the sedentary crop growers, who resent the transformation of arable land into pastures and the trampling underfoot of their lands by herds coming south. The well-digging operations destined to enhance the cattle industry were therefore received with mixed feelings by the population. From these herds, 24 million litres of milk are available each year for local consumption, about 10 litres per capita.

Fisheries. Fresh-water fishing represents an important source of animal protein and an important factor in economic life. Seventy-five thousand tons of fish are reported to be fished out of the Logone, Shari, and Lake Chad Basins every year. The lower Shari produces a number of species of fish that can be used for smoking and drying and can serve also as an export product. The city of Fort Lamy itself is said to buy 600 tons of fish a year. The best and most professional fishermen are found among the Boudouma and the Kouri, living on islands inside Lake Chad; the Kotoko, fishing the Logone River, are also among the most experienced in the former French Equatorial Africa. The fish are mainly salanga caught after returning from their spawning grounds in the lake. There are said to be 125 other species of fish, which the scientific farms are sorting out in order to find those that are most suitable for smoking, drying, and local consumption. Fishing is carried out on the lake, using a plank for a boat or using a dugout canoe sometimes enlivened with a sail. In the marshy areas around the lake, fish are caught with seines and baskets.

D. REGIONAL FOOD SUPPLIES[19]

By virtue of its large herds and fish resources, the live food supplies of Chad are abundant. But the vastness of the territory, combined with an inadequate transportation system, makes the utilization of these food supplies a difficult problem to solve. Practically no significant quantities of animal protein, whether cattle or fish, are stored except on a temporary basis while awaiting shipment elsewhere. If better storage were available, there is a great potential for increased income in food from both land and aquatic origins.

Millet is grown in the Batha, Ouaddai and Salamat areas, and in the region located between Batha in the north and the Aouk in the south. Rice is found in the Logone Valley and in the marshy areas between Logone and Shari. Corn is grown outside most villages of the south and wheat in the region of the Bol Dam on the Logone River. Sweet potatoes, manioc, and yams are the principal crops of the south and southwest, particularly of the well watered valley of the Logone River. Some of this manioc may also be found stored in the ground, but no actual storage and no reserves can be counted upon. Groundnuts are planted in the Borkou district, in the Batha Valley, and in the Mayo Kebbi, and also in the Shari-Baguirmi and along the thirteenth parallel out to the Ouaddai Mountains. The short harvest time of the cereals raises the important question of granaries and stockage. Some of the cereal-growing populations have accepted the concept of reserves and set aside some food for the leaner days. Unfortunately, these stocks are always exhausted before the next crop is in, so preharvest hunger occurs.

Transportation

Transportation in Chad is difficult. There are few permanent bridges on the rivers, so ferries have to be used. There are 29,000 kilometers of roads and trails, but many of them are impassable during certain portions of the year. To prevent some irresponsible truckers from destroying these trails by traveling over them at the wrong time, the government has had to establish roadblocks during certain months. Main arteries link Fort Lamy with Bangui, and also link Fort Lamy with Yaounde (in Cameroun) by way of Bozoum in the Central African Republic. Fort Lamy is linked to Algiers by a well known trail through the Sahara, which is useable several months a year. Fort Lamy is linked to Tunis via Largeau and to Karthoum via Abeche.

Airways play an important role in domestic transportation and would certainly be the most useful means of transport in case of shortage of food in one given area. There are five main airports; one of them, the Fort Lamy Airport, is capable of handling the most powerful jets presently in use. Waterways are navigable only during certain months of the year. The Shari River connects Chad with the Central African Republic and the Republic of the Congo between July first and February first. The Shari is navigable only between Fort Lamy and Fort Archambault, from where an all-weather road leads south. The stretch from Fort Lamy to Lake Chad, which is navigable all year round, is important for transporting fish and natron from the lake to the south. The Logone is navigable beyond Fort Lamy but with great difficulty. The Pende and the Bahr Sara Rivers can also be used to a limited extent. The Ouaddai region is supplied by trucks carrying food over 1150 kilometers of sandy trails.

E. FOOD INDUSTRIES[19][16]

There is little industry in Chad. It consists of little more than a rice mill at the Lai Station, a small dairy farm at Massa Kori that produces butter and cheese, and a few fish-drying and -smoking plants. The only food industry that has grown to any significant size is the meat industry. Unfortunately, the industry is unbalanced, because there are excessive facilities for slaughtering and freezing. On several oc-

casiona a large plant located at Farsha in Fort Lamy has neared bankruptcy even though it handles 82 percent of the total refrigerating and
packing business. Secondary plants exist at Fort Archambault and at
Abéché. The meat industry has grown from 59 tons in 1948 to 3500 tons
in 1959.

F. IMPORT-EXPORT

As already stated, Chad is self-sufficient in terms of food. As a
result, only sugar, salt, flour, tea and coffee, and a few alcoholic beverages are imported. Chad is an exporter of food in the form of meat.
Livestock is exported both on the hoof and as processed meat. One
hundred thirty-five thousand head of cattle and one hundred thirty
thousand sheep are exported on the hoof, three-fourths of which go
to Nigeria and the rest to the Central African Republic and to Cameroun. Packed meat from the plants in Fort Lamy go to Brazzaville,
Gabon, and Cameroun.

III

DIET TYPES

The people of Chad have two separate diet types with several vari-
ables in each. The northern Caucasian Moslem group of pastoralists
eats mutton, cereals, and, when available, milk. The southern Negro
animist group of agriculturists eats tubers, leaves and occasionally
fish. The pastoralists are generally reluctant to eat fish except on rare
occasions when they are destitute or can find nothing else.

As already stated, a million sheep are slaughtered every year, producing approximately 10 million kilos of mutton or four kilos per capita
per year. In the same way, 11,800,000 kilos of beef are processed in
the 20 to 25 refrigerated slaughterhouses of the state, but most of this
beef is eaten by Europeans and by évolués; the pastoralists eat chiefly
mutton. However, these figures hardly correspond to the real consumption because considerable clandestine slaughtering occurs and natural
deaths of animals are not reported.

Especially in the north, couscous is a popular dish. It consists of
finely ground millet or sorghum flour rolled into balls. This is eaten
with green leaves or other vegetables and is seasoned with a spicy
sauce that includes chili and peppers. Palm oil serves as the basis for
the sauce in the south while peanut oil with melon seeds is used in the
north. Nutritional levels follow the typical savannah-type curve: after
harvest families gorge themselves with porridge and wash it down with
merisse (millet beer) by the jarfull; when the lean months set in, the
porridge becomes thinner and thinner (made with the grains of wild
graminae called kreb); the only drink is water.

In the oases the menu is based on a mixture of grain and dates.

IV

ADEQUACY OF FOOD RESOURCES

Unlike other African republics, Chad has adequate food. The inadequacy of diets is chiefly the result of resistance to change, improvidence, and poor transportation. There is not much difference in a country like Chad between food supply in normal times and in times of stress. The nearer a society is to a natural agricultural economy, the less vulnerable it is to great upheavals such as modern revolutions and wars. If the system of exporting frozen meat by air were to break down, only a few people in the southern towns would suffer. The masses would not feel it and most likely would have more food than before because of the inability to transport the excess. Some exchanges between north (dates and millet) and south (manioc) might be interrupted, but little damage would result. The availability of surplus food for foreign armies would depend upon location; where large herds are kept, food would be available but not without considerable resistance from the population.

V

NUTRITIONAL DISEASES

Little information is available on the existence of nutritional diseases. Hospital records indicate some beriberi in the south during certain months.

VI

CONCLUSIONS

Malnutrition in Chad is the result of ingrained cultural traits and poor transportation rather than of population pressures or lack of food.

BIBLIOGRAPHY: STATES OF THE FORMER FRENCH EQUATORIAL AFRICA

1. Bascoulergue, P. R., Influence de l'alimentation sur la dysproteinémie de l'Africain, Medecine Tropicale, 1958, pp. 811-815.
2. Bascoulergue, P., Depoux, R., Charmot, G.: Le Kwashiorker au Moyen Congo. Bulletins de la Societé de Pathologie Exotique, 1958, No. 6, pp. 1008-1016.

3.   Bascoulergue, P., L'alimentation rurale au Moyen Congo - Monographie, S. G. Endémies, AEF, 1959.

4.   Bascoulergue, P., L'arachide, aliment de complement pour leś ecoliers de l'AEF Oléagineux, 1958, Vol. 13, No. 10, pp. 731-733.

4a. Bergeret, B., Les Marches Bamileké de Saison Sèche, Med. Trop., Marseille, 1956, Sept-Oct. Vol. 16, No. 5, pp. 698-708.

5.   Calame, Griaule G., Le Role Spirituel et Social de La Femme dans La Societé, Soudanaise Traditionelle, Diogeǹe, Vol. 37, 1962, pp. 81 and 92.

6.   (The) Central African Republic, Pamphlet by the French Embassy.

7.   Deffontaine, P. in Jean Brunhes Delamarre, M., Geographie Universelle Larousse, Paris 1959.

8.   Food and Agricultural Organization of the United Nations, Production Yearbook 1961, Vol. 15.

8a. Food and Agricultural Organization of the United Nations, Rapport au Gouvernement de la Republique Centrafricaine, No. 1450, Rome 1962.

9.   Food and Agricultural Organization of the United Nations, The State of Food and Agriculture, 1962.

9a. Food and Agricultural Organization of the United Nations, Africa Survey, C61/15, Rome 1962.

10. Fourre, P., Rapport Sur L'Enseignement en Oubangi-Shari, Paris 1955.

11. Geortay, G., Données de Base Pour la Gestion des Paysannats de Culture, Vivriéres en Région Equatoriale Forestiere, Bulletin Inf. de L'INEAC, August 1956, pp. 227-229.

12. Johnston, Bruce, The Staple Food Economies of Western Tropical Africa, Food Research Institute, Stanford University Press, Stanford, Calif., 1958.

13. Kimble, George H. T., Tropical Africa, The Twentieth Century Fund, 2 vol., New York 1960.

13a. Papes, L., Organisme d'Enquéte pour l'Etude des populations de l'A.O.F., Daka, 1947.

14. Patten, George P., Gabon, "Focus"- American Geographical Society, Vol. XII, No. 2, Oct. 1961.

15. Patten, George P., Republic of the Congo (Brazzaville), "Focus" - American Geographical Society, Vol. XIII, No. 2, Oct. 1962.

16. (The) Republic of Chad, Pamphlet by the French Embassy.

17. (The) Republic of the Congo (Brazzaville), Pamphlet by the French Embassy.

18. (The) Statesman's Yearbook 1962-1963. St. Martin's Press, New York.

19. Thompson, Virginia and Adloff, Richard, The Emerging States of French Equatorial Africa, Stanford University Press, Stanford, Calif., 1961.

20. United States Department of Commerce, World Trade Information Service, Basic Data on the Economy of Gabon, Congo, Chad, and Central African Republics, Part I, No. 59-73.

21. United States Department of Commerce, World Trade Information Service, Economic Developments in the Republic of Chad, 1961.

THE STATES OF THE FORMER FRENCH EQUATORIAL AFRICA

LIST OF TABLES

TABLE NO. 1

Production
States of Former French Equatorial Africa
(1948-1962)

Items	Area (000 Ha.)			Yields (T./Ha.)			Production (000 T.)		
	1948/53	1960/61	1961/62	48/53	60/61	61/62	48/53	60/61	61/62
CORN									
Federat.	25			0.5			14		
Congo		2			0.5			1	
Gabon		2			0.5			1	
C.A.R.		72*			0.6			12	
Chad		8.9			1.1			10	
MILLETS & SORGHUM									
Chad	865	1500*		0.6	0.6		634	860	
C.A.R.	76	84.3	75	0.2	0.3		19	19.2	26
RICE									
Federat.	16			0.7			12		
Congo		5			0.7			4	
Chad		20			1			20	
C.A.R.		0.1			1			0.1	
YAMS									
Federat.	38			9			298		
Chad		9.3			4.6			43	
C.A.R.*		18.6			1.9			32.2	
MANIOC									
Congo**		100			8			800	
Chad**		9.3			2.6			25	
Gabon**		37			4.1			152	
C.A.R.		220	220		10	10	2,200	2,200	
DRY BEANS									
Federat.	10			6.3			63		
BANANAS									
C.A.R.		17	17		10	10		170	170
Congo		1			3.5			4	
PLANTAIN									
C.A.R.		17.6			2			35.2	
PALM OIL									
C.A.R.***		18			0.6			10.8	
Congo		6.5						5.2	
GROUNDNUTS									
Federat.	160	240	255	0.5	0.7	0.7	84	190	195
Chad		160			0.8			137	
COTTONSEED									
C.A.R.	151	162	167	0.16	0.12	0.10	22	20	18
Chad	208	273	263	0.19	0.24	0.13	34	64	33
COFFEE									
C.A.R.								6.5	8.1
Congo		30	30				4.4	0.5	0.7
Gabon								0.3	0.4
COCOA									
Congo								0.6	0.8
Gabon							2.3	3.8	2.5
COTTON									
C.A.R.	151	162	167	0.08	0.07	0.06	12	11	10
Chad	208	273	263	0.09	0.1	0.06	17	34	16

*Single and mixed crops combined
**Figures for 1959
***Industrial, cultivated production
Sources: FAO Production Yearbook.
Report No. 1450

TABLE NO. 2

Nutrient Values in Some Equatorial African Foods
per 100 Grams of Product

Item	Proteins in grams	Fats in grams	CHO in grams	P in milli- grams	Ca in milli- grams	Iron in milli- grams	Thiamin mcg	Calories
Sorghum (red)	9.9	2.8	66.15	360	30	8	278	329
Sorghum (white)	11.0	2.8	67.10	320	20	6.5	206	347
Millets	7.9	4.9	70.2	178.5	14	10.9	--	363
Gumbo (dry)	9.18	3.6	18.7	350	650	87.0	--	144
Breadfruit	3.6	0.6	40.5	130	480	10.0	466	182
Peanuts	22.7	52.0	10.0	360	39	15.0	131	601
Manioc	1.3	0.4	71.2	--	95	7.0	127	294
Upland rice	6.1	2.2	71.1	180	20	1.0	200	328
Local rice	7.0	2.3	69.5	200	20	2.0	200	366
Corn	9.5	4.4	69.0	280	20	2.9	210	353
Palm nut	9.1	52.1	11.9	390	140	12.0	52	552
Fish (capitaine)	70.0	--	--	662	170	--	--	--
Termites (fried)	42.0	39.2	--	530	20.4	23.2	220	520
Shrimps	68.1	5.9	--	106	128	37.5	--	325

Source: Organisions d'enquête anthropologique
          Rapport No. 3, Gov't General de l'AOF - 1947

Note: Capitaine is the market name of "Lates nilauticus"

TABLE NO. 3

Summary of Food Resources
Central African Republic 1960
(in 1,000 metric tons)

Foods	Production	Export	Import	Balance Available	Cal. p. d.	Prot. p. d.	Fats p. d.
Millets	19.2	--	--	19.2	111	3.2	1
Corn	12.0	--	--	12.0	80	2.1	1
Rice	0.1	--	0.02	0.12	1	—	--
Manioc	752.1	--	--	752.1	1,398	12.2	3.0
Yams	32.2	--	--	32.2	51	0.7	0.1
Plaintain	35.2	--	--	35.2	43	0.5	0.1
Sugar	—	--	0.5	0.5	4	—	--
Groundnuts	29.6	5.0	--	24.6	214	10	16.9
Sesame	6.8	1.0	--	5.8	61	1.9	5.4
Gourd	5.0	--	--	5.0	27	1.4	2.2
Beef	5.0	--	1.6	6.6	24	2.2	1.6
Goat, Sheep	0.5	--	--	0.5	1	0.1	0.1
Elephant	2.2	--	--	2.2	—	—	--
Buffalo	1.5	--	--	1.5	19	1.2	1.5
Fish	0.2	--	0.1	0.3	1	0.1	
Milk	31.2	--	0.3	31.8	49	2.5	2.8
Cottonseed Oil	0.5	--	--	0.5	--	—	--
Palm Oil	10.8	--	--	10.8	37	—	4.2
Karite butter	0.4	--	--	0.4	8	—	0.9

Total Calories 2,131   38.1   40.9
animal   6.1
veget.   32

Source: Situation alimentaire et nutritionelle
Rapport au Gouvernement de le Republique Centrafricaine
FAO, No. 1450, Rome, 1962.

TABLE NO. 4

Foods Consumed Per Capita Per Day in Selected Areas
Central African Republic 1960

	Bouar	Berberati	Bambari	Nola
Manioc	548.9 Gr.	453 Gr.	489 Gr.	342.7 Gr.
Yams	9.2 Gr.	1.4 Gr.	–	7.1 Gr.
Corn	–	–	–	37.8 Gr.
Sesame seeds	53.7 Gr.	8.9 Gr.	–	0.7 Gr.
Gourd seeds	–	5.1 Gr.	67.3 Gr.	12.1 Gr.
Palm nut	–	3.7 Gr.	–	–
Palm oil	–	6.1 Gr.	–	4.0 Gr.
Groundnut seed	0.5 Gr.	23.9 Gr.	4.3 Gr.	23.3 Gr.
Groundnut oil	9.1 Gr.	3.8 Gr.	1.9 Gr.	1.9 Gr.
Meat (fresh)	antelope 1.6 Gr.	beef 48.9 Gr.	beef 7.3 Gr.	ant. or monkey 24.9 Gr.
Meat (dry)	antelope 3.5 Gr.	alligator 3.5 Gr.	beef 17.9 Gr.	ant. or monkey 26.0 Gr.
Fish (fresh)	0.7 Gr.	9.9 Gr.	2.0 Gr.	1.4 Gr.
Fish (dry)	60.4 Gr.	3.6 Gr.	–	–
Millets (sissengo)	37.7 Gr.	5.6 Gr.	–	–
Greens	–	48.3 Gr.	–	92.0 Gr.
Plantain	–	3.9 Gr.	99.9 Gr.	253.0 Gr.
Mushrooms	30.8 Gr.	12.7 Gr.	10.9 Gr.	4.3 Gr.
Papaya	–	–	–	24.1 Gr.
Citrus fruit	–	–	–	3.3 Gr.
Chili	–	–	–	0.3 Gr.

Source: Situation alimentaire et nutritionelle
Rapport au Gouvernement de le Republique Centrafricaine
FAO, No. 1450, Rome, 1962.

TABLE NO. 5

Daily Per Capita Caloric Equivalents of Diets in Selected Areas
Central African Republic 1960

Nutrients	Bouar		Berberati		Bambari		Nola	
Calories	n.	2,400	n.	2,103	n.	2,288	n.	2,106
Total Protein	Gr.	28.0	Gr.	35.0	Gr.	50.1	Gr.	52.9
Animal Protein	Gr.	4.2	Gr.	15.9	Gr.	16.8	Gr.	26.3
Fats	Gr.	35.2	Gr.	39.8	Gr.	38.3	Gr.	32.3
Carbohydrates	Gr.	479.0	Gr.	385.0	Gr.	423.0	Gr.	388.0
Calcium	Gr.	0.807	Gr.	0.331	Gr.	0.227	Gr.	0.242
Iron	mgm.	12.2	mgm.	4.9	mgm.	15.0	mgm.	?
Vitamin B_1	mgm.	0.54	mgm.	0.4	mgm.	0.37	mgm.	0.66
Vitamin B_2	mgm.	0.23	mgm.	0.3	mgm.	0.54	mgm.	0.73
Vitamin PP	mgm.	14.2	mgm.	14.7	mgm.	7.3	mgm.	12.6
Vitamin C	mgm.	96.0	mgm.	66.0	mgm.	207.0	mgm.	435.0
Vitamin A	UI	1,893	UI	3,200	UI	1,960	UI	4,300
Percentage of Calories:								
Proteins	4.8 percent		6.8 percent		8.9 percent		10.3 percent	
Fats	13.4 percent		17.2 percent		15.2 percent		13.9 percent	
Carbohydrates	81.8 percent		76.0 percent		75.9 percent		75.8 percent	
	100.0 percent		100.0 percent		100.0 percent		100.0 percent	

Source: Situation alimentaire et nutritionelle, Rapport au Gouvernement de le Republique Centrafricaine FAO No. 1450, Rome, 1962

TABLE NO. 6

Nutritional Deficiencies in Selected Areas
Central African Republic 1960

	Bouar Area	Berberati Area	Bambari Area	Nola Area	Bangassou Area	Babinga People
Nos. in sample	1,894	1,150	450	196	1955 79 children	619
Vit. A defic.	4.8 percent	4.3 percent	11.5 percent	7.6 percent	50.74 percent	2.9 percent
Vit. B defic.	3.0 percent	0.39 percent	9.1 percent	2.5 percent	52.39 percent	2.4 percent
Vit. C defic.	3.1 percent	0	0	0	22.32 percent	0.33 percent
Protein defic.	5.2 percent	3.4 percent	12.8 percent	0	73.41 percent	0
Goiter	26.3 percent	21.2 percent	24.8 percent	1.6 percent	24.04 percent	0.33 percent
Hb (80%)	67.0 percent	100 percent	100 percent	68.4 percent	?	74.8 percent

Source: Situation alimentaire et nutritionelle
    Rapport au Gouvernement de le Republique Centrafricaine
    FAO, No. 1450, Rome, 1962.

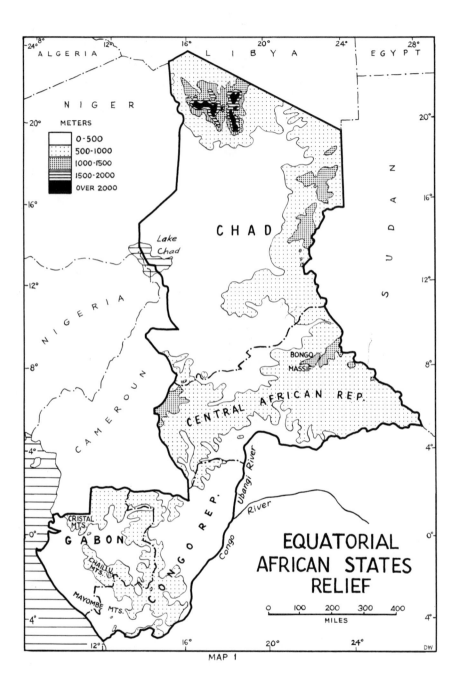

MAP 1

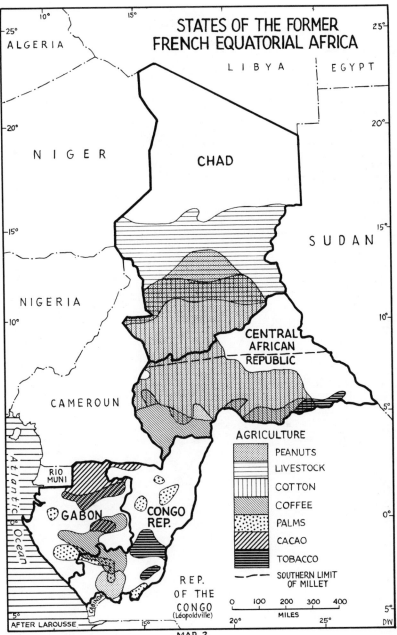

STATES OF THE FORMER
FRENCH EQUATORIAL AFRICA

25°
ALGERIA
LIBYA   EGYPT
20°
NIGER   CHAD
NIGERIA
SUDAN
15°
CENTRAL
AFRICAN
REPUBLIC
CAMEROUN
RIO
MUNI
Atlantic Ocean
GABON   CONGO
REP.

AGRICULTURE
PEANUTS
LIVESTOCK
COTTON
COFFEE
PALMS
CACAO
TOBACCO
SOUTHERN LIMIT
OF MILLET

REP.
OF THE
CONGO
(Léopoldville)

0   100   200   300   400
MILES

AFTER LAROUSSE   DW

MAP 2

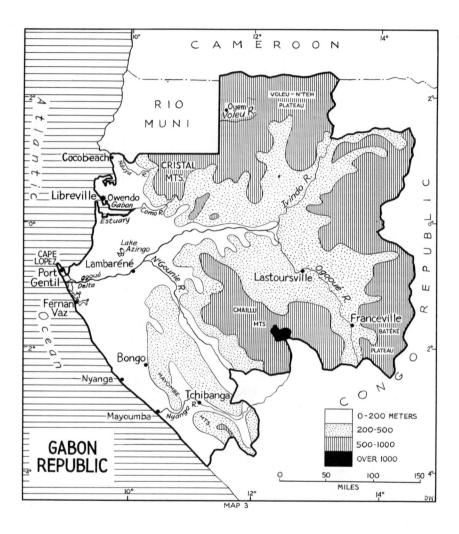

MAP 3

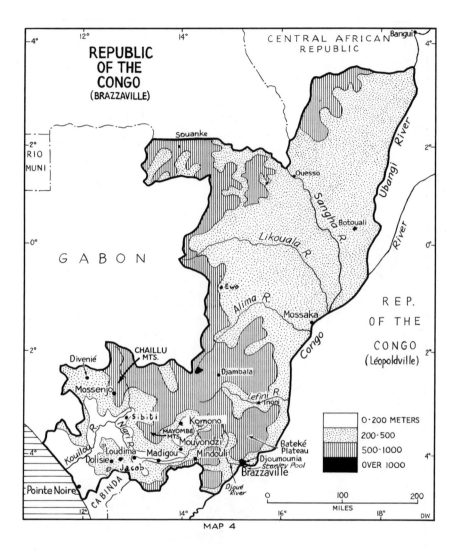

REPUBLIC
OF THE
CONGO
(BRAZZAVILLE)

CENTRAL AFRICAN
REPUBLIC

Bangui

RIO
MUNI

GABON

Souanke

Ouesso

Botouali

Sangha R.

Likouala R.

Ubangi River

River

Ewo

Alima R.

Mossaka

Congo

REP.

OF THE

CONGO

(Léopoldville)

CHAILLU
MTS.

Divenié

Djambala

Mossenjo

Lefini R.

Inoni

Sibiti

Komono

Niari R.

MAYOMBE
MTS.

Mouyondzi

Batéké
Plateau

Kouilou

Loudima

Madigou

Mindouli

Djoumounia

Stanley Pool

Dolisie

Jacob

Brazzaville

Pointe Noire

CABINDA

Djoué
River

0 - 200 METERS
200 - 500
500 - 1000
OVER 1000

0   100   200
MILES

DW

MAP 4

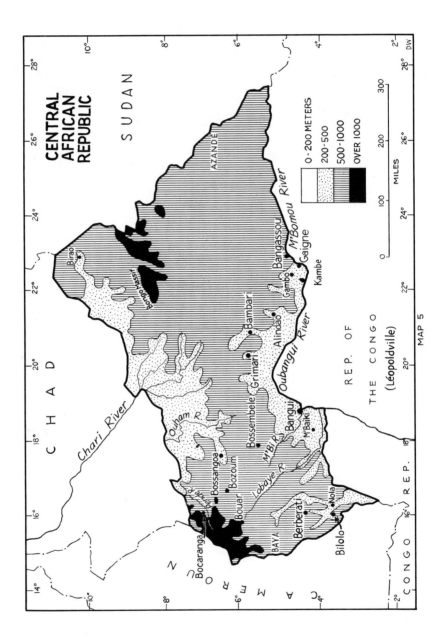

CENTRAL
AFRICAN
REPUBLIC

SUDAN

CHAD

CAMEROUN

REP. OF
THE CONGO
(Léopoldville)

CONGO REP.

0 - 200 METERS
200 - 500
500 - 1000
OVER 1000

MILES

0   100   200   300

MAP 5

Chari River

Ouham R.

Bocaranga
Bossangoa
Bouar
Bozoum
Bossembele
Grimari
Bambari
Alindao
Gambo
Bangassou
Gaigne
Kambe

Bangui
M'Baiki
Berberat
Bilolo
Nola

M'B. R.
Lobaye R.
Oubangui River
M'Bomou River

Birao
Bongo Massif
AZANDE
BAYA

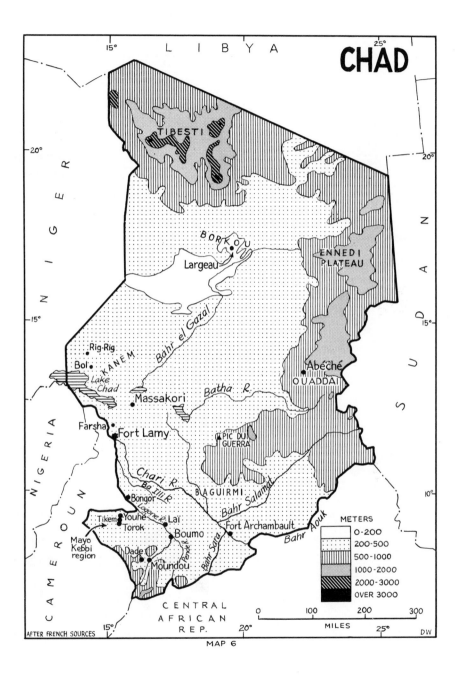

MAP 6

INDEX